INTRODUCTION TO Semimicro Qualitative Analysis

THIRD EDITION

C. H. SORUM

Professor of Chemistry
University of Wisconsin

PRENTICE-HALL, INC. *Englewood Cliffs, N. J.*

Library of Congress Catalog Card Number 60–15091

Printed in the United States of America

49594—C

Preface to the Third Edition

There have been no major changes in procedures in this edition. A new alternative test for antimony has been added and details of many procedures have been modified but the basic methods are the same as in the second edition. The modifications will in every case help insure better analytical results.

The section of the book dealing with the analysis of salts and salt mixtures has been rearranged somewhat for greater clarity.

Parts of Chapter II, which deals with the theory of qualitative analysis, have been rewritten. The section devoted to complex ions has been extended. The following topics have been added: pH; Hydrolysis; Indicators; Oxidation Potentials; Balancing Oxidation-Reduction Equations.

The problems in Chapter II have been replaced by a new set. The questions at the end of the other chapters have been enlarged and rearranged.

The author wishes to express his deep appreciation for the suggestions, comments and criticisms which he has received from users of the previous edition. In particular he is indebted to his colleagues on the freshman chemistry staff at the University of Wisconsin.

C. H. SORUM

Madison, Wisconsin

Note to Instructors

A group of questions will be found at the end of each chapter. These can be used as the basis for an oral review of each chapter's content or they can be assigned as homework. A few problems, with answers, are given at the end of Chapter 2. If a more complete coverage of problems is desired, the author's *How to Solve General Chemistry Problems* Second Edition (Prentice-Hall, Inc., 1958), or some comparable problem book may be used as a companion text.

A list of the required equipment is given on page 228. The student is introduced to each piece of equipment, and any special technique involved in the use of the equipment, at the time it is first used in the plan of analysis. If H_2S gas is used as a precipitating reagent the student will need to prepare two or three hydrogen sulfide bubbling tubes from 6 mm. glass tubing in the manner described on page 90. If each student is to prepare his own H_2S by heating a mixture of sulfur, paraffin, and asbestos in the fashion described in Note 2 on page 90, simple generators of the type illustrated in the figure on that page must be set up. Five-inch stirring rods will need to be cut from ⅛-inch glass rod and firepolished. Otherwise, the items are standard semimicro pieces of the type available at most supply houses.

A list of all reagents used, with directions for preparing all solutions, is given on pages 223 to 228. Tables of ionization constants, instability constants, oxidation potentials and solubility products are given along with the appropriate text material in Chapter 2.

The experimental procedures and specific tests have been checked and rechecked; if the directions are followed with reasonable care, good results will be obtained.

All equations for reactions in solution are presented in net ionic form. This is in conformity with the principle that the equation should indicate the species that predominate in a reacting system. No effort is made to present the detailed mechanisms of the more complex reactions; all that is attempted is a simplified equation that will give a picture of the major species which are involved.

CONTENTS

The practice of qualitative analysis

THE FIRST semester's laboratory work in general chemistry was concerned, to a considerable extent, with the preparation and properties of certain elements and their compounds. In the course of this laboratory work, the student was frequently called upon to *test* for a substance or to prove the *identity* of a substance. Oxygen was *identified* by the fact that it caused a glowing splint to burst into flame. Carbon dioxide produced a white precipitate of calcium carbonate when passed into limewater, whereas solutions containing sulfate ions gave a white precipitate when treated with a solution of barium ions. Further examples might be cited, all pointing to the fact that a student who has had an introductory laboratory course in general chemistry has learned to *identify* various substances.

In the laboratory work with which this book is concerned, *identification* of substances will be of primary interest. The study of qualitative analysis is a study of the ways and means by which substances can be identified. Specifically, inorganic qualitative analysis is concerned with finding out which metallic ions (cations) and acid radicals (anions) are present in substances and mixtures of substances.

A complete system of qualitative inorganic analysis would include methods for detecting all cations (metallic ions) and all anions (acid radicals) as well as all the elements. Not only would procedures be given for the detection of cations of such common metals as copper, tin, iron, aluminum, and zinc and such anions as sulfate, phosphate, and carbonate, but the detection of the less common metals such as rhenium, niobium, platinum, and cerium and such anions as tellurate, molybdate, ferrocyanide, and vanadate would also be included. Such a complete course would be quite involved.

An understanding of the *methods* of qualitative analysis and a knowledge of the *principles* which underlie it can be obtained by a study of the identification of a few common and representative cations and anions. Those considered in this course are the following:

Cations (metallic ions): Ag^+, Pb^{++}, Hg_2^{++}, Hg^{++}, Bi^{+++}, Cu^{++}, Cd^{++}, Sn^{++}, Sn^{++++}, Sb^{+++}, As^{+++}, Fe^{++}, Fe^{+++}, Al^{+++}, Cr^{+++}, Mn^{++}, Zn^{++}, Ni^{++}, Co^{++}, Ba^{++}, Ca^{++}, Mg^{++}, Na^+, K^+, NH_4^+.

Anions (acid radicals): SO_4^{--}, SO_3^{--}, CO_3^{--}, BO_3^{---}, CrO_4^{--}, PO_4^{---}, AsO_4^{---}, S^{--}, Cl^-, Br^-, I^-, NO_3^-, $C_2H_3O_2^-$.

In order to show how qualitative analysis works out in actual practice, let us take a solution containing all the cations listed above and examine the method by which the presence of each cation is proved.

A first thought might be to add some superreagent that would give a different and very characteristic precipitate with each cation in the mixture. Obviously, however, such a procedure would be no good because the mixture of cations, each giving a different and characteristic precipitate, would give a completely confusing mixture of precipitates.

The answer to this objection would be to find a specific reagent for each cation, a reagent that would give a precipitate or colored solution with one, and only one, cation. If there were such a complete set of specific reagents, qualitative analysis would be very simple. Unfortunately, such an ideal collection of reagents does not exist. With three or four exceptions, a reagent that gives a characteristic reaction with one ion either gives a characteristic reaction with other ions as well, or else its characteristic reaction with one ion is interfered with by other ions. In other words, *in order to identify a certain cation it must generally be alone, free from other cations.*

The answer to the question of how to proceed with the detection of the cations in the above solution is thus quite obvious. The cations must first be *separated;* then they can be *identified.* The whole plan of qualitative analysis is a series of *separations* and *identifications.*

The next question is how to go about separating all the cations listed when they are found together in the same solution. It is possible that a system could be worked out whereby the cations could be separated and identified one at a time. The more practical method, employed in all systems of qualitative analysis, is to separate the cations a handful at a time. The procedure, in brief, is as follows: A small handful of cations, three to be specific, is first taken out. This handful of three is then separated into three parts by taking out one and leaving two, and then separating these two from each other. The separated cations are then easily identified by means of characteristic reactions.

Having taken out and separated the first handful, we next take out a second handful, then a third, leaving a fourth and last handful. The original mixture of cations is separated into four handfuls. Each of these handfuls is separated in turn and the separated cations are identified. If the handful is a small one, consisting of only three cations, it is separated by taking out one, leaving two and then separating these two. If the handful is a large one, as is actually the case with the second, third, and fourth handfuls, the large handful is first separated into two small handfuls; then the separation proceeds by taking out first one and then another until each cation has been isolated.

The next question is, How do we go about picking out these handfuls? The handfuls, more correctly referred to as *groups,* are taken out by the addition of a specific reagent, called a *group reagent.* This reagent forms insoluble compounds with the cations in that particular group but permits all other cations to remain in solution. The group is thereby taken out as a mixture of insoluble substances.

Outline 1, page 5, shows the content of each group and the group reagent that is added to precipitate out each group. This outline should be examined carefully, since it gives the whole plan of group separation of cations.

Hydrochloric acid is the group reagent for the first group, called the *silver group.* Separation of the cations of the silver group from all other cations depends on the experimental fact that the chlorides of silver, lead, and mercury(I) are insoluble in dilute HCl, whereas the chlorides of all other metals are soluble.

The group reagent for the second group, the *copper-arsenic group,* is H_2S. Separation of the cations of the copper-arsenic group from the remaining cations depends on the fact that the sulfides of the former are insoluble in HCl, whereas the sulfides of the latter are soluble.

The group reagents for the third group, the *aluminum-nickel group,* are NH_4OH and $(NH_4)_2S$. The sulfides and hydroxides of the cations of the aluminum-nickel group are insoluble in alkaline solution, whereas the sulfides and hydroxides of the cations of the last group, the *barium-magnesium group,* are soluble.

The last question is, How do we go about separating and identifying the cations in each handful? The detailed answers to that question will be left to Chapters 3, 4, 5, and 6. At this point it will be sufficient to call attention to Outlines 2, 3, 4, and 5, on pages 74, 87, 125, and 153, respectively. These outlines show, schematically, how the separation and identification of the cations in each group are carried out.

It is obvious, from what has been said, that the separation and identification of the cations follow an orderly plan. It is also obvious, from an examination of Outlines 2, 3, 4 and 5, that the execution of this orderly plan of separation and identification is going to call for careful and extensive laboratory work, and the understanding of the plan is going to require knowledge of a great many principles and facts. So that the student may have a better chance to learn these principles and facts, so that he may acquire the techniques required for the various procedures, and may learn to recognize the colors and other characteristics of the solutions and precipitates that make identification of the various cations possible, the following program will be followed. A practice solution ("known" solution) containing all the cations of a particular group will first be analyzed. This known solution will then be followed by the unknown solution (or solid) for that group, in which the student goes through the same steps that he has taken with the known. The series of group knowns and unknowns for the four groups will be followed by an unknown that contains combinations of all four cation groups in the form of an alloy.

Thus, bit by bit, separation and identification of the metallic ions will be studied. The student will then be ready to extend his efforts to a study of the identification of anions. This he will do by analyzing salts and salt mixtures.

In keeping with this objective of studying the qualitative procedures of the separate groups before undertaking a complete analysis, the following substances will be analyzed and in the following order.

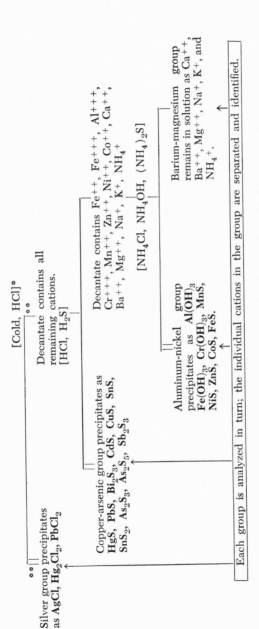

Solution contains Ag^+, Hg_2^{++}, Pb^{++}, Hg^{++}, Bi^{+++}, Cu^{++}, Cd^{++}, Sn^{++}, Sn^{++++}, As^{+++}, $H_2AsO_3^-$, AsO_4^{---}, Sb^{+++}, Fe^{++}, Fe^{+++}, Al^{+++}, Cr^{+++}, Mn^{++}, Zn^{++}, Ni^{++}, Co^{++}, Ca^{++}, Ba^{++}, Mg^{++}, Na^+, K^+ and NH_4^+.

[Cold, HCl]*

Silver group precipitates as **$AgCl$, Hg_2Cl_2, $PbCl_2$**

Decantate contains all remaining cations. [HCl, H_2S]

Copper-arsenic group precipitates as **HgS, PbS, Bi_2S_3, CdS, CuS, SnS, SnS_2, As_2S_3, As_2S_5, Sb_2S_3**

Decantate contains Fe^{++}, Fe^{+++}, Al^{+++}, Cr^{+++}, Mn^{++}, Zn^{++}, Ni^{++}, Co^{++}, Ca^{++}, Ba^{++}, Mg^{++}, Na^+, K^+, NH_4^+

[NH_4Cl, NH_4OH, $(NH_4)_2S$]

Aluminum-nickel group precipitates as **$Al(OH)_3$, $Fe(OH)_3$, $Cr(OH)_3$, MnS, NiS, ZnS, CoS, FeS.**

Barium-magnesium group remains in solution as Ca^{++}, Ba^{++}, Mg^{++}, Na^+, K^+, and NH_4^+.

Each group is analyzed in turn; the individual cations in the group are separated and identified.

* A bracketed formula [cold HCl] means that the substance (HCl in this case) is added as a reagent.

** The notation ⦀ means separation by centrifuging and decanting. The double vertical parallel lines at the left refer to the precipitate and the one vertical line at the right refers to the decantate.

OUTLINE 1: THE SEPARATION OF CATIONS INTO GROUPS

Schedule of Laboratory Work

1. *One silver group known.* This solution contains all the cations of the silver group. It will not contain cations of other groups. Obtain it and all subsequent knowns from the instructor. Follow the directions given in Procedures 1 to 4, inclusive.

2. *One or two silver group unknowns.* These solutions contain cations of the silver group. They will not contain cations of other groups. Obtain these and all subsequent unknowns from the instructor. Follow the directions given in Procedures 1 to 4, inclusive.

3. *One copper-arsenic group known.* This solution contains all the cations of the copper-arsenic group. It will not contain cations of other groups. Follow the directions given in Procedures 5 to 14, inclusive.

4. *One or two copper-arsenic group unknowns.* These solutions contain cations of the copper-arsenic group. They will not contain cations of other groups. Follow the directions given in Procedures 5 to 14, inclusive.

5. *One aluminum-nickel group known.* This solution contains all the cations of the aluminum-nickel group and will not contain cations of other groups. Follow the directions given in Procedures 15 to 21, inclusive.

6. *One or two aluminum-nickel group unknowns.* These solutions contain cations of the aluminum-nickel group. They will not contain cations of other groups. Analyze according to the directions given in Procedures 15 to 21, inclusive.

NOTE

In the presence of phosphates or borates, a modified plan of analysis must be used for the aluminum-nickel group. Unknowns ordinarily issued in the course will not contain phosphates or borates that necessitate using the modified procedure.

7. *One barium-magnesium group known.* This solution contains all the cations of the barium-magnesium group. It will not contain cations of other groups. Follow the directions given in Procedures 22 to 27, inclusive.

8. *One or two barium-magnesium group unknowns.* These solutions contain cations of the barium-magnesium group. They will not

contain cations of other groups. Analyze according to the directions given in Procedures 22 to 27, inclusive.

9. *One alloy.* This solid may contain any or all of the 21 metals. Follow the directions given in Procedure 28.

10. *Preliminary tests and specific tests for anions.* Follow the directions given in Experiments 1, 2, 3, and 4, pages 175, 177, 178, and 179.

11. *Complete analysis of solids for both cations (metallic ions) and anions (acid radicals).* The remainder of the laboratory work will consist of the complete analysis of solid unknowns for cations and anions. Follow the directions given in Chapter 8.

Record of Laboratory Work and Laboratory Reports

A record of all laboratory work is to be kept on the blank pages at the end of each chapter in this manual in accordance with the following directions.

1. As each group known or unknown is being analyzed the outline for that group must be developed in the manual. This outline is similar to those printed in this manual. The object of making such an outline is to enable the student to visualize the steps of the analysis and record his own findings. Each step in the outline must be recorded concurrently with the actual laboratory performance of that step.

2. All confirmatory tests obtained in the analysis of a group known must be approved by the instructor. Confirmatory tests obtained in the analysis of an unknown need not be thus approved.

3. The group known must be finished and the completed outline for this group known must be approved by the instructor before an unknown will be issued. The student must demonstrate to the instructor that he is familiar with the analysis of the group before he is permitted to start the analysis of the unknown.

4. When a group unknown is reported to the instructor, the manual should contain:

(a) The approved outline of the group known.

(b) All equations for the reactions that took place in the analysis of the group known.

(c) The outline for the unknown.

5. The alloy will not be issued until the student is able to demon-

strate to his instructor a proper understanding of the analysis of the alloy.

6. When the alloy is reported the manual should contain:

(a) A composite outline showing how it was analyzed.

(b) Equations for dissolving the metals proved to be present in the alloy.

7. Salts and salt mixtures will be reported in accordance with the instructions given in Chapter 9.

8. The first salt will not be issued until the student can demonstrate a satisfactory understanding of its plan of analysis. Experiments 1, 2, 3, and 4, pages 175, 177, 178, and 179, must be performed before the first salt mixture is analyzed.

9. Special solids will be reported in the same manner as salts.

The theory of qualitative analysis

FROM WHAT has been stated in Chapter 1, it is evident that the whole plan of qualitative analysis is based on the relative solubilities of the compounds formed by the various ions. Separation and identification of cations and anions involve a series of processes of solution and precipitation in which the ion in question eventually appears as a precipitate or as a solution of distinctive color. The study of qualitative analysis is thus largely concerned with solutions, solubility, and formation of precipitates. It is concerned with the best conditions for the formation of precipitates, the best conditions for dissolving certain precipitates, and the best methods for separating one ion from another. It is interested in the best techniques, the best laboratory practices, and the most effective equipment for accomplishing the desired separations and identifications. It wants to know why one substance forms a precipitate while another does not, why one substance dissolves in a specific reagent while another does not, why one ion reacts in one way while another ion reacts in a different manner. It is interested in knowing exactly the manner in which different ions react, exactly what happens when a precipitate forms, and exactly what takes place when a solid dissolves in a specific reagent. It is concerned with representing correctly, in the form of balanced equations, the reactions that take place.

9

Before the specific aspects of qualitative analysis just mentioned are discussed in detail, it is desirable that a number of fundamental concepts be reviewed.

Molarity and Per Cent Strength of Solutions

Since the separation and detection of the ions are dependent upon selective precipitation it is obvious that, if good results are to be obtained, solutions of precise *concentrations* must be used. The concentration of a solution represents the *quantity of solute* which is present in a *definite quantity of solution* or in a *definite quantity of solvent*. Concentrations of solutions used in the present plan of analysis will generally be expressed in terms of *molarity*. In a few instances, solutions of specific *per cent strength* will be used. *The molarity of a solution represents the number of moles of solute per liter of solution.* A *molar solution*, referred to by the notation 1 *M*, contains one mole of solute in a liter of solution. A one-tenth molar solution (0.1 *M*) contains one-tenth mole of solute per liter of solution. A molar solution of H_2SO_4 contains 98 g. of H_2SO_4 per liter of solution. A liter of 0.1 *M* H_2SO_4 will contain 9.8 g. of H_2SO_4. (See problems 1 to 6, page 71.)

"Per cent" means "parts per one hundred parts." Therefore *the per cent strength of a solution represents the number of parts by weight of solute per 100 parts by weight of solution*. If 10 g. of salt were dissolved in 90 g. of water to give 100 g. of solution, the per cent strength of the solution would be 10%. That is

$$\frac{10 \text{ g. of salt}}{100 \text{ g. of solution}} = 0.10.$$

Note that this gives a decimal per cent. This decimal per cent is commonly converted to parts per 100 by multiplying by 100. The standard formula for expressing per cent is, accordingly,

$$\text{per cent strength} = \frac{\text{weight of solute}}{\text{weight of solution}} \times 100\%.$$

(See problems 7 to 12, page 71.)

Rate of Reaction

When two substances that can react with each other are brought together a definite time interval is necessary for the reaction to take place. For one particular reaction the time interval may be as short as 1/100,000 second. For another reaction days or even years may be required for completion. We see, therefore, that certain reactions are inherently more rapid than others; the reason is that some reacting substances are inherently more active than others. For any particular reaction, whether it is inherently slow or inherently rapid, the rate is influenced by certain factors, the most important of which are temperature, the presence of catalysts, and the concentration of the reactants. The influence of the concentration of the reactants is of particular significance in qualitative analysis.

Consider the case in which two substances A and B react to form two products C and D. Then

$$A + B = C + D.$$

The reaction cannot take place unless the reacting molecules come in contact. The rate at which the reaction takes place will then depend on the number of impacts of molecules of A and molecules of B per second. If x molecules of A and x molecules of B are dissolved in 1000 ml. of solution, the reaction will be much slower than when x molecules of each are dissolved in 100 ml., because in the latter case the molecules will not have to travel so far to come together and react. Now suppose that in the 100 ml. we double the number of molecules of A so that we have $2x$ molecules of A and x molecules of B. It is evident that the products C and D will be formed faster because the solution now contains twice as many molecules of A, and the probability that a molecule of A will encounter a molecule of B is greater than when only x molecules of A were present. This effect of the change in the concentration of a reactant on the rate of a reaction is referred to as *mass action*.

Law of Mass Action

In 1867 Guldberg and Waage expressed the law of mass action as follows: *The speed of a chemical reaction is proportional to the molecular concentrations of the reacting molecules.* As units for expressing concentration it is necessary to use, for each reacting substance, the number of moles per liter. In the reaction, $H_2 + I_2 = 2 HI$, the speed is proportional to the product of the molecular concentrations of the H_2 and I_2. This fact is expressed by the formula,

$$\text{speed} \propto [H_2] \times [I_2].$$

The notation $\propto$ means "is proportional to." The notation $[H_2]$ always refers to concentration expressed in units of moles per liter. In this particular case, $[H_2]$ and $[I_2]$ refer to moles of H_2 and I_2, respectively, per liter.

The relationship above may be expressed in the form of an exact mathematical equation as follows:

$$\text{speed} = k \times [H_2] \times [I_2],$$

in which k is a constant for this particular reaction at a particular temperature. It is called the *velocity constant* for this reaction. Each reaction has its own velocity constant at a particular temperature; the velocity constants for different reactions generally have different numerical values.

The following analogy may help clarify the meaning of the velocity constant k: The amount of money a family spends for milk each month is *proportional to* the number of quarts of milk that are purchased. The number of quarts purchased will be equal to the product of the number of persons in the family and the average number of quarts consumed by each person. That means that

money spent $\propto$ number of persons $\times$ average qts. per person.

The amount of money actually spent will be *equal to* the number of quarts purchased times the *price per quart*. Assuming for the purpose of this analogy that the price of milk does not change during the month, then this price is the constant, k, in the equation

money spent $=$ number of persons $\times$ qts. per person $\times$ k.

The price of a quart of milk (that is, the value of the constant k in the analogy) is determined by all the different items of cost that are involved in its production and distribution. In the United States the value of k (the price of milk) is expressed in units of "cents per quart." Suppose that the price is 24 cents per quart and a family of 5 drinks an average of 12 quarts per person. Then

money spent $=$ 5 persons $\times$ 12 qts. per person $\times$ 24¢ per qt.
$=$ 1440¢.

If the money were being spent by a family in England the constant k (the price) would in all probability be different because the items that enter into the cost of producing and distributing the milk would have a different value than in the United States; also, it would be expressed in different units, perhaps pence per quart. If the family lived in France the quantity of milk would probably be given in liters, and the value of k would be expressed in units of "francs per liter." It is obvious that the value of k would be different for nearly every country.

In chemical reactions the velocity constant k defines the units in which the speed is expressed, and includes also all other constant factors that are characteristic of a specific reaction. Just as the value of k in the formula given above varied from one country to another, so the value of the velocity constant will vary from one reaction to another.

Equilibrium in Chemical Reactions

In a great many reactions the products are capable of reacting with each other and begin to do so as soon as they are formed. A familiar example is the gas phase reaction between carbon monoxide and steam where the products, CO_2 and H_2, react with each other as indicated by the lower arrow:

$$CO + H_2O \rightleftharpoons CO_2 + H_2$$

This type of reaction is called an *incomplete reaction* or *reversible reaction*. Incomplete reactions eventually reach a *state of equilibrium*. At equilibrium the rate of the reaction to the right is exactly equal to the rate of the reaction to the left.

At the start of the above reaction the CO and H_2O are present in high concentrations and, therefore, react with each other at maximum speed, but they are gradually used up as the reaction progresses so the speed to the right gradually decreases.

At the beginning of the reaction, CO_2 and H_2 are present in very low concentrations and, therefore, react with each other at a very low rate, but they increase in concentration as the reaction progresses and the speed to the left gradually increases. Finally, the speed to the left exactly equals the speed to the right. That means that the CO, H_2O, CO_2, and H_2 are being used up as fast as they are being formed. There is no further change in the concentration of any reactant. The reaction just keeps on going "round and round" without any apparent change. A state of equilibrium has been reached.

If we were to start with a mixture of CO_2 and H_2, rather than CO and H_2O, a state of equilibrium would again be reached. In this case, at the start of the reaction CO_2 and H_2 are present in high concentration, while CO and H_2O are present in very low concentration. As the reaction proceeds the speed to the left gradually decreases as CO_2 and H_2 are used up while the speed to the right increases as more CO and H_2O are formed. Eventually, the two rates will be the same; the reaction will then be in a state of equilibrium. *It is a characteristic of any true equilibrium reaction that the same state of equilibrium will be reached by starting with either the reactants or the products.*

It is very important to note that it is not a requirement of equilibrium that the substances be present in the reaction vessel in the exact ratio in which they react with each other. Thus, if we were to place 2 moles of CO and 5 moles of steam in a one-liter reaction vessel, 6 moles of CO and 4 moles of steam in a second liter vessel, 8 moles of CO_2 and 3 moles of H_2 in a third vessel, and 3 moles of CO, 2 moles of steam, 4 moles of CO_2 and 7 moles of H_2 in a fourth vessel, a state of equilibrium, represented by the reaction CO + H_2O ⇌ CO_2 + H_2, will be attained in each vessel. However, it will be observed that, in each of the 4 vessels, when CO and H_2O react to form CO_2 and H_2 they always do so in the mole ratio represented by the equation, namely, 1 mole of CO with 1 mole of H_2O to form 1 mole of CO_2 and 1 mole of H_2. In any equilibrium reaction the substances will always *react* with each other in the mole ratio represented by the equation, but they can be present in all sorts of ratios.

Suppose we have, in a liter reaction vessel at a given high temperature, an equilibrium mixture consisting of 0.10 mole of CO, 0.80 mole of H_2O (steam), 0.80 CO_2, and 0.50 mole of H_2 represented by this equation

$$\underset{0.10}{CO} + \underset{0.80}{H_2O} \rightleftharpoons \underset{0.80}{CO_2} + \underset{0.50}{H_2}.$$

Now suppose we were to force into the vessel a quantity of hydrogen gas. This, obviously, will increase the concentration of hydrogen. This increase in concentration of the hydrogen will increase the rate at which it will react with CO_2. As a result the rate of the reaction to the left will be speeded up. This will increase the concentration of the CO and H_2O since they are, at the moment, being formed faster than they are reacting with each other. As time passes and the reaction proceeds the speed to the left gradually decreases as the concentrations of CO_2 and H_2 fall; at the same time the speed to the right gradually increases as the concentrations of CO and H_2O rise. In time the forward and reverse rates will again be equal and equilibrium will again be reestablished. However, at this new equilibrium we will find that the concentrations of the CO, H_2O, and H_2 are greater while the concentration of the CO_2 is less than before the H_2 was added. The increase in concentration of the H_2 has *shifted the equilibrium* to the left as evidenced by the fact that the concentrations of the CO and H_2O on the left have gone up, while the concentration of the CO_2 on the right has gone down. We can state that, in effect, the addition of H_2 (on the right) has pushed the equilibrium toward the left. Had we added more CO or H_2O to the reaction vessel the equilibrium would have been shifted to the right. In an equilibrium, if the concentration of a given reactant is increased, the equilibrium will be pushed toward the opposite side of the reaction. If the concentration of a reactant is reduced, by removing some of that reactant, the equilibrium will be *pulled* toward the same side of the reaction.

If we were to examine carefully, at the new equilibrium point, the increase in the *number of moles* of CO and H_2O on the left and the decrease in the *number of moles* of CO_2 on the right resulting from forcing more H_2 into the reaction vessel, we would find that the increase in the number of moles of CO is the same as the increase in the number of moles of H_2O, and that the decrease in the number of moles of CO_2 is the same as the increase in the number of moles of CO. This is exactly what we would expect from the equation, $CO + H_2O \rightleftharpoons CO_2 + H_2$, since it tells us that CO_2 and H_2 react in the ratio of 1 mole of CO_2 with 1 mole of H_2 to yield 1 mole of CO and 1 mole of H_2O.

Suppose we have, in a reaction vessel of fixed volume at a given high temperature, an equilibrium mixture represented by the following equation:

$$4\,NH_3 + 5\,O_2 \rightleftharpoons 6\,H_2O + 4\,NO.$$

If we now force into this reaction vessel, at the given temperature, some more NO gas the equilibrium will be shifted to the left. At the new equilibrium the concentrations of the NH_3 and O_2 will be higher than before addition of the extra NO and the concentration of the H_2O will be lower. In this case, however, the increase in the *number of moles* of NH_3 and O_2 and the decrease in the *number of moles* of H_2O will not be the same; we will find, as the equation testifies, that in the shift in equilibrium due to addition of more NO, for every 4 additional moles of NH_3 that are produced there will be 5 additional moles of O_2, and 6 moles of H_2O will be used up. These two examples emphasize the very important fact that, in every equilibrium shift, the change in the number of moles of the reactants involved is strictly in accord with the mole relationship specified by the balanced equation for the reaction.

We have noted earlier in this discussion that, for any equilibrium reaction, the reactants can be present in all sorts of ratios. This is illustrated in Table 2.1 which gives the equilibrium concentrations of CO, H_2O, CO_2, and H_2 for the reaction, $CO + H_2O \rightleftarrows H_2 + CO_2$, for five experiments, all carried out at the same temperature.

TABLE 2.1. RELATIVE CONCENTRATION OF REACTANTS IN AN EQUILIBRIUM SYSTEM AT CONSTANT TEMPERATURE

Reaction vessel	[CO]	$[H_2O]$	$[CO_2]$	$[H_2]$	$\dfrac{[CO_2] \times [H_2]}{[CO] \times [H_2O]}$
1	0.20	0.20	0.50	0.40	5.00
2	0.10	0.18	0.30	0.31	5.16
3	0.10	0.80	0.80	0.50	5.00
4	0.30	0.50	0.90	0.83	4.98
5	0.75	0.20	0.80	0.94	5.01

Note: The notations $[CO_2]$, $[H_2O]$, $[CO]$, and $[H_2]$ mean concentration in moles per liter of the substance within the bracket.

An examination of the data in Table 2.1 reveals one very striking fact. The answer obtained when the product of the concentrations of the products, H_2 and CO_2, is divided by the product of the concentrations of the reactants, CO and H_2O, is, within the limits of experimental error, the same for each experiment. That is,

$$\frac{[CO_2] \times [H_2]}{[CO] \times [H_2O]} = \text{a constant.}$$

Similar data from the thousands of equilibria that have been studied confirm the fact that *in every reacting system in equilibrium at a given temperature the product of the concentrations of the products divided by the product of the concentrations of the reactants is a constant.* This constant, referred to by the letter, K, is called the *Equilibrium Constant* for the particular reaction at the particular temperature. For the reaction

$$A + B \rightleftharpoons C + D$$

the formula for the equilibrium constant, K, is,

$$K = \frac{[C] \times [D]}{[A] \times [B]}.$$

It will be referred to as the *Equilibrium Formula.*

It is obvious that, if

$$\frac{[C] \times [D]}{[A] \times [B]}$$

is constant, then

$$\frac{[A] \times [B]}{[C] \times [D]}$$

will also be constant; the latter constant will be the reciprocal of the former. By common agreement among scientists, the product of the concentrations of the products is placed in the numerator.

For the reaction $SO_2 + NO_2 \rightleftharpoons SO_3 + NO$,

$$K = \frac{[SO_3] \times [NO]}{[SO_2] \times [NO_2]}.$$

When a reaction involves more than 1 mole of a specific reactant, the concentration of that reactant is raised to a power equal to the number of moles. Thus, for the reaction $2\,SO_2 + O_2 \rightleftharpoons 2\,SO_3$,

$$K = \frac{[SO_3]^2}{[SO_2]^2 \times [O_2]}.$$

For the reaction $N_2 + 3\,H_2 \rightleftharpoons 2\,NH_3$,

$$K = \frac{[NH_3]^2}{[N_2] \times [H_2]^3}.$$

For the reaction $H_2 + I_2 \rightleftharpoons 2\,HI$,

$$K = \frac{[HI]^2}{[H_2] \times [I_2]}.$$

For the reaction $4\,NH_3 + 5\,O_2 \rightleftharpoons 4\,NO + 6\,H_2O$,

$$K = \frac{[NO]^4 \times [H_2O]^6}{[NH_3]^4 \times [O_2]^5}.$$

And for the general reaction, $aA + bB \rightleftharpoons cC + dD$,

$$K = \frac{[C]^c \times [D]^d}{[A]^a \times [B]^b}.$$

The reason for raising the concentration of a reactant to a power equal to the number of moles becomes more evident if we show each mole as a separate reactant by writing the equation for the reaction in the form

$$N_2 + H_2 + H_2 + H_2 \rightleftharpoons NH_3 + NH_3.$$

The equilibrium constant, K, can then be expressed in the form

$$K = \frac{[NH_3] \times [NH_3]}{[N_2] \times [H_2] \times [H_2] \times [H_2]} = \frac{[NH_3]^2}{[N_2] \times [H_2]^3}.$$

The equilibrium constant possesses the following fundamental characteristics:

1. At constant temperature its numerical value is definite and is independent of the original concentrations of the reactants. This means that in a reaction of the type

$$CO + H_2O \rightleftharpoons H_2 + CO_2,$$

the equilibrium constant in the systems containing, originally,

0.3 mole of H_2O and 0.3 mole of CO
0.6 mole of H_2O and 0.3 mole of CO
0.3 mole of H_2O and 0.6 mole of CO
0.6 mole of H_2O and 0.1 mole of CO

will be the same. The difference in the four systems will consist of different concentrations of the four substances at equilibrium.

2. The equilibrium constant is different for different reactions.

3. The larger the equilibrium constant, the more complete the reaction.

4. The equilibrium constant for a given reaction is different for different temperatures. For some reactions the value of the constant is increased when the temperature is increased, for others it is decreased.

5. The equilibrium constant is not changed by change of pressure or change of concentration or by the presence of a catalyst.

The numerical value of the equilibrium constant for a given reaction is obtained by inserting the experimentally determined values of the concentrations in the Equilibrium Formula for the reaction. Thus, for the reaction,

$$SO_2 + NO_2 \rightleftharpoons SO_3 + NO,$$
$$0.60 \quad\quad 0.80 \quad\quad 0.90 \quad\quad 1.1$$

the calculation, using the equilibrium concentrations given in moles per liter, becomes

$$K = \frac{[SO_3] \times [NO]}{[SO_2] \times [NO_2]} = \frac{0.90 \times 1.1}{0.60 \times 0.80} = 2.1.$$

For the reaction,

$$2\,SO_2 + O_2 \rightleftharpoons 2\,SO_3$$

0.20   0.30   0.60

$$K = \frac{[SO_3]^2}{[SO_2]^2 \times [O_2]} = \frac{(0.60)^2}{(0.20)^2 \times (0.30)} = 30.$$

(See problems 13, 14, 15, page 72.)

Ionization Equilibrium

When weak electrolytes such as acetic acid and ammonia are dissolved in water partial ionization takes place. This incomplete ionization reaches a state of equilibrium that may be represented by the following equations.

$$HC_2H_3O_2 \rightleftharpoons H^+ + C_2H_3O_2^-.$$

$$NH_4OH \rightleftharpoons NH_4^+ + OH^-.$$

Since these ionization equilibria are true chemical equilibria, their equilibrium constants can be calculated from the equilibrium formula. Such ionization equilibrium constants are called *ionization constants*. For the two reactions given above the mass law equations are

$$K = \frac{[H^+] \times [C_2H_3O_2^-]}{[HC_2H_3O_2]}, \qquad K = \frac{[NH_4OH]}{[NH_4^+] \times [OH^-]}.$$

The ionization constant can be calculated if the concentrations of ions in the solution are known. For example:

In a 0.10 molar solution of acetic acid, which ionizes according to the equation

$$HC_2H_3O_2 \rightleftharpoons H^+ + C_2H_3O_2^-,$$

the acid is known, from experimental measurements, to be ionized to the extent of only 1.34 per cent. The reaction is therefore only 1.34 per cent complete. The concentration of ions and molecules in the solution is therefore:

$HC_2H_3O_2$ (molecules),

         $0.10 \times 98.66\% = 0.09866$ mole per liter.

Hydrogen ion (H^+)

         $0.10 \times 1.34\% = 0.00134$ mole per liter.

Acetate ion ($C_2H_3O_2^-$)

         $0.10 \times 1.34\% = 0.00134$ mole per liter.

The equilibrium constant is

$$K = \frac{0.00134 \times 0.00134}{0.09866} = 0.000018 = 1.8 \times 10^{-5}.$$

This value of K (ionization constant) is a measure of the tendency of acetic acid to ionize. In the case of acids the ionization constant is a measure of the strength of the acid. The larger the constant, the greater the hydrogen ion concentration, and, consequently, the stronger the acid. This relationship is shown in Table 2.2 which gives values of the ionization constants of several acids at 20°C.

TABLE 2.2. IONIZATION CONSTANTS OF ACIDS
AND BASES AT 20°C

Acetic	$HC_2H_3O_2$		1.8×10^{-5}
Arsenic	H_3AsO_4	$K_1 =$	2.5×10^{-4}
		$K_2 =$	5.6×10^{-8}
		$K_3 =$	3.0×10^{-13}
Arsenious	H_3AsO_3	$K_1 =$	$6 \quad \times 10^{-10}$
Boric	H_3BO_3	$K_1 =$	6.0×10^{-10}
Carbonic	H_2CO_3	$K_1 =$	4.2×10^{-7}
		$K_2 =$	4.8×10^{-11}
Chromic	H_2CrO_4	$K_1 =$	1.8×10^{-1}
		$K_2 =$	3.2×10^{-7}
Formic	$HCHO_2$		2.1×10^{-4}
Hydrocyanic	HCN		4.0×10^{-10}
Hydrofluoric	HF		6.9×10^{-4}
Hydrogen sulfide . . .	H_2S	$K_1 =$	1.0×10^{-7}
		$K_2 =$	1.3×10^{-13}
Hypochlorous	$HClO$		3.2×10^{-8}
Nitrous	HNO_2		4.5×10^{-4}
Oxalic	$H_2C_2O_4$	$K_1 =$	3.8×10^{-2}
		$K_2 =$	5.0×10^{-5}
Phosphoric	H_3PO_4	$K_1 =$	7.5×10^{-3}
		$K_2 =$	6.2×10^{-8}
		$K_3 =$	1.0×10^{-12}
Sulfurous	H_2SO_3	$K_1 =$	1.3×10^{-2}
		$K_2 =$	5.6×10^{-8}
Ammonium hydroxide .	NH_4OH		1.8×10^{-5}

In polyprotic acids such as carbonic acid, K_1 represents the ionization constant of the hydrogen ion formed according to the equation

$$H_2CO_3 \rightleftharpoons H^+ + HCO_3^-.$$

The ionization constant of the second hydrogen ion, represented by the equation

$$HCO_3^- \rightleftharpoons H^+ + CO_3^{--},$$

is designated by K_2. (See problem 16, page 72.)

It should be recalled, in connection with the ionization of acids, that it is generally postulated that the replaceable H from the covalent molecule, HCl for example, coordinates with the O in the covalent H_2O molecule to form the H_3O^+ ion. The reaction taking place when HCl or any similar compound is dissolved in water to form an acid is then

$$HCl + H_2O = H_3O^+ + Cl^-.$$

The H_3O^+ ion is called the *hydronium ion*. This hydronium ion is essentially a hydrated hydrogen ion. The hydrogen ion in turn is a *proton*, inasmuch as it is the hydrogen nucleus stripped of its lone electron. In the discussions that follow, the positive ion that forms when an acid is dissolved in water will be referred to as the hydrogen ion, H^+, rather than as a proton or a hydronium ion. This usage of the term hydrogen ion is for convenience and to avoid confusion and does not imply lack of agreement with the above postulate. It will always be understood that H^+ is a convenient symbol for an ion which is undoubtedly hydrated.

The Common Ion Effect

A solution of the weak acid, acetic acid, contains hydrogen ions and acetate ions in equilibrium with acetic acid molecules.

$$HC_2H_3O_2 \rightleftharpoons H^+ + C_2H_3O_2^-.$$

If sodium acetate crystals are dissolved in this acetic acid solution, the concentration of acetate ions will be greatly increased because the sodium acetate, being a salt and hence a strong electrolyte, is completely ionized into Na^+ and $C_2H_3O_2^-$ ions. This increase in the concentration of acetate ions will speed up the rate at which H^+ ions will combine with $C_2H_3O_2^-$ ions. This will shift the equilibrium of the acetic acid ionization to the left. As a result of this shift in the equilibrium the concentration of H^+ ions will be decreased and the concentration of un-ionized $HC_2H_3O_2$ molecules will be increased; in other words, the degree of ionization of the $HC_2H_3O_2$ will be decreased. Such a decrease in the ionization of an electrolyte resulting from an increase in the concentration of one of its ions is an example of the *common ion effect.*

The ionization of any weak acid will be depressed by addition of a soluble salt of the acid. Thus the ionization of H_3PO_4 is depressed by the addition of Na_3PO_4 or K_3PO_4, while the ionization of H_2SO_3 will be depressed by the addition of Na_2SO_3 or K_2SO_3.

The ionization of a weak acid can be depressed also by addition of a strong acid; in this case the hydrogen ion is the common ion whose concentration is increased. Thus the ionization of the weak acid H_2S will be decreased by the addition of HCl. The equations for the ionization of H_2S can be represented as

$$H_2S \rightleftharpoons H^+ + HS^-$$

$$HS^- \rightleftharpoons H^+ + S^{--}.$$

Obviously, if the hydrogen ion concentration of a solution of H_2S is increased by addition of the strong acid, HCl, the above equilibria will be shifted to the left; as a result of this shift the concentration of S^{--} ions will be decreased and the concentration of H_2S molecules will be increased. We see from this that the concentration of sulfide ions in a solution of H_2S will go down if the concentration of the hydrogen ions goes up, and vice versa. This very important fact is put to good practical use in the precipitation of the cations of the copper-arsenic and aluminum-nickel groups. The separation of the cations of these two groups is best accomplished by precipitating the sulfides of the copper-arsenic group with a fairly low concentration of sulfide ions and the sulfides of the aluminum-nickel group with a much higher concentration of sulfide ions. A low concentration of sulfide ions is obtained by keeping the solution acidic with HCl, while the high sulfide ion concentration is achieved by keeping the solution alkaline with NH_4OH.

Just as the ionization of a weak acid is depressed appreciably by addition of a salt of that acid, the ionization of a weak base is depressed by addition of a salt of the base. Thus the ionization of NH_4OH is depressed by addition of NH_4Cl. The ionization reaction for NH_4OH is

$$NH_4OH \rightleftharpoons NH_4^+ + OH^-.$$

It is evident that, if the concentration of NH_4^+ ions is increased by addition of the soluble salt NH_4Cl, the equilibrium point will be shifted to the left. As a result of this equilibrium shift the concentration of NH_4OH molecules will be increased while the concentration of OH^- ions will be decreased. When the concentration of NH_4^+ ions increases, the concentration of OH^- ions decreases and vice versa. This fact will be put to practical use in the analysis of the aluminum-nickel and barium-magnesium groups.

The Weak Electrolyte, Water

Precise measurements show that a liter of pure water contains 1×10^{-7} moles of H^+ ions and 1×10^{-7} moles of OH^- ions. That means that water is a very weak electrolyte. The reaction for its ionization is

$$(1) \qquad H_2O \rightleftharpoons H^+ + OH^-.$$

Since water contains both H^+ ions and OH^- ions it is both an acid and a base. The ionization constant for water can be represented by the formula

$$(2) \qquad K = \frac{[H^+] \times [OH^-]}{[H_2O]}.$$

A liter of water (1000 g.) will contain 55.5 moles of H_2O (1000 g. $\div$ 18 g./mole = 55.5555555 moles). As already noted, a liter of pure water at 25°C contains 1×10^{-7} mole of H^+ ions and 1×10^{-7} mole of OH^- ions. If we substitute these values in equations (1) and (2) we obtain

$$(3) \qquad \underset{55.5 - 1 \times 10^{-7}}{H_2O} \rightleftharpoons \underset{1 \times 10^{-7}}{H^+} + \underset{1 \times 10^{-7}}{OH^-}$$

$$(4) \qquad K = \frac{(1 \times 10^{-7}) \times (1 \times 10^{-7})}{(55.5 - 1 \times 10^{-7})}.$$

If H^+ ions (in the form of a strong acid, HCl, for example) are added to water, the equilibrium in reaction (3) will be shifted to the left in accordance with the common ion effect already discussed. As a result of this shift the concentration of the un-ionized H_2O molecules will be increased, while the concentration of the OH^- ions will be decreased. However, no matter how high the value of $[H^+]$ becomes there will always be some OH^- ions in any water solution. Likewise, no matter how high the value of $[OH^-]$ may be there will always be some H^+ ions present. Even if the concentration of H^+ ions added is so high that the concentration of OH^- ions is reduced practically to zero, the concentration of un-ionized H_2O molecules could increase only from 55.5555554 to 55.5555555; for all practical purposes that is no change at all. In other words, the concentration of H_2O molecules in equilibrium with H^+ and OH^- ions is constant. Therefore, equation (4) becomes

$$(5) \qquad K = \frac{(1 \times 10^{-7})\,(1 \times 10^{-7})}{\text{constant whose value is } 55.5}.$$

This constant, whose value is 55.5, can be multiplied by the ionization constant, K, to give a new constant which is called the *ion product constant* for water; it is designated by the symbol K_w. The numerical value of K_w will therefore be $1 \times 10^{-7} \times 1 \times 10^{-7}$, or 1×10^{-14}. That is,

$$(6) \qquad K_w = [H^+] \times [OH^-] = 1 \times 10^{-14}.$$

Equation (6) tells us that *the product of the* H^+ *ion and* OH^- *ion concentration in pure water or any water solution is always* 1×10^{-14}.

In pure water the H^+ and OH^- ion concentrations are the same; each is equal to 1×10^{-7} mole per liter. Therefore, pure water is neutral. If the H^+ ion concentration is greater than 1×10^{-7} mole per liter, the OH^- ion concentration will be less than 1×10^{-7}; the solution will then be acidic, but the product of the two ion concentrations will still be 1×10^{-14}. If $[H^+]$ is less than 1×10^{-7}, $[OH^-]$ will be greater than 1×10^{-7}; the solution will then be alkaline but the product of $[H^+]$ and $[OH^-]$ will still be 1×10^{-14}.

Complex Ions

When a simple ion combines with one or more other ions or with one or more neutral molecules to form a new ion, this new ion is called a *complex ion*. The complex hydronium ion H_3O^+ is formed when an H^+ ion combines with a molecule of H_2O. A copper ion combines with four NH_3 molecules to form the complex ion $Cu(NH_3)_4^{++}$, while an Fe^{+++} ion combines with six SCN^- ions to form the $Fe(SCN)_6^{---}$ ion. Other complex ions that will be encountered in qualitative analysis are $Ag(NH_3)_2^+$, $PbCl_4^{--}$, $Cd(NH_3)_4^{++}$, $Cd(CN)_4^{--}$, $Cu(CN)_2^-$, SnS_3^{--}, SbS_3^{---}, AsS_4^{---}, $Ni(NH_3)_6^{++}$, $Co(NH_3)_6^{+++}$, $FeCl_4^-$, $Zn(NH_3)_4^{++}$, $Fe(CN)_6^{----}$, $Al(OH)_4^-$, $Zn(OH)_4^{--}$, $Cr(OH)_4^-$, $Sn(OH)_4^{--}$, $Sn(OH)_6^{--}$, $Co(SCN)_4^{--}$, FeF_6^{---}, $HgCl_4^{--}$, and $CuCl_4^{--}$.

All complex ions are unstable to a greater or lesser degree and dissociate, in characteristic fashion to give, usually, the ions or molecules from which they were formed. Table 2.3 gives the dissociation equations for a number of complex ions.

TABLE 2.3. COMPLEX ION EQUILIBRIA

Equation	Instability constant
$Ag(NH_3)_2^+ \rightleftharpoons Ag^+ + 2\,NH_3$	6×10^{-8}
$Ag(CN)_2^- \rightleftharpoons Ag^+ + 2\,CN^-$	1.8×10^{-19}
$Cu(NH_3)_4^{++} \rightleftharpoons Cu^{++} + 4\,NH_3$	4.7×10^{-15}
$Cu(CN)_2^- \rightleftharpoons Cu^+ + 2\,CN^-$	5×10^{-28}
$Cd(NH_3)_4^{++} \rightleftharpoons Cd^{++} + 4\,NH_3$	7.5×10^{-8}
$Cd(CN)_4^{--} \rightleftharpoons Cd^{++} + 4\,CN^-$	1.4×10^{-19}
$Co(NH_3)_6^{+++} \rightleftharpoons Co^{+++} + 6\,NH_3$	2.2×10^{-34}
$Fe(CN)_6^{----} \rightleftharpoons Fe^{++} + 6\,CN^-$	1×10^{-35}
$Ni(NH_3)_6^{++} \rightleftharpoons Ni^{++} + 6\,NH_3$	1.8×10^{-9}
$Zn(NH_3)_4^{++} \rightleftharpoons Zn^{++} + 4\,NH_3$	3.4×10^{-10}

Since the above equations represent true equilibrium reactions, their equilibrium constants can be represented in the conventional manner. The equilibrium equation when applied to these reactions yields, for the equation

$$Ag(NH_3)_2^+ \rightleftharpoons Ag^+ + 2\,NH_3,$$

for example, the familiar expression

$$K_{\text{Inst.}} = \frac{[Ag^+] \times [NH_3]^2}{[Ag(NH_3)_2^+]}.$$

For a complex ion which is very stable, and hence is only slightly dissociated, the quantities in the numerator will be very small, the quantity in the denominator will be relatively large, and the value of K will be very small. On the other hand, a complex ion that is relatively unstable and hence dissociates to a fairly high degree, will have a relatively large K. The value of K is therefore a measure of the instability of the ion; if K is very small the ion is very stable, if K is large the ion is relatively instable. For that reason K is called the *instability constant* and is designated by the symbol $K_{\text{Inst.}}$. The instability constants for the ions cited are given in Table 2.3. Certain of these ions, it will be noted, are extremely stable while others are quite unstable.

Having noted a number of specific complex ions certain questions arise. How can an ion such as Co^{+++}, for example, hang on to 6 molecules of NH_3? Why does the copper complex ion with ammonia contain 4 molecules of NH_3 while the nickel complex contains 6 molecules?

Complex ions are formed in accordance with a theory which postulates that, over and above its usual electrovalence, a metal ion has a so-called auxiliary valence which gives it a definite capacity for combining with, or attaching to itself, other ions or molecules. These ions or molecules are referred to as *ligands*. The bonding by which the ligand is more or less firmly attached to the central cation is most generally covalent in character and results from a mutual sharing of a pair of electrons by the central ion and the ligand. Since both of the shared electrons are donated by the ligand a coordinate bond is presumed to be formed. For that reason the resulting compounds are called *coordination compounds* and the maximum number of ligands that a central ion is able to attach to itself is called its *coordination number*. Since it is postulated that the ligand donates a pair of electrons it follows that, to be able to function as a ligand, an ion or molecule must have at least one pair of unshared electrons. All anions meet this requirement and can, under proper conditions, serve as ligands. There is, however, a great difference in the tendency of different anions to donate their unshared electrons. Nitrate ions are very weak electron donors and, hence, rarely appear in complex ions. On the other hand cyanide ions have a strong tendency to donate electrons, and hence form complex ions with a great many cations; these complex ions are, generally, very stable.

A large number of neutral molecules, such as H_2O, NH_3, and CO, have a strong tendency to donate their unshared electrons to cations and, accordingly, form stable complexes.

Since, in forming a positive ion, the metal atom has given up one or more electrons (Ni^{++}, Cu^{++}, Cr^{+++}) it follows that every cation should be able to accept pairs of electrons from donor ligands and thereby form a complex ion. The tendency to accept such donated electrons varies greatly among different cations. The best acceptors are those cations that have a high charge ($+2$, $+3$, and $+4$), small diameters and incompletely filled valence shells, particularly with underlying d orbitals. The high charge and small diameter mean that the donated electrons will be strongly attracted by the positive nucleus of the cation; an extensive incompletely filled valence shell gives the ion the necessary spaces (orbitals) in which the donated electrons can be shared. The best acceptors are the ions of the b periodic group elements; they have relatively small diameters and high charge. Because their atoms are formed by addition of d-orbital electrons they may have s, p, and d orbitals available for electron acceptance. In contrast, the group Ia and IIa cations are poor acceptors and form few complex ions presumably because they have large diameters, small charges, and no incomplete d orbitals.

The question of the coordination number that should be assigned to a particular cation can be answered only by examination of its complex ions. Co^{+++} and Ni^{++} each have a coordination number of 6; this is deduced from the fact that they combine with 6 molecules of NH_3. Cu^{++} can combine with a maximum of 4 molecules of NH_3, and is presumed, therefore, to have a coordination number of 4. The belief that Co^{+++} has a coordination number of 6 is strengthened by the fact that it forms the following complex ions: $Co(SCN)_6^{---}$; $Co(NO_2)_6^{---}$; $Co(NH_3)_5Cl^{++}$; $Co(NH_3)_4Cl_2^+$; $CoCl_4(H_2O)_2^-$. As the last three of these cobalt complexes indicate, the ligands need not all be of the same species.

The charge carried by the complex ion is the algebraic sum of the charges on the central ion and the attached ions or molecules. $Co(SCN)_6^{---}$ has a charge of -3 because the one Co^{+++} and six SCN^- give a net value of -3. One Co^{+++}, plus one Cl^-, plus 5 neutral NH_3's give the $Co(NH_3)_5Cl^{++}$ complex a net charge of $+2$.

The precise nature of the bonding that exists between central ion and ligand and the manner in which it is achieved has been and still is the subject of much thought and speculation. The structures of the $Cd(NH_3)_4^{++}$ and $Fe(CN)_6^{----}$ ions which are developed below illustrate where this bonding is presumed to occur.

For the cadmium atom the arrangement of the electrons in its valence shell ($4d$, $5s$, and $5p$) is:

The cadmium ion will then have the following structure:

Since the Cd^{++} ion has one empty $5s$ orbital and three empty $5p$ orbitals in its valence shell it can accept four pairs of electrons and will, thus, have a coordination number of 4. The NH_3 molecule, with the structure.

$$\begin{array}{c} H \\ :\overset{\cdot\cdot}{N}\!:\!H \\ H \end{array}$$

can serve as a ligand by donating one pair of unshared electrons. Four NH_3 molecules will thus coordinate with one Cd^{++} ion to form the $Cd(NH_3)_4^{++}$ ion. Since the ion was formed by coordination in one $5s$ orbital and three $5p$ orbitals it is said to have an sp^3 structure.

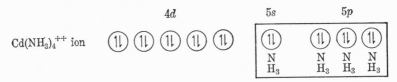

The iron atom has the structure shown below.

The Fe^{++} ion has the following structure.

Since this ion has a total of six vacant orbitals (two $3d$, one $4s$ and three $4p$) a coordination number of 6 is logical.

The CN^- ion has the structure $:C:::N:$; six CN^- ions will each donate one pair of unshared carbon electrons to the Fe^{++} ion to form the $Fe(CN)_6^{----}$ ion.

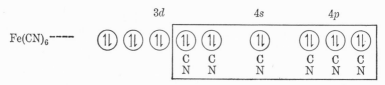

An examination will show that this complex ion has a d^2sp^3 structure.

A complex ion is always named as a derivative of the central ion (the cation). The constituent parts of the ion are named in the following order: anion, neutral molecule, central ion (cation). For anions whose names end in *ide*, the *ide* changes to *o* (chlor*ide* becomes chlor*o*, cyan*ide* becomes cyan*o*, hydrox*ide* becomes hydrox*o*, etc.). For anions whose names end in *ate* or *ite* the *e* changes to *o* (sulf*ate* becomes sulf*ato*, sulf*ite*, becomes sulf*ito*, cyan*ate* becomes cyan*ato*, etc.). Neutral molecules have specific names; thus NH_3 is ammine, H_2O is aquo.

In a negative complex ion the name used to designate the central ion always ends in *ate* and is derived from the name from which the symbol of the element is derived. [$Ag(CN)_2{}^-$ is the dicyano*argentate* ion and $Pb(OH)_4{}^{--}$ is the tetrahydroxo*plumbate* ion.] In a positive complex ion the common name of the central ion is used. [$Ag(NH_3)_2{}^+$ is the diammine*silver* ion and $PbCl^+$ is the mono-chloro*lead* ion.]

A Roman numeral enclosed in parentheses shows the oxidation state of the central element.

In accordance with the above rules:

$Fe(H_2O)_2Cl_4{}^-$ is the tetrachlorodiaquoferrate(III) ion;

$FeCl^{++}$ is monochloroiron(III);

$Sn(OH)_4{}^{--}$ is tetrahydroxostannate(II);

$Sn(OH)_6{}^{--}$ is hexahydroxostannate(IV);

$Co(NH_3)_5Cl^{++}$ is monochloropentamminecobalt(III);

$CuCl_4{}^{--}$ is tetrachlorocuprate(II);

$Cu(NH_3)_4{}^{++}$ is tetramminecopper(II);

$Ag(S_2O_3)_2{}^{---}$ is dithiosulfatoargentate(I);

and $Fe(CN)_6{}^{----}$ is hexacyanoferrate(II).

In water solution, and in the absence of a more readily attachable ligand, nearly all central ions will coordinate with water molecules. That means that any and every ion that is not coordinated, either fully or in part, with other ions or groups, is coordinated, in whole or in part, with H_2O. Speaking exactly, aluminum ions are $Al(H_2O)_6{}^{+++}$, not simply Al^{+++}, and the $CrCl^{++}$ ion is really the $Cr(H_2O)_5Cl^{++}$ ion. Because it would become tedious and cumbersome to always indicate the degree of hydration of an ion, and because the degree of hydration appears to have no effect on the stoichiometric behavior of an ion as it is represented in a balanced equation, we shall not, except in rare instances, represent a simple or partially coordinated ion in its hydrated form. We shall, however, have the same understanding that has already been declared for the H^+ ion. We acknowledge that it is hydrated, but we will not represent it as such.

The exact composition of the complex ions that are formed when the two reactants are brought together in solution may vary with the concentration of the complexing species. Thus, when solid AgI is treated with a solution of KI of moderate concentration the predominant complex species is AgI_2^-. As the concentration of I^- ions is increased, the AgI_3^{--} ions become the predominant species, although AgI_2^- ions are still present. The equilibrium picture is probably represented by the equations

$$AgI \quad + \ I^- \ \rightleftharpoons \ AgI_2^-.$$

$$AgI_2^- + \ I^- \ \rightleftharpoons \ AgI_3^{--}.$$

Inasmuch as the reagent that provides the complexing ion is always present in relatively high concentrations in all the systems which will be encountered in qualitative analysis, we will follow the policy in this book of using that complex ion formula that experimental evidence indicates to be the one that predominates at high concentrations of the complexing ion.

Molecular Equations, Detailed Ionic Equations, and Net Equations

Practically every separation and identification in qualitative analysis involves one or more reactions in solution. The discussion of these reactions will require the writing of equations, so it will be in order to say something about the manner in which the equation for a chemical reaction in solution may be presented. Three kinds of equations may be written: molecular equations, detailed ionic equations, and net equations. The difference between these three kinds of equations can best be shown by using them to represent typical reactions.

The *molecular equation* for the reaction that takes place when a solution of the strong acid HCl is neutralized by a solution of the strong base NaOH is

$$NaOH + HCl = NaCl + H_2O.$$

This balanced equation gives the formula of the solid NaOH that was used in preparing the solution of sodium hydroxide, of the HCl gas that was used in preparing the solution of hydrochloric acid, of the solid sodium chloride that would be recovered if the resulting solution were evaporated to dryness, and of the water molecules that are formed as the product. It tells us that one mole of NaOH will neutralize exactly one mole of HCl to form exactly 1 mole of NaCl and 1 mole of H_2O; in other words, it represents the exact stoichiometry of the reaction. It enables us to calculate how many grams of solid NaOH would have to be dissolved in water in order to give a solution that would exactly neutralize a solution formed by dissolving a definite number of grams of HCl in water, and it allows us to calculate exactly how many grams of NaCl would be recovered if the resulting solution were evaporated to dryness. The molecular equation makes no pretense whatever of telling anything about the mechanism of the reaction that takes place; it gives simply the molecular species of the substances used in preparing the solutions and represents the molecular ratio in which they react.

NaOH, HCl, and NaCl are strong electrolytes; in dilute solutions of strong electrolytes the solute is completely ionized. (NaOH and NaCl, being electrovalent compounds, are 100% ionized in the solid state.) Therefore, a solution of NaOH contains Na^+ and OH^- ions but no NaOH molecules, a solution of HCl contains H^+ and Cl^- ions but practically no HCl molecules, and a solution of NaCl contains Na^+ and Cl^- ions but no NaCl molecules. Water is such an extremely weak electrolyte that it exists almost exclusively in the form of H_2O molecules. This means that when a solution of NaOH reacts with a solution of HCl to form a solution of NaCl and H_2O, what actually happens is that a solution of Na^+ and OH^- ions reacts with a solution of H^+ and Cl^- ions to form a solution of Na^+ and Cl^- ions containing also H_2O molecules. The *detailed ionic equation* for the reaction would then be

$$Na^+ + OH^- + H^+ + Cl^- = Na^+ + Cl^- + H_2O.$$

We note that all the sodium exists as Na^+ ions on the right side of the equation as well as on the left side. Likewise, all the chlorine appears as Cl^- ions on both right and left. Evidently, then, nothing happens to either Na^+ or Cl^- ions. Therefore we can cancel Na^+ and Cl^- from both sides of the equation. That means that the only thing that actually happens is that H^+ ions combine with OH^- ions to form H_2O molecules. We can therefore represent the simple over-all picture of what actually takes place by the following *net equation:*

$$H^+ + OH^- = H_2O.$$

The reaction that takes place when a solution of the weak base NH_4OH is neutralized by the strong acid HCl can be represented by the following *molecular equation:*

$$NH_4OH + HCl = NH_4Cl + H_2O.$$

What has already been said about the molecular equation

$$NaOH + HCl = NaCl + H_2O$$

applies exactly to this equation; it gives the molecular species of the substances used in preparing the two solutions and the molecular species of the products, and represents the exact stoichiometry of the reaction, but it makes no pretense whatever of telling anything about the mechanism of the reaction that takes place. It should be noted at this point that there is some question about the molecular species that are present in the solution formed when NH_3 gas is dissolved in water. The assumption is made in this discussion that NH_3 reacts with H_2O to form NH_4OH in the manner represented by the equilibrium reaction

$$NH_3 + H_2O \rightleftharpoons NH_4OH$$

and that the predominant molecular species is NH_4OH. The NH_4OH exists, in turn, in equilibrium with NH_4^+ and OH^- ions as represented by the equation

$$NH_4OH \rightleftharpoons NH_4^+ + OH^-.$$

As has already been noted, HCl is a strong acid; a dilute solution of HCl contains, therefore, H^+ and Cl^- ions but practically no unionized HCl molecules. Ammonium hydroxide, however, is a weak electrolyte. Therefore a solution of NH_4OH contains a large number of NH_4OH molecules and relatively few NH_4^+ and OH^- ions. The three species exist in equilibrium as represented by the following equation:

$$NH_4OH \rightleftharpoons NH_4^+ + OH^-.$$

NH_4Cl is a salt and, accordingly, a strong electrolyte: a solution of NH_4Cl contains NH_4^+ and Cl^- ions but no NH_4Cl molecules.

This means that what actually happens in the reaction of hydrochloric acid with ammonium hydroxide is that a solution of H^+ and Cl^- ions reacts with a solution containing a few NH_4^+ and OH^- ions in equilibrium with a great many NH_4OH molecules to form a solution containing NH_4^+ and Cl^- ions and H_2O molecules. We can represent the actual situation by the equation

$$H^+ + Cl^- + NH_4OH + NH_4^+ + OH^-$$
$$= NH_4^+ + Cl^- + H_2O.$$

The ionic theory postulates that when electrolytes react in solution the detailed reaction is between ions. Therefore what really happens in the above reaction is that the H^+ ions from HCl react with the OH^- ions from NH_4OH to form H_2O molecules. This reduces the concentration of OH^- ions, and therefore reduces the rate at which OH^- ions and NH_4^+ ions combine to form NH_4OH. However, molecules of NH_4OH continue to ionize, so, as fast as the OH^- ions are used up, additional molecules of NH_4OH ionize to give more OH^- ions. This process goes on until, eventually, all the NH_4OH has ionized to give NH_4^+ and OH^- ions, and all these OH^- ions have combined with H^+ ions to form H_2O molecules. We can represent the *detailed reaction* picture as follows:

$$NH_4OH$$
$$H^+ + Cl^- + \quad \uparrow\downarrow \quad = NH_4^+ + Cl^- + H_2O.$$
$$NH_4^+ + OH^-$$

In arriving at a simple equation that will represent the net result of the above detailed reaction, we first note that the NH_4OH will eventually all dissociate into NH_4^+ and OH^- in the manner already explained. That means that we can strike out the "NH_4OH." Since NH_4^+ and Cl^- appear on both sides of the equation, they can be canceled out. That leaves

$$H^+ + OH^- = H_2O,$$

representing the net result of the detailed reaction process. This is exactly the same as the final equation for the reaction of sodium hydroxide with hydrochloric acid. There is, however, a very important and significant difference between the reaction of hydrochloric acid with the strong electroylte NaOH and its reaction with the weak electroylte NH_4OH, and it is highly desirable that the equation show this difference. As has already been pointed out, a solution of NaOH contains Na^+ and OH^- ions and no NaOH molecules. By contrast, a solution of NH_4OH contains a large number of NH_4OH molecules and very few NH_4^+ and OH^- ions. A more correct and more realistic description of what happens in the reaction of hydrochloric acid with ammonium hydroxide would be to say that a solution of H^+ and Cl^- ions reacts with a solution of NH_4OH molecules. The actual situation would then be represented by the following equation:

$$H^+ + Cl^- + NH_4OH = NH_4^+ + Cl^- + H_2O.$$

The only common ion that can be canceled is the Cl^- ion. This leaves the following *net equation:*

$$H^+ + NH_4OH = NH_4^+ + H_2O.$$

This net equation tells us that the *predominant species* involved in the reaction are H^+ ions and NH_4OH molecules. It represents correctly the stoichiometry of the reaction between the predominant species. It does not, however, pretend to represent the actual mechanism of the reaction.

Summarizing, we can say that the *molecular equation* gives the formulas of the molecular species of the substances used in making up the reacting solutions and the formulas of the molecular species that can be recovered as products; it represents the correct stoichiometric ratio in which these substances react; it does not represent the mechanism of the reaction and does not imply that the molecules as such either take part in the reaction or exist in solution. The *detailed ionic equation* attempts to give a correct and detailed picture of the reaction process. The *net equation gives the predominant species involved in the reaction and represents the correct stoichiometric ratio in which they react.* In reactions between strong electrolytes the net equation represents a simple summary of the ionic reactions that actually take place. When a weak electrolyte or "insoluble" electrolyte is a reactant, the net equation does not pretend to represent the actual mechanism of the reaction.

Because the net equation shows the species that predominate in a reacting system and because, in qualitative analysis, we are more interested in the species that are present than how they come and go, we will as a general rule use the net equation rather than the detailed ionic equation. When the exact mechanism of a reaction process is under discussion, the detailed ionic equation will be presented. In using the net equation it must be recognized that the identities of the predominant species may be a matter of question. Likewise, in presenting a detailed ionic equation it must be understood that one cannot be absolutely certain, beyond the shadow of a doubt, about the detailed mechanism of any reaction.

The following examples will emphasize further the relationship between the three kinds of equations.

(a) The reaction of hydrogen sulfide gas with a solution of lead chloride:

Molecular: $PbCl_2 + H_2S = \textbf{PbS} + 2\,HCl.$

Detailed: $H_2S \rightleftharpoons 2\,H^+ + S^{--}.$

$PbCl_2 \longrightarrow Pb^{++} + 2\,Cl^-.$

$Pb^{++} + S^{--} \longrightarrow \textbf{PbS}.$

Net: $Pb^{++} + H_2S = \textbf{PbS} + 2\,H^+.$

(b) The reaction of hydrochloric acid with solid calcium carbonate:

Molecular: $\textbf{CaCO}_3 + 2\,HCl = CaCl_2 + H_2O + CO_2.$

Detailed: $\textbf{CaCO}_3 \rightleftharpoons Ca^{++} + CO_3^{--}.$

$2\,HCl \longrightarrow 2\,H^+ + 2\,Cl^-.$

$CO_3^{--} + 2\,H^+ \longrightarrow H_2O + CO_2.$

Net: $\textbf{CaCO}_3 + 2\,H^+ = H_2O + CO_2 + Ca^{++}.$

It is obvious from what has been stated that, to write a correct net equation, a decision must be made as to whether a substance exists predominantly as an ion or as a neutral unit (molecule or neutral ionic crystal such as solid $CaCO_3$). The following summary will aid in making this decision:

1. The following soluble compounds, being *strong electrolytes,* exist in solution as *ions.*

    (a) All soluble salts. (See Solubility Rules page 188.)
    (b) All soluble metal hydroxides. (See Solubility Rules page 189.)
    (c) The following common acids: H_2SO_4, HNO_3, HCl, HBr, HI.

2. The following soluble compounds, being *weak electrolytes,* exist in solution predominantly as *molecules.*

(a) All soluble acids not listed in (1).
(b) Ammonia.
(c) Water.

3. All *insoluble substances* (solids, liquids, gases) exist as *molecules* or neutral ionic units.

4. Complex ions are soluble weak electrolytes and exist predominately as undissociated ions.

Buffer Action

Hydrochloric acid is classed as a strong acid; that means that in dilute solution it is 100% ionized. A liter of 0.01 molar hydrochloric acid will, therefore, contain 0.01 mole of H^+ ions. If a quantity of solid Na_3PO_4 is dissolved in 0.01 M HCl, the concentration of the hydrogen ions in the acid will be reduced; this can be proved by demonstrating that the rate at which a quantity of magnesium metal liberates hydrogen from the acid to which Na_3PO_4 has been added is slower than the rate at which the same quantity of magnesium liberates hydrogen from pure 0.01 M HCl. The rate at which a given quantity of magnesium liberates hydrogen from an acid is proportional to the hydrogen ion concentration of the acid; therefore a slower rate of evolution of H_2 means a lower concentration of hydrogen ions.

The reduction in the concentration of the hydrogen ions when Na_3PO_4 is added can be accounted for in the following manner: Na_3PO_4 is a salt and therefore is a strong electrolyte. That means that when it is dissolved in water it yields a great many PO_4^{---} ions. These PO_4^{---} ions will combine with the H^+ ions from the 0.01 M HCl to form the weak acid, H_3PO_4. As a result, the hydrogen ion concentration of the solution is reduced.

Although the Na_3PO_4 has reduced the concentration of hydrogen ions in the 0.01 M *HCl*, it has not changed the total available hydrogen in the solution. This can be proved by demonstrating that the total quantity of hydrogen gas that an excess of magnesium will liberate from a liter of 0.01 M HCl to which Na_3PO_4 has been added is exactly the same as the quantity of hydrogen that an excess of magnesium will liberate from a liter of pure 0.01 M HCl. The fact that the total available hydrogen has not been changed by the addition of Na_3PO_4 can be accounted for in the following way: H_3PO_4 ionizes according to the equations

$$H_3PO_4 \rightleftharpoons H^+ + H_2PO_4^-$$

$$H_2PO_4^- \rightleftharpoons H^+ + H PO_4^{--}$$

$$H PO_4^- \rightleftharpoons H^+ + PO_4^{---}.$$

When hydrogen ions are removed from solution by the magnesium metal in accordance with the reaction

$$Mg + 2 H^+ = Mg^{++} + H_2$$

the ionization equilibria for H_3PO_4 will be shifted to the right. Eventually, all the H_3PO_4 will have ionized and the hydrogen ions will all have been given off as hydrogen gas. The PO_4^{---} ions take hydrogen ions out of solution and store them as H_3PO_4 molecules, but these hydrogen ions are available when they are needed.

The soluble salt of any weak acid will reduce the concentration of hydrogen ions in the same way that Na_3PO_4 does.

Just as a soluble salt of a weak acid will tie up H^+ ions, the soluble salt of a weak base will tie up OH^- ions. Ammonium chloride will, for example, reduce the OH^- ion concentration of a solution of NaOH or KOH. The NH_4^+ ions from the NH_4Cl will combine with the OH^- ions from the NaOH and tie them up in the form of molecules of the weak base, NH_4OH. The concentration of OH^- ions in the solution will thereby be reduced, but the total available alkalinity will not be altered.

The ability of the salt of a weak acid to tie up hydrogen ions in the form of molecules of the weak acid, and the ability of the salt of a weak base to tie up hydroxyl ions, is the basis of a phenomenon known as *buffer action*. If a small amount of strong acid is added to pure water or a dilute solution of acid in water, the hydrogen ion concentration of the water or solution is noticeably increased. If the same small amount of acid is added to the same amount of solution containing the soluble salt of a weak acid, the increase in hydrogen ion concentration is so slight that, for all practical purposes, it is negligible. The anions of the salt of the weak acid have taken the H^+ ions as fast as they were added and have tied them up in the form of molecules of the weak acid. The net result is that the hydrogen ion concentration has changed only very slightly. This maintenance of a practically constant hydrogen ion concentration in spite of the addition of hydrogen ions is called *buffer action*. The solution of the substance which is capable of exerting the buffer action is called a *buffer solution*.

The ability of the salt of a weak acid to reduce the hydrogen ion concentration of a solution of a strong acid is put to practical use in the identification of arsenic in Procedure 13 of the copper-arsenic group analysis. The solution on which the confirmatory test for arsenic is to be made contains some nitric acid. Sodium acetate is added to the solution. The acetate ions from the sodium acetate combine with the hydrogen ions in the solution to form the weak acid $HC_2H_3O_2$. The result of this action is that the hydrogen ion concentration of the solution is brought down low enough to permit the characteristic identifying precipitate of Ag_3AsO_4 to form.

Hydrolysis

Since water is both an acid and a base it will show the buffering phenomenon that has already been discussed. The phenomenon is in this instance referred to as *hydrolysis*. Thus, if the soluble salt of a weak acid and a strong base, such as $NaC_2H_3O_2$, is added to water, the $C_2H_3O_2^-$ ions will tie up some of the H^+ ions in the form of $HC_2H_3O_2$ molecules. This will cause the equilibrium in the reaction, $H_2O \rightleftarrows H^+ + OH^-$, to be shifted to the right. As a result the concentration of OH^- ions will be increased; since the shift is caused by removal of H^+ ions the resulting solution will show an alkaline reaction. The Na^+ ions have no attraction for OH^- ions and will, therefore, not enter into or have any effect on the reaction. The net equation for the hydrolysis reaction is

$$(1) \qquad C_2H_3O_2^- + H_2O \rightleftharpoons HC_2H_3O_2 + OH^-.$$

The anion of any weak acid will show a similar reaction with water.

If the salt of a weak base and a strong acid, such as NH_4Cl, is added to water the NH_4^+ ions will tie up some of the OH^- ions in the form of NH_4OH molecules. This removal of OH^- ions will shift the ionization equilibrium for water to the right, will thereby increase the concentration of H^+ ions, and will yield an acidic solution. The Cl^- ions have very little attraction for H^+ ions and will therefore have practically no effect on the reaction. The net equation for the hydrolysis reaction is

$$(2) \qquad NH_4^+ + H_2O \rightleftharpoons NH_4OH + H^+.$$

The hydrolysis of cations of the less electropositive metals can be represented by net equations of the type

$$(3) \quad Al(H_2O)_6^{+++} + H_2O \rightleftharpoons Al(H_2O)_5OH^{++} + H_3O^+.$$

This accounts for the acidic reaction of a solution of $AlCl_3$.

When the salt of a weak acid and a weak base is dissolved in water, both anion and cation will undergo hydrolysis. What the reaction of this solution will be toward an indicator will depend upon the relative strength of the acid and base that are formed.

Since the reactions given above reach a state of equilibrium, each will have an equilibrium constant. For the hydrolysis of acetate ion,

$$C_2H_3O_2{}^- + H_2O \rightleftharpoons HC_2H_3O_2 + OH^-,$$

the equilibrium constant will be represented by the equation

$$(4) \qquad K = \frac{[HC_2H_3O_2] \times [OH^-]}{[C_2H_3O_2{}^-] \times [H_2O]}.$$

In comparison with the concentrations of the other ions involved in this reaction, $[H_2O]$ is very large; this is particularly true in dilute solution. Since $[H_2O]$ is so large, and since the degree of hydrolysis is in most instances very small, the change in the value of $[H_2O]$ when the equilibrium is shifted is negligible; $[H_2O]$ can therefore be considered to be constant. In dilute solutions the value of $[H_2O]$ is approximately 55.55 moles per liter. This constant value of $[H_2O]$ can then be multiplied by the equilibrium constant, K, in equation (4) to give a new constant, K_h, called the *hydrolysis constant*. The formula for the hydrolysis constant will then be

$$(5) \qquad K_h = \frac{[HC_2H_3O_2] \times [OH^-]}{[C_2H_3O_2{}^-]}.$$

For the hydrolysis of the ammonium ion, equation (2),

$$(6) \qquad K_h = \frac{[NH_4OH] \times [H^+]}{[NH_4{}^+]}.$$

The Concept of pH

The degree of acidity of a solution is determined by the concentration of H^+ ions. Rather than say that a solution has a hydrogen ion concentration of 10^{-5} moles per liter (indicating thereby that it is very weakly acidic) it is common practice to state, more simply, that the solution has a *pH of 5*. The number 5 is the negative of the logarithm of the number 10^{-5}. From this example we see that *pH is the negative of the logarithm of the* $[H^+]$ *of a solution.* Since the number 5 is the logarithm of $\frac{1}{10^{-5}}$, *pH can also be defined as the logarithm of the reciprocal of* $[H^+]$.

Suppose the hydrogen ion concentration of a solution is 2.0×10^{-4} moles per liter. The logarithm of 2.0×10^{-4} is -3.7. Therefore, the pH is 3.7.

Pure water is neutral to indicators. The $[H^+]$ of pure water is 10^{-7}. The pH of pure water is, therefore, 7. It follows that *a pH of 7 represents neutrality.*

If H^+ ions are added to pure water the $[H^+]$ of the resulting solution will be greater than 10^{-7}, 2×10^{-4} for example, or 10^{-2}, or 5×10^{-1}. The negative of the logarithms of these three numbers are, respectively, 3.7, 2, and 0.3. It follows, therefore, that *a pH less than 7 represents acidity;* the lower the pH the greater the degree of acidity.

If OH^- ions, in the form of NaOH, for example, are added to pure water the $[OH^-]$ of the resulting solution will be greater than 10^{-7} and it will show an alkaline (basic) reaction. As $[OH^-]$ increases $[H^+]$ must decrease, since $[H^+] \times [OH^-]$ must always equal 1×10^{-14}. An $[OH^-]$ value of 10^{-5} means that the $[H^+]$ of the solution must be 10^{-9} and an $[OH^-]$ value of 2×10^{-4} means that $[H^+]$ is 5×10^{-11}. But an $[H^+]$ value of 10^{-9} is a pH of 9 and an $[H^+]$ value of 5×10^{-11} is a pH of 10.3. Since these solutions are alkaline it follows that *a pH greater than 7 represents alkalinity;* the higher the pH the more alkaline the solution.

Indicators

The indicators commonly used in the laboratory are weak organic acids; a few are weak organic bases. They ionize according to the reaction

$$HIn \rightleftharpoons H^+ + In^-.$$
$$\text{Color A} \qquad\qquad \text{Color B}$$

They owe their utility as indicators to the fact that the un-ionized molecule, HIn, has one color while the anion, In^-, has a different color. If H^+ ions (in the form of an acid) are added to a solution containing the indicator, the ionization equilibrium will be shifted to the left. This will increase the concentration of HIn and decrease the concentration of In^-. As a result the solution will take on the color of the molecule, HIn. If OH^- ions are added they will react with the H^+ ions and the equilibrium will be pulled to the right. This will cause the solution to have the color of the ion, In^-. In litmus the molecule is red while the ion is blue; in phenolphthalein the molecule is colorless and the ion is red.

Amphoterism

Among the complex ions that will be encountered in the study of qualitative analysis $Zn(OH)_4^{--}$, $Sn(OH)_4^{--}$, $Cr(OH)_4^-$, and $Al(OH)_4^-$ are of particular interest because their formation illustrates the *amphoteric* character of the hydroxides of the metals involved. Using zinc as an example, if a solution of sodium hydroxide is added, drop by drop, to a solution of a soluble zinc salt, a white precipitate, $Zn(OH)_2$, will first form. If the addition of the sodium hydroxide solution is continued, the solid $Zn(OH)_2$ will gradually dissolve until, finally, a water-clear solution is obtained. This clear solution is found to contain the complex ion, $Zn(OH)_4^{--}$. The net equation to account for its formation when excess base is added to the precipitate of $Zn(OH)_2$ is

$$Zn(OH)_2 + 2\,OH^- \rightleftharpoons Zn(OH)_4^{--} \quad \text{(tetrahydroxozincate ion)}.$$

The $Zn(OH)_2$ that is precipitated when a solution of a zinc salt is treated with NaOH will dissolve in any strong acid in accordance with the following net equation:

$$Zn(OH)_2 + 2\,H^+ = Zn^{++} + 2\,H_2O.$$

There is nothing unusual about this latter reaction; $Zn(OH)_2$ is the basic hydroxide of a metal, and basic hydroxides react with acids to form salts and water. The solubility of $Zn(OH)_2$ in excess sodium hydroxide is, however, unique. It means that $Zn(OH)_2$ will react with either a strong acid or a strong base. *A hydroxide that has the property of reacting with either a strong acid or a strong base is said to be amphoteric.*

The hydroxides of aluminum, chromium, tin, lead, and antimony, like $Zn(OH)_2$, are amphoteric: They react with strong acids in the manner typical of the basic hydroxides of metals. They react with strong bases to form stable complex ions. Although there is some question about the composition of some of these hydroxo complexes, we will represent all of them by the same general formula, $M(OH)_4^-$, ($Zn(OH)_4^{--}$, $Al(OH)_4^-$, $Cr(OH)_4^-$, $Sn(OH)_4^{--}$, $Pb(OH)_4^{--}$, $Sb(OH)_4^-$).

If a solution of a strong acid is added, drop by drop, to a solution containing any one of the above complex hydroxo ions, the hydroxide of the metal is completely precipitated when the neutral point is reached. On further addition of acid the hydroxide dissolves to form a solution containing the cation of the metal. This behavior indicates that there exists an equilibrium of the type represented by the net equation

$$Cr(OH)_3 + OH^- \text{ (excess)} \rightleftharpoons Cr(OH)_4^-.$$

The hydrogen ions (acid) that are added remove OH^- ions, and thereby reduce the rate of reaction to the right. This causes the equilibrium to be shifted to the left, which causes $Cr(OH)_3$ to precipitate. When the excess OH^- ions have all been neutralized, the acid dissolves the basic hydroxide in the conventional manner indicated by the net equation

$$Cr(OH)_3 + 3 H^+ = Cr^{+++} + 3 H_2O.$$

If solutions of the complex hydroxo ions formed by dissolving the amphoteric hydroxides in sodium hydroxide are concentrated by evaporation solid salts of compositions represented by the formulas Na_2ZnO_2, Na_2SnO_2, and $NaAlO_2$ will crystallize out. This indicates that the solutions may have contained the ions ZnO_2^{--}, SnO_2^{--}, and AlO_2^-. The presence of these ions can be accounted for by equilibria of the type

$$Sn(OH)_4^{--} \rightleftharpoons SnO_2^{--} + 2 H_2O.$$

The question will arise as to why, among the many metal hydroxides, the six discussed above should be amphoteric while the others are not. We will find, if we examine the periodic table that, with the exception of chromium, the metals in question lie along the borderline between the characteristically nonmetallic elements in the upper right section of the table and the more characteristically metallic elements that occupy the rest of the table. Accordingly, these hydroxides, although predominantly basic, are also somewhat acidic in character.

The separation of aluminum, chromium, and zinc ions from iron, cobalt, nickel, and manganese ions depends upon the fact that the hydroxides of the first three elements are amphoteric whereas the hydroxides of the last four are not. If a solution containing a mixture of the cations of these seven metals is treated with an excess of sodium hydroxide, the hydroxides of iron, cobalt, nickel, and manganese, which are not amphoteric, will form precipitates, while the amphoteric hydroxides, $Al(OH)_3$, $Cr(OH)_3$, and $Zn(OH)_2$, will dissolve in excess NaOH to give the soluble $Al(OH)_4^-$, $Cr(OH)_4^-$, and $Zn(OH)_4^{--}$ ions. (See Procedure 16, page 130.)

Equilibria Involving Solids and Precipitates

Up to this point the various equilibrium systems that have been discussed have largely involved reactions in which all the predominant reacting species were in solution. Since the practice of qualitative analysis is concerned, to a very large degree, with the formation of precipitates and the dissolving of precipitates, it follows that, from both a practical and theoretical point of view, the most significant equilibria are those involving solids and precipitates. Consideration of equilibria involving solids brings up immediately certain practical questions whose answers are fundamental to an understanding of qualitative analysis. Why are some substances soluble in water while others are insoluble? Why will a certain combination of ions yield a precipitate under one set of conditions but not under another? What are the best conditions for removing the maximum quantity of an ion from solution? Just exactly what happens when precipitation takes place? Just exactly what happens when a substance dissolves in a specific solvent? Why will one solid dissolve in a specific reagent while another will not?

The most important questions of all, "Why are some substances soluble in water while others are not?" and "Why are some substances very soluble while others are slightly soluble?" cannot, unfortunately, be answered in any simple straightforward manner. We can marshal a lot of experimental data, and from these data, we can draw up solubility rules of the sort given on page 188. With these rules as a guide we can answer a great many questions of fact and we can predict, by analogy to related compounds, whether or not a certain compound will be soluble, but the fundamental question, "Why is $BaSO_4$ insoluble while $MgSO_4$ is soluble?" we are not able to answer with any degree of exactness. All we can say is that the attraction of water molecules for the Mg^{++} ions and SO_4^{--} ions that constitute the crystal of $MgSO_4$ is so great compared with the attraction of the units of the crystal for each other that water is able to tear the crystal apart and carry the ions into solution. The attraction of water molecules for Ba^{++} and SO_4^{--} ions is not great enough to compete successfully with the attraction of the units of the crystal for each other, so $BaSO_4$ does not go into solution.

When it comes to knowing *what happens when* a precipitate does form or a precipitate does dissolve, we are on much firmer ground. The fundamental concept that will serve as a guide in answering questions relating to the formation and dissolving of precipitates is that of *solubility product.*

Solubility Product

If an excess of sugar is mixed with water at a certain temperature the sugar will dissolve until the solution is saturated. To all appearances the sugar will then stop dissolving. If, however, we were to examine this saturated solution with eyes that would enable us to see molecules, we would observe that, in the saturated solution, sugar molecules are still going into solution at a steady rate. However, other sugar molecules are coming out of solution at the same rate. The net result is that the amount of solid sugar in the beaker remains the same. We say that the solid sugar is in *equilibrium* with its saturated solution, meaning thereby that the *rate* at which sugar is dissolving is exactly the same as the *rate* at which it is precipitating. We can represent this equilibrium condition by the equation

solid sugar $\rightleftharpoons$ sugar molecules in solution.

Had we watched the entire process from the time the sugar was first mixed with the water until the solution became saturated, we would have noted that, from the very first moment the sugar was dropped into the water, the solid sugar molecules went into solution at a definite steady rate per unit amount of surface and that this rate stayed absolutely constant all the time. We would have observed that just as soon as some sugar molecules had gone into solution an occasional molecule would hop out back on to the solid sugar. As the concentration of sugar molecules in solution increased, the number that came out of solution on to the sugar in a given space of time increased. Finally, when the concentration was sufficiently high, molecules came out of solution exactly as fast as they went in. The solution was then saturated. It is important to note that we observed that the rate at which sugar dissolved from a given amount of solid sugar surface was absolutely constant and was not influenced by the concentration of the sugar molecules already in the solution. The rate at which the sugar molecules came out of solution was, however, directly proportional to the concentration of sugar molecules in solution.

If we were to mix an excess of solid silver chloride, AgCl, which is a strong electrolyte, with water we would observe somewhat the same thing that we observed with sugar, but with one important difference: Solid AgCl dissolves at a steady rate per unit surface, and this rate is the same from start to finish. However, no AgCl molecules are observed in solution; only Ag^+ ions and Cl^- ions. Nevertheless, just as sugar molecules came out of solution, so Ag^+ ions and Cl^- ions come out of solution in the form of ion pairs and deposit as solid AgCl. As the concentration of Ag^+ and Cl^- ions in solution increases, the rate at which the $Ag^+–Cl^-$ ion pairs precipitate out of solution increases. This condition is what we would expect since, according to the mass law, the rate of a reaction is proportional to the concentration of the reactants. Finally, this rate of precipitation is equal to the *constant rate* at which AgCl is going into solution. Equilibrium is then established, not between solid AgCl and AgCl molecules in solution, but between solid AgCl and Ag^+ ions and Cl^- ions in solution. This equilibrium can be represented by the equation

$$AgCl \,(solid) \;\rightleftharpoons\; Ag^+ + Cl^-.$$

If we now add some Cl^- ions (in the form of NaCl) to the saturated solution in which Ag^+ and Cl^- ions are in equilibrium with solid AgCl, we observe that the rate at which the $Ag^+–Cl^-$ ion pairs come out of solution increases for a short time. Since the rate at which AgCl is dissolving is constant, as it has been all the time, AgCl is now precipitating faster than it is dissolving. As a result the amount of solid precipitate in the beaker increases. That means, of course, that Ag^+ ions and Cl^- ions are now being removed from solution faster than they are going into solution. As the concentration of Ag^+ ions and Cl^- ions in solution is reduced by their removal at a faster rate than they are dissolved, the rate at which they precipitate slows down. Finally, the rate at which $Ag^+–Cl^-$ ion pairs precipitate is again equal to the constant rate at which AgCl dissolves and equilibrium again exists. We now find that the solution contains more Cl^- ions than Ag^+ ions. However, we make **one** very important observation: The product of the molar concentrations of the Ag^+ ions and Cl^- ions in the new equilibrium solution is exactly the same as their product in the saturated solution to which no extra Cl^- ions had been added. If we had extended the experiment by adding additional Cl^- ions or additional Ag^+ ions, we would find that, *at a definite temperature, the product of the concentrations of the Ag^+ and Cl^- ions in equilibrium with solid AgCl is always constant.* Had we extended our study to other slightly soluble electrolytes, we would find that in every case the product of the concentrations of the ions in equilibrium with a specific precipitate is a constant. Each slightly soluble electrolyte has its own constant product. This constant product is called the *solubility product*. It is commonly referred to by the notation "K_{sp}" or "SP."

The fact that the product of the concentrations of the ions in equilibrium with a precipitate is a constant is strictly in accord with what has already been learned about equilibrium systems. Since the reaction

$$AgCl(solid) \rightleftharpoons Ag^+ + Cl^-$$

is a true equilibrium it follows the equilibrium law and will, therefore, have an equilibrium constant. That is,

$$\frac{[Ag^+] \times [Cl^-]}{[AgCl](solid)} = K.$$

We know from our study of solutions that the amount of excess solid solute in contact with a saturated solution at a given temperature has no effect on the concentration of the solute; that is, on the solubility of the solute. The amount of solute in a given amount of saturated solution at a given temperature will be the same whether we have a mere speck of excess solute or a very large amount. That means that, in the case of AgCl, the amount of excess solid AgCl has no effect whatever on the concentration of Ag^+ ions and Cl^- ions in a saturated solution. Since the solid AgCl has no effect at all, we can call this effect unity or, what amounts to the same thing, we can leave it out of the mass law equation entirely. The equation then becomes

$$K = [Ag^+] \times [Cl^-].$$

This equation tells us, simply, that the product of the concentrations (in moles per liter) of the solute ions in a saturated solution of a very slightly soluble electrolyte is constant at a given temperature. This constant, K, is the *solubility product constant*, or simply the *solubility product*.

The solubility product is the product of the concentrations of the solute ions in a saturated solution of a slightly soluble electrolyte. That means that, in a saturated solution of a slightly soluble electrolyte, the product of the concentrations of the ions is just equal to the solubility product of that electrolyte. If the product of the concentrations of the Ag^+ and Cl^- ions in a solution is *less* than K_{sp} for AgCl the solution is *unsaturated*. If, on the other hand, the prod-

TABLE 2.4. SOLUBILITY PRODUCTS AT 20°

Aluminum hydroxide	$[Al^{+++}] \times [OH^-]^3$	5	$\times 10^{-33}$
Barium carbonate	$[Ba^{++}] \times [CO_3^{--}]$	1.6	$\times 10^{-9}$
Barium chromate	$[Ba^{++}] \times [CrO_4^{--}]$	8.5	$\times 10^{-11}$
Barium sulfate	$[Ba^{++}] \times [SO_4^{--}]$	1.5	$\times 10^{-9}$
Barium oxalate	$[Ba^{++}] \times [C_2O_4^{--}]$	1.5	$\times 10^{-8}$
Bismuth sulfide	$[Bi^{+++}]^2 \times [S^{--}]^3$	1	$\times 10^{-70}$
Cadmium hydroxide	$[Cd^{++}] \times [OH^-]^2$	2	$\times 10^{-14}$
Cadmium sulfide	$[Cd^{++}] \times [S^{--}]$	6	$\times 10^{-27}$
Calcium carbonate	$[Ca^{++}] \times [CO_3^{--}]$	6.9	$\times 10^{-9}$
Calcium oxalate	$[Ca^{++}] \times [C_2O_4^{--}]$	1.3	$\times 10^{-9}$
Calcium sulfate	$[Ca^{++}] \times [SO_4^{--}]$	2.4	$\times 10^{-5}$
Chromium hydroxide	$[Cr^{+++}] \times [OH^-]^3$	7	$\times 10^{-31}$
Cobalt sulfide	$[Co^{++}] \times [S^{--}]$	5	$\times 10^{-22}$
Cupric hydroxide	$[Cu^{++}] \times [OH^-]^2$	1.6	$\times 10^{-19}$
Cupric sulfide	$[Cu^{++}] \times [S^{--}]$	4	$\times 10^{-36}$
Ferric hydroxide	$[Fe^{+++}] \times [OH^-]^3$	6	$\times 10^{-38}$
Ferrous hydroxide	$[Fe^{++}] \times [OH^-]^2$	2	$\times 10^{-15}$
Ferrous sulfide	$[Fe^{++}] \times [S^{--}]$	4	$\times 10^{-17}$
Lead carbonate	$[Pb^{++}] \times [CO_3^{--}]$	1.5	$\times 10^{-13}$
Lead chromate	$[Pb^{++}] \times [CrO_4^{--}]$	2	$\times 10^{-16}$
Lead iodide	$[Pb^{++}] \times [I^-]^2$	8.3	$\times 10^{-9}$
Lead sulfate	$[Pb^{++}] \times [SO_4^{--}]$	1.3	$\times 10^{-8}$
Lead sulfide	$[Pb^{++}] \times [S^{--}]$	4	$\times 10^{-26}$
Magnesium carbonate	$[Mg^{++}] \times [CO_3^{--}]$	4	$\times 10^{-5}$
Magnesium hydroxide	$[Mg^{++}] \times [OH^-]^2$	8.9	$\times 10^{-12}$
Magnesium oxalate	$[Mg^{++}] \times [C_2O_4^{--}]$	8.6	$\times 10^{-5}$
Manganese hydroxide	$[Mn^{++}] \times [OH^-]^2$	2	$\times 10^{-13}$
Manganese sulfide	$[Mn^{++}] \times [S^{--}]$	8	$\times 10^{-14}$
Mercurous chloride	$[Hg_2^{++}] \times [Cl^-]^2$	1.1	$\times 10^{-18}$
Mercuric sulfide	$[Hg^{++}] \times [S^{--}]$	1	$\times 10^{-50}$
Nickel hydroxide	$[Ni^{++}] \times [OH^-]^2$	1.6	$\times 10^{-16}$
Nickel sulfide	$[Ni^{++}] \times [S^{--}]$	1	$\times 10^{-22}$
Silver arsenate	$[Ag^+]^3 \times [AsO_4^{---}]$	1	$\times 10^{-23}$
Silver bromide	$[Ag^+] \times [Br^-]$	5	$\times 10^{-13}$
Silver carbonate	$[Ag^+]^2 \times [CO_3^{--}]$	8.2	$\times 10^{-12}$
Silver chloride	$[Ag^+] \times [Cl^-]$	2.8	$\times 10^{-10}$
Silver chromate	$[Ag^+]^2 \times [CrO_4^{--}]$	1.9	$\times 10^{-12}$
Silver iodate	$[Ag^+] \times [IO_3^-]$	3	$\times 10^{-8}$
Silver iodide	$[Ag^+] \times [I^-]$	8.5	$\times 10^{-17}$
Silver phosphate	$[Ag^+]^3 \times [PO_4^{---}]$	1.8	$\times 10^{-18}$
Silver sulfide	$[Ag^+]^2 \times [S^{--}]$	1	$\times 10^{-50}$
Silver thiocyanate	$[Ag^+] \times [CNS^-]$	1	$\times 10^{-12}$
Stannous sulfide	$[Sn^{++}] \times [S^{--}]$	1	$\times 10^{-24}$
Zinc hydroxide	$[Zn^{++}] \times [OH^-]^2$	5	$\times 10^{-17}$
Zinc sulfide	$[Zn^{++}] \times [S^{--}]$	1	$\times 10^{-20}$

uct of the concentrations of the Ag^+ and Cl^- ions is greater than K_{sp} for AgCl, silver chloride will settle out as a precipitate. Furthermore, AgCl will keep on precipitating until enough Ag^+ and Cl^- ions have been removed to lower the product of their concentrations to the value of the solubility product.

Determinition of Solubility Products

The solubility products of the slightly soluble electrolytes listed in Table 2.4 were in most instances determined in the following manner. The solubility of the compound in pure water at 20°C. was determined with great accuracy. From these solubility data the solubility product was then calculated. To illustrate, the solubility of $BaSO_4$ was found to be exactly 1×10^{-5} mole of $BaSO_4$ per liter. Since the $BaSO_4$ is 100 per cent ionized, and since the ionization equation, $BaSO_4 \rightleftarrows Ba^{++} + SO_4^{--}$, shows that 1 mole of $BaSO_4$ yields 1 mole of Ba^{++} and 1 mole of SO_4^{--}, the saturated solution will contain 1×10^{-5} mole of Ba^{++} and 1×10^{-5} mole of SO_4^{--} per liter.

$$K_{sp} = [Ba^{++}] \times [SO_4^{--}] = 1 \times 10^{-5} \times 1 \times 10^{-5} = 1 \times 10^{-10}.$$

The solubility product in the above case is calculated for the simplest type of salt, namely, one that yields one positive ion and one negative ion from each molar unit that dissociates. In its more general form the solubility product formula requires that the concentration of each ion be raised to a power equal to the number of that ion derived from one molar unit of the compound. This is in accord with the mass law formula (page 17).

$$Mg(OH)_2 \rightleftarrows Mg^{++} + 2\,OH^-, \qquad K_{sp} = [Mg^{++}] \times [OH^-]^2,$$

$$Ag_3PO_4 \rightleftarrows 3\,Ag^+ + PO_4^{---}, \qquad K_{sp} = [Ag^+]^3 \times [PO_4^{---}].$$

The solubility of $Mg(OH)_2$ is 0.000150 mole per liter. Since the dissolved $Mg(OH)_2$ is completely ionized, the Mg^{++} ion concentration will be 0.000150 mole per liter. The OH^- ion concentration will be twice this amount, since each molecule produces two hydroxyl ions.

The solubility product is therefore

$$[Mg^{++}] \times [OH^-]^2 = K_{sp},$$

$$0.00015 \times (0.0003)^2 = 1.35 \times 10^{-11}.$$

If the solubility product is a very small number it shows that the substance is very slightly soluble and that only very low concentrations of its ions can exist together in solution; if the product is a large number the solubility is greater. In comparing solubility products as a means of estimating the relative solubilities of substances it is important to remember that the solubility product is a fair basis of comparison only if the molar units of the substances being compared yield the same number of ions. One molar unit of AgCl and one molar unit of $MgCO_3$ each yield two ions, one positive, one negative. The solubility product of AgCl is represented by the product, $[Ag^+] \times [Cl^-]$, while the solubility product of $MgCO_3$ is represented by the product $[Mg^{++}] \times [CO_3^{--}]$. It follows, therefore, that if the solubility products of the two substances are equal, the same number of moles of each must have dissolved in a liter of solution. Vice versa, if the same number of moles of each dissolve in a liter of solution, the two solubility products will be the same. When the two substances yield a different number of ions per molar unit their solubility products do not indicate directly their relative solubilities. Suppose, for example, that the two substances $Ba(OH)_2$ and $CaCrO_4$ are both soluble to the same extent of 0.01 of a mole per liter. That means that a liter of the saturated solution of $CaCrO_4$ will contain 0.01 mole of Ca^{++} and 0.01 mole of CrO_4, and the solubility product of $CaCrO_4$ will be 0.01×0.01 or 0.0001. A liter of a saturated solution of $Ba(OH)_2$ will contain 0.01 mole of Ba^{++} and 0.02 mole of OH^-. The solubility product equation for $Ba(OH)_2$ is $[Ba^{++}] \times [OH^-]^2$. The solubility product of $Ba(OH)_2$ will accordingly be $(0.01) \times (0.02)^2$, or 0.000004. That means that, although the molar solubilities of $CaCrO_4$ and $Ba(OH)_2$ are the same, the solubility product of $CaCrO_4$ is 25 times as great as that of $Ba(OH)_2$. (See problems 17 to 20, page 72.)

Effect of a Common Ion on the Formation of a Precipitate

If 1 mole of $Pb(NO_3)_2$ and 1 mole of Na_2SO_4 are brought together in a liter of solution at 20°C., precipitation takes place until 0.0207 g. of Pb^{++} ions remains in solution. If an excess of 0.0006 mole of Na_2SO_4 is present in the solution, only 0.0035 g. of lead ions remains in solution. Such a result is entirely in accordance with the solubility product principle and the equilibrium which is involved. If we examine the equation representing the equilibrium,

$$PbSO_4 \text{ (solid)} \rightleftharpoons Pb^{++} + SO_4^{--},$$

it is apparent that, if the concentration of SO_4^{--} in the solution is increased, the equilibrium will be shifted to the left. This will reduce the concentration of Pb^{++} ions in solution and will cause more $PbSO_4$ to be precipitated.

The solubility product equation is

$$[Pb^{++}] \times [SO_4^{--}] = K_{sp},$$

and the experimentally determined value of K_{sp} for $PbSO_4$ at 20°C is 1×10^{-8}. Since the product of the concentrations of the Pb^{++} and SO_4^{--} ions can never exceed 1×10^{-8}, it is obvious that as the concentration of sulfate ion in solution is increased the concentration of the lead ions must be reduced. If we wish to leave as little of the lead ions as possible in solution we must add a large excess of sulfate ions. In general, to get maximum precipitation of a compound, AB, and thereby leave a minimum concentration of A^+ ions in solution, an excess of the reagent, B^-, should be added

$$AB \text{ (solid)} \rightleftharpoons A^+ + \mathbf{B^-}.$$

Since the solubility of a solid usually decreases as the temperature decreases, it is obvious that maximum precipitation will result if the temperature is kept as low as possible. Also, one should, whenever a choice is possible, precipitate the ion that is to be removed from solution in the form of its least soluble compound. A glance at Table 2.4 will show that Pb^{++} ions will be removed from solution more completely if they are precipitated as $PbCrO_4$ ($K_{sp} = 2 \times 10^{-16}$) than if they are precipitated as $PbSO_4$. ($K_{sp} = 1 \times 10^{-8}$)

It should be noted that the solubility product equation is valid only in case the salt is relatively insoluble. Further, the common ion effect cannot be extended indefinitely; the precipitate may react with the excess ions to form a complex ion.

Dissolving Precipitates

A precipitate will go into solution if the product of the concentrations of its ions in solution is less than its solubility product. It will keep on dissolving until the product of the concentration of its ions in solution equals the solubility product. Just how a precipitate is dissolved in actual practice, just what happens when a precipitate dissolves, and just why a certain solvent will dissolve one precipitate but will not dissolve another can best be shown by considering some specific cases.

Ag_3PO_4 is soluble in dilute HNO_3. That means that when HNO_3 is added to solid Ag_3PO_4 a condition is created in which the product of the concentrations of PO_4^{---} and $(Ag^+)^3$ is less than the solubility product for Ag_3PO_4. The actual solution process probably proceeds somewhat as follows: When Ag_3PO_4 is brought in contact with water or a water solution the following equilibrium is set up:

(a) $$Ag_3PO_4 \rightleftharpoons 3\,Ag^+ + PO_4^{---}.$$

This is a true equilibrium in that the *rate* at which silver ions and phosphate ions combine to form solid Ag_3PO_4 is exactly equal to the *rate* at which solid Ag_3PO_4 dissolves and dissociates into Ag^+ and PO_4^{---} ions. The rate at which Ag^+ and PO_4^{---} ions combine is directly proportional to the concentration of each ion. The rate at which Ag_3PO_4 dissolves from unit surface of solid Ag_3PO_4 is constant at a given temperature; that is, Ag_3PO_4 dissolves at a constant rate, and this rate is not affected by the concentration of the Ag^+ and PO_4^{---} ions in solution. If the strong acid HNO_3 is added to the system, the H^+ ions which it provides will combine with the PO_4^{---} ions and tie them up in the form of molecules of the *weak acid*, H_3PO_4.

(b) $$PO_4^{---} + 3\,H^+ \rightleftharpoons H_3PO_4.$$

This will reduce the concentration of PO_4^{---} ions in solution. This reduction in the concentration of PO_4^{---} ions will reduce the rate at which Ag^+ ions and PO_4^{---} ions combine to form solid Ag_3PO_4. Since Ag_3PO_4 keeps right on dissolving at the same constant rate, we now have a situation in which solid Ag_3PO_4 is being formed at a *slower rate* than it is dissolving. If the rate at which Ag^+ and PO_4^{---} ions combine is kept slowed down by adding enough HNO_3 to give enough H^+ ions to tie up enough PO_4^{---} ions and, thereby, keep their concentration low, the Ag_3PO_4 will eventually all go into solution.

Exactly the same sort of thing happens when Ag_3AsO_4 is dissolved by HNO_3. The equilibrium that exists between solid Ag_3AsO_4 and its ions in the saturated solution is represented by equation (a).

(a) $$Ag_3AsO_4 \rightleftharpoons 3\,Ag^+ + AsO_4^{---}.$$

(b) $$AsO_4^{---} + 3\,H^+ \rightleftharpoons H_3AsO_4.$$

The H^+ ions from HNO_3 combine with the AsO_4^{---} ions to form the *weak electrolyte* H_3AsO_4. This reduces the concentration of AsO_4^{---} ions in solution and, thereby, slows down the rate at which Ag^+ ions and AsO_4^{---} ions combine to form solid Ag_3AsO_4. Since the rate at which the solid Ag_3AsO_4 dissolves from unit surface of the solid is constant, solid Ag_3AsO_4 will now be dissolving faster than it is being precipitated; if the difference in rate is maintained by adding enough HNO_3, the Ag_3AsO_4 will eventually all dissolve. It should be emphasized that the HNO_3 does not make the solid Ag_3AsO_4 (or Ag_3PO_4) go into solution any faster; the presence of the HNO_3 simply causes the precipitate of Ag_3AsO_4 to form more slowly.

The product of the concentrations of the ions that are in equilibrium with a precipitate is, by definition, the solubility product. Therefore, to say that Ag_3AsO_4 dissolves because the concentration of AsO_4^{---} ions is reduced to such a low value that the rate at which Ag^+ and AsO_4^{---} combine to form solid Ag_3AsO_4 is slower than the rate at which Ag_3AsO_4 dissolves, is equivalent to saying that the concentration of AsO_4^{---} has been lowered below the solubility product concentration for Ag_3AsO_4. As long as the concentration of the ions in solution is less than the concentration required to equal the solubility product constant, the solid will precipitate at a slower rate than it dissolves. Stated differently, a solid will dissolve if the concentration of its ions in solution is less than the concentration required to equal the solubility product. The inevitable result, if this situation is maintained, is that the solid will all go into solution.

We will find that $AgCl$ will not dissolve in HNO_3. Why? Like all other sparingly soluble electrolytes, solid silver chloride exists in equilibrium with its ions in saturated solution according to the equation

$$\textbf{AgCl}\,(\text{solid}) \rightleftharpoons \textbf{Ag}^+ + \textbf{Cl}^-.$$

At equilibrium the rate at which Ag^+ and Cl^- combine to form solid $AgCl$ per unit of solid surface is equal to the constant rate at which solid $AgCl$ dissolves. When HNO_3 is added there is no change in the concentration of either the Ag^+ ions or Cl^- ions (except for a negligible dilution effect). Hydrogen ions do not tie up Cl^- ions; neither do NO_3^- ions tie up Ag^+ ions. The reason is that both HCl and $AgNO_3$ are strong electrolytes. Since the concentrations of Ag^+ and Cl^- ions remain the same, the rate at which they combine to form solid $AgCl$ remains the same, and $AgCl$ continues to precipitate just as fast as it dissolves.

If we re-examine the three cases that we have considered and also note a number of additional cases, we will arrive at the following general interpretation of what happens when any solid electrolyte is dissolved: First, the solid electrolyte exists in equilibrium with its ions as represented by equation (a).

(a) $Ag_3PO_4 \rightleftharpoons 3\,Ag^+ + PO_4^{---}$,

(b) $PO_4^{---} + 3\,H^+ \rightleftharpoons H_3PO_4$.

The solvent ion or molecule (H^+ in this case) then reacts with one of these ions (PO_4^{---} in this case) and ties it up in the form of a stable substance (H_3PO_4 in this case) in accordance with a second equation, (b). This reduces the concentration of the ion (PO_4^{---}) with which the solvent has combined below the solubility product concentration required for equation (a). As a result, the rate with which the two ions in equation (a) combine to form the precipitate is slowed down and, as a consequence, the precipitate dissolves faster than it precipitates. Eventually it will be completely dissolved.

The stable substance formed in (b) may be either a weak electrolyte, a nonelectrolyte, a complex ion, or a highly insoluble precipitate. In most instances (b) represents an incomplete reaction; in a few cases the reaction is complete. In any case (a) and (b) have an ion in common, and it is imperative that the concentration of this common ion in reaction (b) always be kept lower than the equilibrium solubility product concentration needed for reaction (a). As long as this requirement is met the precipitate will keep on going into solution faster than it precipitates and will eventually be completely dissolved. In effect, lowering the concentration of the common ion causes the equilibrium in reaction (a) to be shifted (pulled) to the right; this shift leads, eventually, to the complete dissolving of the precipitate. If the concentration of the common ion in equilibrium (b) is less than the concentration required to satisfy the equilibrium in (a) the total reaction will run "down hill," from the precipitate in (a) to the stable substance in (b).

Ag_3PO_4 and Ag_3AsO_4 dissolved in HNO_3 because the anions, PO_4^{---} and AsO_4^{---}, were tied up in the form of the weak acids H_3PO_4 and H_3AsO_4. The weak acids were formed because Ag_3PO_4 and Ag_3AsO_4 are salts of weak acids. We can state that, as a general rule, *the insoluble salt of a weak acid will dissolve in a strong acid.* In agreement with this rule the phosphates, arsenates, carbonates, sulfites, borates, and chromates of all metals are soluble in strong acids.

AgCl will not dissolve in HNO_3 because, being the salt of a strong acid, its anion cannot be tied up by H^+ ions. Likewise AgBr, AgI, $PbSO_4$, and $BaSO_4$ are not soluble in strong acids such as HNO_3, HCl, or H_2SO_4 because they are themselves salts of strong acids. We can conclude from these examples that *the insoluble salt of a strong acid will not dissolve in a strong acid;* since weak acids provide fewer H^+ ions, the salts of strong acids obviously will not dissolve in weak acids either.

Mercury(II) sulfide is the salt of the weak acid, H_2S. In accordance with the rule stated above, it should be soluble in the strong acid HCl. Actually, it is not dissolved by HCl. The reason is that HgS is so highly insoluble that the concentration of sulfide ions in equilibrium with solid HgS in equation (a) is so small that it is much lower than the concentration of sulfide ions in equation (b) even when the equilibrium point in the latter equation is shifted far to the right by a high concentration of H^+ ions.

(a) $$\mathbf{HgS} \rightleftharpoons Hg^{++} + S^{--},$$

(b) $$S^{--} + 2\,H^+ \rightleftharpoons H_2S.$$

The failure of HgS to be dissolved by HCl emphasizes the fact that if a solid electrolyte is to dissolve, not only must one of its ions be tied up in the form of a weak electrolyte, a complex ion, or other stable substance, but the concentration of this ion in equilibrium with the stable substance must always be less than its concentration in equilibrium with the solid electrolyte.

AgCl, which is insoluble in all acids will, however, dissolve in ammonium hydroxide. Here is what happens.

(a) $$\mathbf{AgCl} \rightleftharpoons Ag^+ + Cl^-,$$

(b) $$Ag^+ + 2\,NH_3 \rightleftharpoons Ag(NH_3)_2^+.$$

The NH_3 from NH_4OH ($NH_4OH \rightleftharpoons NH_3 + H_2O$) combines with Ag^+ to form the stable complex ion, $Ag(NH_3)_2^+$, in accordance with equation (b). This reduces the concentration of Ag^+ below the equilibrium value required for equation (a).

Silver iodide, AgI, will not dissolve in NH_4OH. It is so insoluble that the concentration of Ag^+ ions in the equilibrium

(a) $$\mathbf{AgI} \rightleftharpoons Ag^+ + I^-$$

is always less than the concentration of Ag^+ ions in the equilibrium

(b) $$Ag^+ + 2\,NH_3 \rightleftharpoons Ag(NH_3)_2^+.$$

AgI can be dissolved by CN^- ions. The reason is that the complex $Ag(CN)_2^-$ ion which is involved in the process represented by the equations

(a) $$AgI \rightleftharpoons Ag^+ + I^-,$$

(b) $$Ag^+ + 2 CN^- \rightleftharpoons Ag(CN)_2^-,$$

is very stable and, as a result, holds the Ag^+ ion in equilibrium at a concentration which is even lower than the concentration of Ag^+ ions in equilibrium with AgI. The fact that the instability constant for $Ag(CN)_2^-$ (see Table 2.3) is 1.8×10^{-19}, while the constant for $Ag(NH_3)_2^+$ is 6×10^{-8} shows that $Ag(CN)_2^-$ is much more stable than $Ag(NH_3)_2^+$. In this instance as in all the other cases that we have discussed, a high concentration of the solvent ion or molecule (CN^-, in this case) shifts equation (b) to the right and keeps the concentration of the common ion at a very low level.

When the hydroxide of a metal is dissolved by an acid in the manner already discussed under amphoterism, the conditions that we have set up for dissolving a precipitate are realized.

(a) $$Zn(OH)_2 \rightleftharpoons Zn^{++} + 2 OH^-,$$

(b) $$OH^- + H^+ \rightleftharpoons H_2O.$$

The common ion is OH^-, the solvent ion is H^+, and the stable, soluble molecule is H_2O.

When an amphoteric hydroxide dissolves in a strong base the requirements that we have set up are again fulfilled.

(a) $$Zn(OH)_2 \rightleftharpoons Zn^{++} + 2 OH^-,$$

(b) $$Zn^{++} + 4 OH^- \rightleftharpoons Zn(OH)_4^{--}.$$

The common ion is Zn^{++}, and the stable, soluble substance is the complex ion.

Although $Mg(OH)_2$ is very sparingly soluble in water, it is readily dissolved by a solution of NH_4Cl, NH_4NO_3, or $(NH_4)_2SO_4$. The following reactions are involved.

(a) $$Mg(OH)_2 \rightleftharpoons 2 OH^- + Mg^{++},$$

(b) $$OH^- + NH_4^+ \rightleftharpoons NH_4OH.$$

The NH_4^+ ions from the ammonium salt combine with the OH^- ions formed in equation (a) and tie them up as molecules of NH_4OH in the manner represented by equation (b).

In certain cases it is not possible to find any solvent that will form a soluble ion or molecule of sufficient stability to cause the solid to dissolve. In some such cases one can resort to the technique of destroying an ion by having it take part in a complete reaction. That is what happens when the sulfides of copper, lead, bismuth, and cadmium are dissolved in nitric acid in the analysis of the copper group.

(a) $\mathbf{CuS} \rightleftharpoons Cu^{++} + S^{--}$,

(b) $S^{--} + 2\,NO_3^- + 4\,H^+ = S + 2\,NO_2 + 2\,H_2O$.

The common ion in this case is S^{--}.

The dissolving of carbonates and sulfites by a strong acid illustrates the special case where the soluble substance that is formed is not only sparingly ionized but is also present in very low concentration due to the fact that it is partially decomposed into an insoluble gaseous product.

(a) $\mathbf{CaCO_3} \rightleftharpoons Ca^{++} + CO_3^{--}$,

(b) $CO_3^{--} + 2\,H^+ \rightleftharpoons H_2CO_3 \rightleftharpoons H_2O + CO_2$.

A very insoluble substance which, accordingly, is in equilibrium with a very low concentration of ions, will not only be very difficult to dissolve at all but will also dissolve very slowly. In such a case it may be expedient to work on both of its ions at the same time. That is what is believed to happen when HgS is dissolved in a mixture of HNO_3 and HCl.

(a) $\mathbf{HgS} \rightleftharpoons Hg^{++} + S^{--}$,

(b₁) $Hg^{++} + 4\,Cl^-$ (from HCl) $\rightleftharpoons HgCl_4^{--}$,

(b₂) $S^{--} + 2\,NO_3^- + 4\,H^+ = S + 2\,NO_2 + 2\,H_2O$.

In certain instances the dissolving of one solid electrolyte is attended by the precipitation of another electrolyte. Thus if a solution of NaCl is added to some solid Ag_3PO_4, the Ag_3PO_4 dissolves, but a precipitate of AgCl forms.

(a) $\mathbf{Ag_3PO_4} \rightleftharpoons 3\,Ag^+ + PO_4^{---}$,

(b) $Ag^+ + Cl^- \rightleftharpoons AgCl$.

AgCl is less soluble than Ag_3PO_4. That means that the concentration of Ag^+ ions required to exceed the solubility product for AgCl in reaction (b) is less than the solubility product concentration of Ag^+ in reaction (a).

When $PbSO_4$ is dissolved by Na_2CO_3 solution the following equilibria are set up.

(a) $$PbSO_4 \rightleftharpoons Pb^{++} + SO_4^{--},$$

(b) $$Pb^{++} + CO_3^{--} \rightleftharpoons PbCO_3.$$

If the concentration of carbonate ions is kept very high, by using a saturated solution of Na_2CO_3, the concentration of Pb^{++} ions in equilibrium (b) will be kept so low that it will be below the concentration of Pb^{++} required for equilibrium (a). As a result $PbSO_4$ will go into solution more rapidly than it is being precipitated. Any water-insoluble salt will behave as did $PbSO_4$; in each instance the cation (metal) of which the solid is composed will be precipitated as the carbonate but the anion will go into the solution. This, therefore, provides a convenient method for preparing a solution of the anions of water-insoluble salts. (See Procedure 30 c, page 183.) Since the metal carbonates are all readily soluble in dilute acids, digestion of an acid-insoluble salt with sodium carbonate solution, followed by treatment of the metal carbonate with dilute acid, is a convenient method for preparing a solution containing the cations of such a solid.

It should be pointed out that the common ion involved in the solution equilibria that have just been discussed may be involved in other equilibria that have no direct connection with the actual dissolving process. For example, solid As_2S_5 is readily dissolved by a solution of $(NH_4)_2S$, the stable soluble complex ion, AsS_4^{---}, being formed in the process. (See Note 2, Procedure 6.) The two reactions directly involved can be considered to be

(a) $$As_2S_5 \rightleftharpoons 2 As^{+++++} + 5 S^{--},$$

(b) $$As^{+++++} + 4 S^{--} \rightleftharpoons AsS_4^{---}.$$

However, the As^{+++++} ions are very strongly hydrolyzed according to the equilibrium reaction

(c) $$As^{+++++} + 4 H_2O \rightleftharpoons H_3AsO_4 + 5 H^+.$$

Reaction (c) is not directly involved in the solution process. However, it does play a very important role in determining the concentration of As^{+++++} ions that are in equilibrium with the solid As_2S_5.

A substance that will dissolve a precipitate will obviously keep that precipitate from forming in the first place. Thus Ag_3PO_4 and Ag_3AsO_4 will not precipitate from a solution when the hydrogen ion concentration (acidity) is too high, while $Mg(OH)_2$ will not precipitate from a solution which contains a high concentration of NH_4^+ ions. The latter case is of particular interest since, in the precipitation of the cations of the aluminum-nickel group, ammonium chloride is deliberately added so as to prevent $Mg(OH)_2$ from being precipitated when NH_4OH is added as a group reagent. (See Note 4, page 127.)

Chemical Reactions

One of the major problems faced in qualitative analysis is that of deciding whether or not a reaction will take place when two or more substances are brought together in solution and, if they do react, of knowing what products are formed. In the majority of instances the decision is relatively simple if certain rules of chemical behavior, based on experimental facts, are kept in mind; in some cases, however, the answers are determined by very specific properties of the reactants. The next few pages of this chapter will present those rules of chemical behavior, and those facts that will aid in determining what reactions take place in the procedures outlined in this book.

We will note, as we follow through the analytical procedures that are presented, that all the chemical reactions encountered fall into one of the three following classes:

1. Direct combination of an anion with a cation.
2. Complex ion formation.
3. Oxidation-reduction.

Direct Combination of an Anion with a Cation

The large majority of reactions in qualitative analysis involve simple, direct combinations of an anion with a cation. One can state that, *as a general rule, whenever two electrolytes are brought together in solution, or under such conditions that a solution can form, the positive ion of one electrolyte will always* **tend** *to combine with the negative ion of the other electrolyte to form a compound;* the chemical formula of the compound will be determined by the valences of the combining ions. The simple combination of oppositely charged ions to form a compound will actually take place only if:

1. The resulting compound is insoluble or decomposes to give an insoluble substance, or

2. The resulting compound is a weak electrolyte, and hence is only slightly ionized, and

3. Neither of the ions becomes involved in an oxidation-reduction reaction.

The solubility rules, given on page 188, identify most of the *insoluble compounds;* the schemes of analysis include any insoluble compounds not covered by the solubility rules.

The *weak electrolytes* with which we will be concerned are H_2O, the weak base NH_4OH, the weak acids H_2S, $HC_2H_3O_2$, H_3BO_3, H_3AsO_4, H_3PO_4, H_2CO_3, H_2SO_3, and the complex ions. Two of the weak acids, H_2CO_3 and H_2SO_3, are unstable and decompose to give the sparingly soluble gases CO_2 and SO_2.

Complex Ion Formation

Complex ions have already been discussed on page 24. Although it is not possible to state simple rules that will enable us to know when a complex ion will be formed and what its formula will be, the following generalizations provide some clues.

1. The cations of the b-Group elements in the periodic table have a strong tendency to form complex ions. The Silver, Copper-Arsenic and Aluminum-Nickel group elements are made up, predominantly, of b-Group cations and, accordingly, form many stable complex ions.

2. The Group Ia and IIa metals form few complex ions. For this reason no complex ions are encountered in the Barium-Magnesium group.

3. All cations except those in the Barium-Magnesium group form stable complex chloro-ions of the type $HgCl_4^{--}$, particularly in solutions of high Cl^- ion concentration, as, for example, when a metal or its sulfide is dissolved in aqua regia.

4. When a precipitate redissolves in an excess of the precipitating ion or molecule a complex ion must be formed. Thus when the $Cu(OH)_2$, $Cd(OH)_2$, $Zn(OH)_2$, $Ni(OH)_2$, and $Co(OH)_2$, which are precipitated when NH_4OH is added to solutions of the respective cations redissolve in an excess of NH_4OH, we can be sure that complex ions of the type $Cu(NH_3)_4^{++}$ and $Ni(NH_3)_6^{++}$ are formed. Likewise, when $Al(OH)_3$ dissolves in excess OH^- and $Cd(CN)_2$

dissolves in excess CN^-, complex ions of the types $Al(OH)_4^-$ and $Cd(CN)_4^{--}$ must be formed.

Oxidation-Reduction Reactions

The following facts and generalizations will help determine whether or not an oxidation-reduction reaction will occur.

1. In order that a particular ion or molecule shall be able to function as an *oxidizing agent* it must contain an atom that can exist in more than one oxidation state; furthermore, in the particular ion or molecule the atom must be present in the *higher* of two oxidation states. Chromium has an oxidation number of 6 in $Cr_2O_7^{--}$ and 3 in Cr^{+++}. Therefore $Cr_2O_7^{--}$ is able to function as an oxidizing agent.

2. In order that a particular ion or molecule shall be able to function as a *reducing agent* it must contain an atom that can exist in more than one oxidation state; furthermore, in this particular ion or molecule the atom must be present in the *lower* of two oxidation states. Sulfur has an oxidation number of -2 in H_2S and 0 in S. Therefore H_2S is able to function as a reducing agent.

3. When an oxidizing agent and a reducing agent are brought together in solution, an oxidation-reduction reaction will take place provided the former is a strong enough oxidizing agent and the latter is a strong enough reducing agent. Whether or not they are strong enough to react can be decided by noting their relative positions in a *Table of Oxidation Potentials* such as Table 2.5.

A Table of Oxidation Potentials consists of a list of equilibrium reactions in which a substance on the left loses one or more electrons and is thereby converted to a substance on the right. Since a loss of electrons means that a substance has been oxidized and since the substance which is oxidized must thereby be functioning as a reducing agent it follows that *each substance on the left is functioning as a reducing agent.* The fact that the reactions reach a state of equilibrium means that, in each reaction, the substance on the right will react to form the substance on the left. To do so it must gain one or more electrons. When a substance gains electrons it is reduced, and during this process of being reduced it is functioning as an oxidizing agent. That means that all of *the substances on the right are oxidizing agents.*

On the extreme right in the table will be found, opposite each equation, a number, in volts. This number represents the *driving*

TABLE 2.5. STANDARD OXIDATION POTENTIALS
IN ACID SOLUTION

Reaction	Potential, $E°$ (in volts)
1. $K \rightleftarrows K^+ + e^-$	2.925
2. $Ba \rightleftarrows Ba^{++} + 2e^-$	2.90
3. $Ca \rightleftarrows Ca^{++} + 2e^-$	2.87
4. $Na \rightleftarrows Na^+ + e^-$	2.714
5. $Mg \rightleftarrows Mg^{++} + 2e^-$	2.37
6. $Al \rightleftarrows Al^{+++} + 3e^-$	1.66
7. $Mn \rightleftarrows Mn^{++} + 2e^-$	1.18
8. $Zn \rightleftarrows Zn^{++} + 2e^-$	0.763
9. $Cr \rightleftarrows Cr^{+++} + 3e^-$	0.74
10. $H_2Te \rightleftarrows Te + 2H^+ + 2e^-$	0.72
11. $AsH_3 \rightleftarrows As + 3H^+ + 3e^-$	0.60
12. $H_3PO_2 + H_2O \rightleftarrows H_3PO_3 + 2H^+ + 2e^-$	0.50
13. $Fe \rightleftarrows Fe^{++} + 2e^-$	0.440
14. $Cr^{++} \rightleftarrows Cr^{+++} + e^-$	0.41
15. $Cd \rightleftarrows Cd^{++} + 2e^-$	0.403
16. $H_2Se \rightleftarrows Se + 2H^+ + 2e^-$	0.40
17. $Pb + SO_4^{--} \rightleftarrows PbSO_4 + 2e^-$	0.356
18. $Co \rightleftarrows Co^{++} + 2e^-$	0.277
19. $H_3PO_3 + H_2O \rightleftarrows H_3PO_4 + 2H^+ + 2e^-$	0.276
20. $Ni \rightleftarrows Ni^{++} + 2e^-$	0.250
21. $Sn \rightleftarrows Sn^{++} + 2e^-$	0.136
22. $Pb \rightleftarrows Pb^{++} + 2e^-$	0.126
23. $HS_2O_4^- + 2H_2O \rightleftarrows 2H_2SO_3 + H^+ + 2e^-$	0.08
24. $H_2 \rightleftarrows 2H^+ + 2e^-$	0.000
25. $HCHO + H_2O \rightleftarrows HCOOH + 2H^+ + 2e^-$	−0.056
26. $PH_3 \rightleftarrows P + 3H^+ + 3e^-$	−0.06
27. $2S_2O_3^{--} \rightleftarrows S_4O_6^{--} + 2e^-$	−0.08
28. $H_2S \rightleftarrows 2H^+ + S + 2e^-$	−0.141
29. $Sn^{++} \rightleftarrows Sn^{++++} + 2e^-$	−0.15
30. $H_2SO_3 + H_2O \rightleftarrows SO_4^{--} + 4H^+ + 2e^-$	−0.17
31. $2Hg + 2Cl^- \rightleftarrows Hg_2Cl_2 + 2e^-$	−0.2676
32. $Cu \rightleftarrows Cu^{++} + 2e^-$	−0.337
33. $S + 3H_2O \rightleftarrows H_2SO_3 + 4H^+ + 4e^-$	−0.45
34. $2I^- \rightleftarrows I_2 + 2e^-$	−0.5355
35. $H_3AsO_3 + H_2O \rightleftarrows H_3AsO_4 + 2H^+ + 2e^-$	−0.559
36. $MnO_4^{--} \rightleftarrows MnO_4^- + e^-$	−0.564
37. $H_2O_2 \rightleftarrows O_2 + 2H^+ + 2e^-$	−0.682
38. $Fe^{++} \rightleftarrows Fe^{+++} + e^-$	−0.771
39. $Ag \rightleftarrows Ag^+ + e^-$	−0.7991
40. $NO_2 + H_2O \rightleftarrows NO_3^- + 2H^+ + e^-$	−0.80
41. $Hg \rightleftarrows Hg^{++} + 2e^-$	−0.854
42. $NO + 2H_2O \rightleftarrows NO_3^- + 4H^+ + 3e^-$	−0.96
43. $NO + H_2O \rightleftarrows HNO_2 + H^+ + e^-$	−1.00

TABLE 2.5. STANDARD OXIDATION POTENTIALS
IN ACID SOLUTION (Cont.)

Reaction	Potential, $E°$ (in volts)
44. $I^- + H_2O \rightleftarrows HOI + H^+ + 2e^-$	−1.00
45. $2 Br^- \rightleftarrows Br_2 (aq) + 2e^-$	−1.065
46. $H_2SeO_3 + H_2O \rightleftarrows SeO_4^{--} + 4 H^+ + 2e^-$	−1.15
47. $2 H_2O \rightleftarrows O_2 + 4 H^+ + 4e^-$	−1.229
48. $Mn^{++} + 2 H_2O \rightleftarrows MnO_2 + 4 H^+ + 2e^-$	−1.23
49. $2 Cr^{+++} + 7 H_2O \rightleftarrows Cr_2O_7^{--} + 14 H^+ + 6e^-$	−1.33
50. $2 Cl^- \rightleftarrows Cl_2 (aq) + 2e^-$	−1.3595
51. $Cl^- + 3 H_2O \rightleftarrows ClO_3^- + 6 H^+ + 6e^-$	−1.45
52. $Pb^{++} + 2 H_2O \rightleftarrows PbO_2 + 4 H^+ + 2e^-$	−1.455
53. $Cl^- + H_2O \rightleftarrows HOCl + H^+ + 2e^-$	−1.49
54. $Mn^{++} + 4 H_2O \rightleftarrows MnO_4^- + 8 H^+ + 5e^-$	−1.51
55. $Ce^{+++} \rightleftarrows Ce^{++++} + e^-$	−1.61
56. $PbSO_4 + 2 H_2O \rightleftarrows PbO_2 + SO_4^{--} + 4 H^+ + 2e^-$	−1.685
57. $MnO_2 + 2 H_2O \rightleftarrows MnO_4^- + 4 H^+ + 3e^-$	−1.695
58. $Bi^{+++} + 3 H_2O \rightleftarrows HBiO_3 + 5 H^+ + 2e^-$	−1.70
59. $2 H_2O \rightleftarrows H_2O_2 + 2 H^+ + 2e^-$	−1.77
60. $Co^{++} \rightleftarrows Co^{+++} + e^-$	−1.82
61. $2 SO_4^{--} \rightleftarrows S_2O_8^{--} + 2e^-$	−1.91
62. $O_2 + H_2O \rightleftarrows O_3 + 2 H^+ + 2e^-$	−2.07
63. $2 F^- \rightleftarrows F_2 + 2e^-$	−2.65
64. $2 HF (aq) \rightleftarrows F_2 + 2 H^+ + 2e^-$	−3.06

force or *potential,* in volts, with which the reaction from left to right takes place. It is a measure of the intensity with which the substance on the left reacts to form the substance on the right. It represents the change in free energy when the reactant on the left forms the product on the right. The greater the change in free energy, the higher the voltage, the more reactive the substance on the left. As you go down the table the voltage gradually decreases from +2.925 at the top to −3.06 at the bottom. That means that *the substance at the top and on the left is the strongest reducing agent,* while the substance at the bottom on the left is the weakest reducing agent. Every substance on the left is a stronger reducing agent than every substance below itself on the left and a weaker reducing agent than every substance above itself on the left.

In contrast, *the substance at the bottom and on the right is the strongest oxidizing agent,* while the substance at the top on the right is the weakest oxidizing agent. Any substance on the right is a stronger oxidizing agent than any substance above itself on the

TABLE 2.6. STANDARD OXIDATION POTENTIALS
IN ALKALINE SOLUTION

Reaction	Potential, $E°$ (in volts)
65. $K \rightleftarrows K^+ + e^-$	2.925
66. $Al + 4\,OH^- \rightleftarrows Al(OH)_4{}^- + 3e^-$	2.35
67. $HPO_3{}^- + 3\,OH^- \rightleftarrows PO_4{}^{---} + 2\,H_2O + 1e^-$	1.12
68. $S_2O_4{}^{--} + 4\,OH^- \rightleftarrows 2\,SO_3{}^{--} + 2\,H_2O + 2e^-$	1.12
69. $CN^- + 2\,OH^- \rightleftarrows CNO^- + H_2O + 2e^-$	0.97
70. $SO_3{}^{--} + 2\,OH^- \rightleftarrows SO_4{}^{--} + H_2O + 2e^-$	0.93
71. $Sn(OH)_4{}^{--} + 2\,OH^- \rightleftarrows Sn(OH)_6{}^{--} + 2e^-$	0.90
72. $Sn + 4\,OH^- \rightleftarrows Sn(OH)_4{}^{--} + 2e^-$	0.76
73. $Cr(OH)_4{}^- + 4\,OH^- \rightleftarrows CrO_4{}^{--} + 4\,H_2O + 3e^-$	0.48
74. $H_2O_2 + 2\,OH^- \rightleftarrows O_2 + 2\,H_2O + 2e^-$	0.076
75. $Mn(OH)_2 + 2\,OH^- \rightleftarrows MnO_2 + H_2O + 2e^-$	0.05
76. $Cu(NH_3)_2{}^+ + 2\,NH_3 \rightleftarrows Cu(NH_3)_4{}^{++} + e^-$	0.0
77. $Co(NH_3)_6{}^{++} \rightleftarrows Co(NH_3)_6{}^{+++} + e^-$	−0.1
78. $Co(OH)_2 + OH^- \rightleftarrows Co(OH)_3 + e^-$	−0.17
79. $4\,OH^- \rightleftarrows O_2 + 2\,H_2O + 4e^-$	−0.401
80. $I^- + 2\,OH^- \rightleftarrows IO^- + H_2O + 2e^-$	−0.49
81. $Ni(OH)_2 + 2\,OH^- \rightleftarrows NiO_2 + 2\,H_2O + 2e^-$	−0.49
82. $MnO_4{}^{--} \rightleftarrows MnO_4{}^- + e^-$	−0.54
83. $MnO_2 + 4\,OH^- \rightleftarrows MnO_4{}^- + 2\,H_2O + 3e^-$	−0.57
84. $MnO_2 + 4\,OH^- \rightleftarrows MnO_4{}^{--} + 2\,H_2O + 2e^-$	−0.60
85. $Br^- + 2\,OH^- \rightleftarrows OBr^- + H_2O + 2e^-$	−0.76
86. $2\,OH^- \rightleftarrows H_2O_2 + 2e^-$	−0.88
87. $O_2 + 2\,OH^- \rightleftarrows O_3 + H_2O + 2e^-$	−1.24

right, but it is a weaker oxidizing agent than any substance below itself on the right.

Most significant of all, *any substance on the left will reduce any substance below itself and on the right. Any substance on the right will oxidize any substance above itself and on the left. A substance on the left will not reduce a substance above itself and on the right. A substance on the right will not oxidize a substance below itself and on the left.* Summarizing, it can be stated that *an oxidizing agent with a lower potential will oxidize any reducing agent with a higher potential* and a *reducing agent with a higher potential will reduce any oxidizing agent with a lower potential.*

Applying these rules we see that Fe^{+++} ions [equation (38)] will oxidize I^- ions [equation (34)] but will not oxidize Br^- [equation (45)]. $Cr_2O_7{}^{--}$ ions [equation (49)] will oxidize Sn^{++} [equation (29)]. H_2SO_3 [equation (30)] will reduce $NO_3{}^-$ [equation (42)].

Not only will the table tell us whether or not two substances will react with each other but it indicates what reaction products will be formed and provides a simple basis for balancing the equation. Thus, equations (49) and (35) show that H_3AsO_3 will reduce $Cr_2O_7^{--}$ to Cr^{+++} and will itself be oxidized to H_3AsO_4. The two half-reactions are

$$Cr_2O_7^{--} + 14\,H^+ + 6\,e^- = 2\,Cr^{+++} + 7\,H_2O$$

$$H_3AsO_3 + H_2O = H_3AsO_4 + 2\,H^+ + 2e^-$$

Since 6 electrons are added in the first reaction while only 2 are given off in the second, it is necessary to triple the coefficients in the second reaction so that the number of electrons in the two reactions will cancel out. When this is done and the two reactions are totaled by adding up the substances on each of the two sides of the equality signs the following balanced equation is obtained:

$$3\,H_3AsO_3 + Cr_2O_7^{--} + 8\,H^+ = 3\,H_3AsO_4 + 2\,Cr^{+++} + 4\,H_2O.$$

It should be emphasized that the potentials given in the table are for 1 molal solution at 25°C. Since the reactions represent true equilibria it follows from the mass law that increasing the concentration of a reactant will increase its potential. Increase in temperature also generally increases the potential. For these reasons substances which, according to the table, do not react at 25° in 1 molal solution are found to do so at higher temperature and concentration. (See question 23, page 73.)

Balancing Oxidation-Reduction Equations

In any oxidation-reduction reaction the oxidation number of at least one element is increased, and the oxidation number of at least one element is decreased. Thus in the reaction

$$Sn^{++} + 2\,Fe^{+++} = Sn^{++++} + 2\,Fe^{++}$$

tin is *oxidized* from an oxidation number of 2 in Sn^{++} to 4 in Sn^{++++}. At the same time iron is *reduced* from an oxidation number of 3 in Fe^{+++} to 2 in Fe^{++}. Here Fe^{+++} is said to be the *oxidizing agent*, while Sn^{++} is said to be the *reducing agent*.

In the reaction

$$Cr_2O_7^{--} + 3\,H_2S + 8\,H^+ = 2\,Cr^{+++} + 3\,S + 7\,H_2O,$$

chromium is *reduced* from an oxidation number of 6 in $Cr_2O_7^{--}$ to 3 in Cr^{+++}, while sulfur is *oxidized* from an oxidation number of -2 in H_2S to 0 in S. $Cr_2O_7^{--}$ is the *oxidizing agent* or *oxidant*, H_2S is the *reducing agent* or *reductant*.

In determining the oxidation number of a specific element in a given molecule or ion the following rules are applied.

1. In an elemental ion, such as Sn^{++++} or S^{--}, the oxidation number is equal to the charge on the ion. Thus, in Sn^{++++} and S^{--} the oxidation numbers of Sn and S are, respectively, $+4$ and -2.

2. The oxidation number of any free element, such as O_2 and S, is zero.

3. In its compounds or ions H has an oxidation number of $+1$. (The exceptions to this rule are the metal hydrides such as CaH_2, where the oxidation number of H is -1.)

4. In its compounds or ions O has an oxidation number of -2. (The exceptions to this rule are OF_2, in which the oxidation number of O is $+2$, and the peroxides, such as H_2O_2 and Na_2O_2, in which its oxidation number is -1.)

5. In any neutral molecule the total positive oxidation numbers equal the total negative oxidation numbers. In an ion the charge on the ion equals the difference between the positive and negative oxidation numbers. In the compound, H_3AsO_4, the total oxidation number for the four atoms of oxygen is -8; since the three hydrogen atoms have a total oxidation number of $+3$, the oxidation number of arsenic is $+5$. In the ion, $Cr_2O_7^{--}$, the total oxidation number for the seven atoms of oxygen is -14; since the charge on the ion is -2 the total positive oxidation number is $+12$, or $+6$ for each of the two atoms of chromium.

If we examine the two equations given above, and any other equation that we wish to select, we will find that, *in every balanced oxidation-reduction equation the total increase in oxidation number of the element (or elements) oxidized equals the total decrease in oxidation number of the element (or elements) reduced.* In the first of the two equations given above one atom of tin has its oxidation number increased from $+2$ to $+4$; the total increase in oxidation number is 2. Two atoms of iron each have their oxidation number reduced from $+3$ to $+2$; the total decrease in oxidation number is 2. In the second balanced equation three atoms of S are each oxidized from an oxidation number of -2 in H_2S to 0 in free S; the total increase in oxidation number is 6. Two atoms of Cr are each reduced from an oxidation number of $+6$ in Cr_2O_7 to $+3$ in Cr^{+++}; the total decrease in oxidation number is 6.

We will notice, also, if we examine the two equations above and any other balanced equation, that *the sum of charges of the ions on each of the two sides of the balanced equation is the same.* In the first equation the sum of the charges on the one Sn^{++} and two Fe^{+++} ions on the left is $+8$; the total net charge on the one Sn^{++++} ion and the two Fe^{++} ions on the right is also $+8$. In the second equation the sum of the charges on the one $Cr_2O_7^{--}$ ion and the eight H^+ ions is $+6$. The total charge on the two Cr^{+++} ions on the right is also $+6$.

We can use the above facts (the equality in the total increase and decrease in oxidation number and the equality of the net charge on the two sides of the equation) as a means of balancing oxidation-reduction equations. To illustrate how this can be done we will balance the equation for the reaction that occurs when a solution of $FeSO_4$, which has been acidified with H_2SO_4, is treated with a solution of $KMnO_4$. The steps in this balancing process are:

1. Write the formulas for the reactants and products.

$$Fe^{++} + MnO_4^- = Fe^{+++} + Mn^{++}.$$

2. Identify the element or elements oxidized and the element or elements reduced. Note the initial and final oxidation number of each of these elements. Note the change in oxidation number of each of these elements.

Fe is oxidized;   Mn is reduced.

3. Select a sufficient number of moles of each reactant so that the total increase in oxidation number equals the total decrease.

4. Equalize the sum of the charges on each side of the equation by adding the necessary H^+ ions. (If the solution is alkaline the charges can be equalized by adding OH^- ions. If the solution is neutral either H^+ or OH^- ions may be added; H_2O will provide these ions.)

As the equation is written in step 3 the net charge on the left (from the five Fe^{++} ions and the one MnO_4^- ion) is $+9$ and the net charge on the right (from the five Fe^{+++} ions and the one Mn^{++} ion) is $+17$. By adding eight H^+ ions to the left the charge on each side will be $+17$.

$$5\,Fe^{++} + MnO_4^- + 8\,H^+ = 5\,Fe^{+++} + Mn^{++}.$$

5. Complete the balancing by adding enough H_2O to equalize the number of atoms of H on each side. If the balancing has been correct up to this point equalizing the atoms of H will also equalize the atoms of O.

$$5\,Fe^{++} + MnO_4^- + 8\,H^+ = 5\,Fe^{+++} + Mn^{++} + 4\,H_2O.$$

If more than one element is oxidized (and/or reduced) the total increase in oxidation number is the sum of the increases for each element. The oxidation of FeS by HNO_3 illustrates such a reaction.

Step 1. $FeS + NO_3^- = NO + SO_4^{--} + Fe^{+++}$

Step 3. $FeS + 3\,NO_3^- = 3\,NO + SO_4^{--} + Fe^{+++}$

Step 4.
$$FeS + 3\,NO_3^- + 4\,H^+ = 3\,NO + SO_4^{--} + Fe^{+++}$$
Step 5.
$$FeS + 3\,NO_3^- + 4\,H^+ = 3\,NO + SO_4^{--} + Fe^{+++} + 2\,H_2O.$$

If more than one gram atom of the element (or elements) oxidized and/or reduced is present in a mole of reactant the minimum number of moles of product formed per mole of reactant must be given in Step 1. Thus, when As_2S_3 is oxidized by HNO_3 to yield H_3AsO_4 and SO_4^{--}, one mole of As_2S_3 will yield two moles of H_3AsO_4 and three moles of SO_4^{--}. The successive steps in the balancing process will then be:

Step 1. $As_2S_3 + NO_3^- = NO + 3SO_4^{--} + 2H_3AsO_4$

$$
\begin{array}{c}
\overbrace{\hspace{8cm}}^{\text{Increase of 4}} \\
\overbrace{\hspace{4.5cm}}^{\text{Increase of 24}}
\end{array}
$$

Step 2. $\overset{+6\ -6}{As_2S_3} + \underset{+5}{NO_3^-} = \underset{+2}{NO} + \overset{+18}{3SO_4^{--}} + \overset{+10}{2H_3AsO_4}$

Decrease of 3

Total increase of 28

Step 3.

$$3As_2S_3 + 28NO_3^- = 28NO + 9SO_4^{--} + 6H_3AsO_4$$

Step 4.

$$3As_2S_3 + 28NO_3^- + 10H^+ = 28NO + 9SO_4^{--} + 6H_3AsO_4$$

Step 5.

$$3As_2S_3 + 28NO_3^- + 10H^+ + 4H_2O = 28NO +$$
$$9SO_4^{--} + 6H_3AsO_4.$$

In a reaction of the type

$$Mg = Mg^{++} + 2e$$

magnesium is oxidized. This *oxidation* of Mg involves an increase of its oxidation number from 0 in Mg to $+2$ in Mg^{++}; also, it involves a *loss of 2 electrons.* Likewise, in a reaction of the type

$$Cl_2 + 2e = 2Cl^-,$$

in which chlorine is reduced, the oxidation number of chlorine is reduced from 0 to -1. In this reaction chlorine *gains 1 electron.* From this it can be concluded that *oxidation means a loss of electrons* while *reduction means a gain of electrons* and that the increase in the oxidation number of an atom during oxidation is numerically equal to the number of electrons which it loses in the process and that the decrease in the oxidation number of an atom during reduction is equal to the number of electrons which it gains in the process. That being the case, one can, in Step 2 in the balancing process, substitute "loss of electrons" for "increase in oxidation number" and "gain of electrons" for "decrease in oxidation number." The final result will be the same. (See questions 21 and 22, page 72.)

The Periodic Table

Attention has already been called to the manner in which the periodic table may be of value in accounting for and explaining the reactions of specific ions and in systematizing the information relating to the behavior of certain groups of ions. Since the study of qualitative analysis is concerned with the chemical behavior of ions and molecules, and since the periodic table provides the best available organized picture of the properties of the elements and their compounds, one should expect the periodic table to serve as a useful guide in many phases of qualitative analysis. Specific examples of this usefulness will appear as the various analytical separations are carried out.

The close similarity in the chemical behavior of chlorides, bromides, and iodides, which is to be expected from the location of the three halogens in Group VIIa, causes them to interfere with each other in their identification. However, the lower reactivity of iodine, and the consequent greater reducing power of the iodide ion, enables one to liberate iodine from an iodide with an oxidizing agent that will not be reduced by either bromide ion or chloride ion.

The marked similarity in the solubilities and colors of phosphates and arsenates is to be expected from the position of arsenic and phosphorus in Group Va. This similarity becomes a complicating factor in the identification of these two anions.

The fact that the barium-magnesium group is composed entirely of metals from periodic Groups Ia and IIa while the silver, copper-arsenic, and aluminum-nickel groups are made up exclusively of metals from other groups accounts for certain very marked differences in the character of the reactions that are observed in the barium-magnesium group as compared with those that take place in the other three groups. The metals in Groups Ia and IIa exist, in their compounds or ions, in only one oxidation state. Therefore there are no oxidation-reduction reactions among the barium-magnesium group equations. A number of the transition metals and metals in the right half of the periodic table have several oxidation states; therefore one finds numerous oxidation-reduction reactions among the equations for the silver, copper-arsenic and aluminum-nickel groups. The cations of the strongly electropositive metals in Groups Ia and IIa form few stable complex ions; by contrast, the transition metals are strongly inclined to form complex ions. As a result no complex ions are encountered in the barium-magnesium group, while complex ions are very common in the other three groups. Certain of these complex ions play a prominent role in the separation and identification.

The aluminum-nickel group includes some of the metals that fall along the borderline between metals and nonmetals. One is therefore not surprised to find that the amphoteric character of the hydroxides of these borderline elements is utilized to effect their separation.

The nonmetallic character of arsenic, antimony, and tin, as indicated by their position in the periodic table, accounts for the acid character of their sulfides; this acid character is the basis for the separation of the sulfides of arsenic, antimony, and tin from the more basic sulfides of mercury, lead, bismuth, copper, and cadmium.

The close similarity of the oxides and sulfides of the various cations is noted at several points during the analysis. This close similarity is to be expected from the fact that oxygen and sulfur both fall at the top of Group VIa.

Colloids

Many of the precipitates formed during the operations of qualitative analysis consist of fine particles showing all the properties of substances in the colloidal state. They may be coagulated, and they adsorb electrolytes from solution. The precipitates are often so finely divided that they do not settle when centrifuged, and they cannot be removed by filtration because the particles are so small that they pass through the pores of the filter paper. The substances that cause the most trouble in this respect are hydroxides and sulfides of the metals, and occasionally elementary sulfur.

Coagulation. Since such colloidal suspensions are composed of small electrically charged aggregates, they are coagulated by electrolytes. The precipitating reagents used in qualitative analysis are electrolytes; consequently, the excess of the precipitant helps coagulate the precipitate. In certain cases, as in the precipitation of the copper-arsenic and the aluminum-nickel group, the presence of a strong electrolyte ($NH_4C_2H_3O_2$ or NH_4Cl) helps assure coagulation of the precipitate.

Washing precipitates. Cold water tends to cause certain insoluble substances to be dispersed in a colloidal condition, the sulfides being especially susceptible. In this finely dispersed state the particles of solid remain in suspension. To avoid this dispersion, hot wash water may be used; also the wash water may contain a small amount of $NH_4C_2H_3O_2$ or some other electrolyte.

Occlusion. Because of the large surface possessed by finely divided precipitates, appreciable amounts of solute are adsorbed when precipitates of this kind are formed. This adsorption, or occlusion as it is sometimes called, often complicates the separation of cations. In certain cases, however, this adsorption of solute proves to be a boon. Aluminum is identified by the fact that $Al(OH)_3$ adsorbs the dye "aluminon" from solution to form a characteristic red gelatinous mass referred to as a "lake"; $Mg(OH)_2$ forms a blue "lake" with another dye.

PROBLEMS

The following problems and questions will illustrate some of the principles discussed in Chapter II. For a more comprehensive list of problems and detailed explanations of the solution of the various types of problems, the student is referred to Sorum's *How to Solve General Chemistry Problems, Second Edition*, Prentice-Hall, Englewood, N. J., 1958.

1. How many grams of K_2SO_4 will be required to prepare 1.00 liter of $0.500 M K_2SO_4$? *Ans.* 87.1 g.

2. If 12 g. of NaOH are dissolved in enough water to give 500 ml. of solution, what is the molarity of the solution? *Ans.* 0.60 *M*

3. How many grams of KOH will be required to prepare 400 ml. of $0.12 M$ KOH? *Ans.* 2.7 g.

4. Calculate the molarity of the solution formed when 8.85 g. of H_2SO_4 are dissolved in enough water to give 45.0 ml. of solution. *Ans.* 2.00 *M*

5. How many moles of hydrogen gas will be liberated from 400 ml. of $0.40 M$ HCl by an excess of magnesium? *Ans.* 0.08 mole

6. If 12.0 g. of NaOH were required to neutralize 82.0 ml. of sulfuric acid, calculate the molarity of the acid. *Ans.* 1.83 *M*

7. Sixty grams of a 12% solution of KNO_3 in water were evaporated to dryness. How many grams of dry KNO_3 were obtained? *Ans.* 7.2 g.

8. How many grams of $MgCl_2$ would have to be dissolved in 20 g. of water to give a 20% solution? *Ans.* 5 g.

9. Fifteen grams of salt were dissolved in 60 g. of water. What was the per cent strength of the resulting solution? *Ans.* 20%

10. You are given 100 g. of a 10.0% solution of $NaNO_3$ in water. How many more grams of $NaNO_3$ would you have to dissolve in the 100 g. of 10.0% solution to change it to a 20.0% solution? *Ans.* 12.5 g.

11. To what volume must 44.20 ml. of a 70.00% solution of sulfuric acid whose density is 1.610 g./ml. be diluted to give $0.4000 M H_2SO_4$? *Ans.* 1275 ml.

12. In $3.58 M H_2SO_4$ there is 29.0% H_2SO_4. Calculate the density of $3.58 M H_2SO_4$. *Ans.* 1.21 g./ml.

13. PCl_5 is 20 mole per cent dissociated into PCl_3 and Cl_2 at equilibrium at a given temperature and in a liter vessel in accordance with the equation, $PCl_5 \rightleftarrows PCl_3 + Cl_2$. One mole of pure PCl_5 was introduced into a liter reaction vessel at the given temperature. How many moles of each component were present at equilibrium?

Ans. 0.2 mole PCl_3, 0.2 mole Cl_2, 0.8 mole PCl_5

14. A liter reaction vessel in which the following reaction had reached a state of equilibrium, $CO + Cl_2 \rightleftarrows COCl_2$, was found to contain 0.3 mole of CO, 0.2 mole of Cl_2, and 0.8 mole of $COCl_2$. Calculate the equilibrium constant for the reaction. *Ans.* 13.3

15. One mole of SO_3 was placed in a liter reaction vessel at a certain temperature. When equilibrium was established in the reaction, $2\,SO_3 \rightleftarrows 2\,SO_2 + O_2$, the vessel was found to contain 0.60 mole of SO_2. Calculate the equilibrium constant for the reaction. *Ans.* 0.68

16. A 0.10 M solution of NH_4OH is 1.3% ionized at 20°C. Calculate the ionization constant for NH_4OH at 20°C. *Ans.* 1.7×10^{-5}

17. A solution in equilibrium with a precipitate of AgBr was found to contain 8.0×10^{-7} mole of Ag^+ per liter and 4.0×10^{-7} mole of Br^- per liter. Calculate the solubility product of AgBr. *Ans.* 3.2×10^{-13}

18. A saturated solution of CdS in water at 25°C was found to have a concentration of 1.2×10^{-13} mole of CdS per liter. Calculate the solubility product of CdS at 25°C. *Ans.* 1.4×10^{-26}

19. The solubility of CaC_2O_4 in water at 20°C, as determined by saturating pure water with solid CaC_2O_4, is 6.1×10^{-3} gram per liter of solution. Calculate the solubility product of CaC_2O_4. *Ans.* 2.3×10^{-9}

20. The solubility product of AgCl is 2.8×10^{-10}. What concentration of Ag^+ must be present to just start precipitation of AgCl from a solution containing 1.0×10^{-4} mole of Cl^- per liter?

Ans. 2.8×10^{-6} mole per liter

21. Complete and balance each of the following reactions (in acidic solution).

(a) $Mn^{++} + HBiO_3 \rightleftarrows MnO_4^- + Bi^{+++}$.

(b) $H_2SO_3 + ClO_3^- = SO_4^{--} + Cl^-$.

(c) $Cr_2O_7^{--} + Sn^{++} = Cr^{+++} + Sn^{++++}$.

(d) $Sb_2S_3 + NO_3^- = NO + S + Sb_2O_5$.

(e) $(NH_4)_2S_2O_3 + MnO_4^- = Mn^{++} + SO_4^{--} + NO$.

(f) $FeS + SO_4^{--} = SO_2 + Fe^{+++}$.

(g) $Fe_2Fe(CN)_6 + NO_3^- = NO + CO_2 + Fe^{+++}$.

22. Complete and balance each of the following reactions (in alkaline solution).

(a) $Sn(OH)_4^{--} + MnO_4^- = MnO_2 + Sn(OH)_6^{--}$.

(b) $Cr(OH)_4^- + H_2O_2 = CrO_4^{--} + H_2O$.

(c) $S_2O_4^{--} + CrO_4^{--} = Cr(OH)_4^- + SO_4^{--}$.

(d) $CN^- + Cu(NH_3)_4^{++} = Cu(CN)_2^- + CNO^-$.

23. In each instance given below the two substances are brought together at 25°C in acidic 1 molal solution. In those cases where a reaction occurs write the balanced equation.

(a) H_3PO_3 and NO_3^-. (e) HNO_2 and Br^-.

(b) Fe^{+++} and I^-. (f) $Cr_2O_7^{--}$ and Fe^{++}.

(c) H_2SO_3 and MnO_4^-. (g) Sn^{++} and Ce^{++++}.

(d) Sn^{++++} and H_3AsO_3. (h) $S_2O_8^{--}$ and Bi^{+++}.

REFERENCES

For detailed discussions of the theories and practice of qualitative analysis, the student is referred to the following texts.

Bailar, J. C., *The Chemistry of the Coordination Compounds*. Reinhold, New York, 1956.

Curtman, L. J., *Introduction to Semimicro Qualitative Chemical Analysis*. Macmillan, New York, 1954.

Gilreath, E., *Qualitative Analysis*. McGraw-Hill, New York, 1954.

Hogness, T. R., and Johnson, W. C., *Qualitative Analysis and Chemical Equilibrium*. Henry Holt, New York, 1954.

King, E. J., *Qualitative Analysis and Electrolytic Solutions*. Harcourt, Brace, New York, 1959.

Latimer, W. H., *Oxidation Potentials*. Prentice-Hall, Englewood Cliffs, N. J., 1952.

McAlpine, P. K., and Soule, B. A., *Fundamentals of Qualitative Chemical Analysis*. Van Nostrand, New York, 1956.

Moeller, T., *Qualitative Analysis*. McGraw-Hill, New York, 1958.

Welcher, F. J., and Hahn, R. B., *Semimicro Qualitative Analysis*. Van Nostrand, New York, 1955.

Wiig, E. O., Line, W. R., and Flagg, J. F., *Semimicro Qualitative Analysis*. Van Nostrand, New York, 1954.

West, P. W., and Vick, M. M., *Qualitative Analysis*. Macmillan, New York, 1959.

CHAPTER THREE

The silver group

SOLUTION CONTAINING Ag^+, Hg_2^{++}, Pb^{++}, Hg^{++}, Bi^{+++}, Cu^{++}, Cd^{++}, Sn^{++}, Sn^{++++}, As^{+++}, Sb^{+++}, Al^{+++}, Cr^{+++}, Fe^{++}, Fe^{+++}, Mn^{++}, Zn^{++}, Ni^{++}, Co^{++}, Ba^{++}, Ca^{++}, Mg^{++}, K^+, Na^+, NH_4^+, $H_2AsO_3^-$ and AsO_4^{---}.

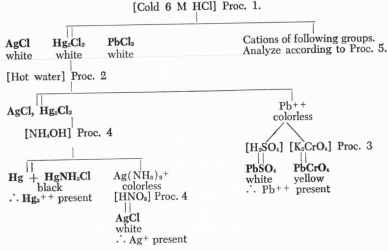

[Cold 6 M HCl] Proc. 1.

AgCl　**Hg₂Cl₂**　**PbCl₂**　　　　Cations of following groups.
white　　white　　white　　　　　　Analyze according to Proc. 5.

[Hot water] Proc. 2

AgCl, Hg₂Cl₂　　　　　　　　　　Pb^{++}
　　　　　　　　　　　　　　　　colorless
　　[NH₄OH] Proc. 4
　　　　　　　　　　　　[H₂SO₄] [K₂CrO₄] Proc. 3

Hg + HgNH₂Cl　　$Ag(NH_3)_2^+$　　**PbSO₄**　**PbCrO₄**
black　　　　　　colorless　　　white　　yellow
∴ **Hg₂⁺⁺** present　[HNO₃] Proc. 4　　∴ Pb^{++} present

AgCl
white
∴ Ag^+ present

OUTLINE 2: ANALYSIS OF THE SILVER GROUP

Precipitation and Analysis of the Silver Group

The chlorides of silver, mercury(I), and lead are insoluble in cold water and cold dilute hydrochloric acid; the chlorides of all other metals are soluble. (See Solubility Rule 3, page 188.) This fact is the basis for the separation of silver, mercury(I), and lead from all other metallic ions.

When HCl or some other soluble chloride is added to a cold solution containing all the common cations, $AgCl$, Hg_2Cl_2, and $PbCl_2$ are precipitated. All other metals remain in solution as soluble chlorides (see Outline 2). The ions of silver, mercury(I), and lead constitute the silver group. Since HCl is used to separate this group of ions from other cations by precipitating them as insoluble chlorides, it is called the *group reagent* for the silver group.

■ ■ ■ Procedure 1: Precipitation of the silver group

Place 5 drops of the solution to be analyzed in a 3-in. test tube and add 5 drops of water (see Note 1). Add 2 drops of 6 M HCl and mix thoroughly by stirring the contents of the test tube with a glass stirring rod. With a few drops of cold water, wash down into the solution any precipitate that adheres to the inside of the test tube above the level of the solution (see Note 2). Centrifuge (see Note 3). Test for complete precipitation by adding another drop of 6 M HCl to the clear supernatant solution in the test tube (see Note 4). When precipitation is complete, centrifuge (see Note 5) and then decant (see Note 6). Save the decantate, which contains the cations of the following groups, for Procedure 5 (see Note 7). Wash the precipitate once with 5 drops of cold water (see Note 8), adding the washing to the decantate being saved for Procedure 5. Allow the precipitate to remain in the test tube and analyze it according to Procedure 2 (see Notes 9 and 14).

NOTES

1. The dropwise addition of water, solutions, or liquid reagents is done with a medicine dropper. All liquid-reagent bottles are fitted with droppers. Each student's desk will be provided with several medicine droppers. Droppers should be tested to see that they deliver drops of such volume that from 20 to 23 are required to give 1 ml. of liquid. With a given liquid the smaller the tip of the dropper the smaller the drop delivered.

2. In the present system of semimicro analytical procedures, solid precipitates are separated from liquids by centrifuging and decantation rather than by filtration. The centrifugal force imparted by the whirling centrifuge causes the heavy precipitate to be thrown to the bottom of the tube, the lighter liquid remaining on top. Any precipitate that happens to be clinging to the sides of the tube above the level of the liquid will remain there and will not be thrown down with the rest of the precipitate. Its presence on the walls of the tube will interfere with subsequent decantation. Therefore, any precipitate adhering to the inside walls of the test tube should always be washed down with a few drops of water or other appropriate reagent before the solution is centrifuged.

3. The test tube containing the material to be centrifuged must always be balanced in the centrifuge by a test tube containing an equal amount of water or other solution.

4. In all future procedures in which precipitation is used to accomplish a separation of substances, it shall be understood that a test for complete precipitation must always be made. If the test shows that precipitation is not complete, add some more of the precipitating reagent, mix thoroughly by stirring the contents of the test tube with a glass stirring rod, and then centrifuge.

5. The length of centrifuging time required will depend upon the nature of the precipitate. Most precipitates require only 15 to 30 seconds of centrifuging; however, some very finely divided ones may require several minutes. Proper centrifuging should give a clear supernatant liquid, with the precipitate packed into the bottom of the tube. If the supernatant liquid is not clear, more centrifuging is required.

6. As a result of settling by centrifuging, most precipitates are so well packed into the bottom of the test tube that the supernatant liquid can be decanted (poured off) without much danger of disturbing the precipitate. The last drop of decantate can even be removed from the lip of the test tube by gentle tapping. Some precipitates, however, are so light and fluffy that decantation of the supernatant liquid can be accomplished only with great care, and even then a part of the supernatant liquid must be allowed to remain behind with the precipitate. In a few instances, to be noted in later procedures, the precipitate is so light that decantation cannot be accomplished even with the exercise of great care; in such instances the top 75–80 per cent of the supernatant liquid is drawn off with a medicine dropper.

If the decantate is to be discarded, as in a washing operation, the loss of bits of precipitate in the decantate is of no consequence. If, however, the decantate is to be submitted to further analysis it must not contain any precipitate; if precipitate does get into the decantate the process of centrifuging and decantation must be repeated.

Because the 3-in. test tubes are of such small diameter ($\frac{3}{8}$ in.), surface tension may cause the failure of decantate to flow out over the lip of the tilted tube. In such a case, if the lip of another test tube or the end of a stirring rod is touched to the solution at the lip of the tube, the decantate will flow out.

7. If the solution being analyzed is known to contain only cations of the silver group (see Schedule of Laboratory Work, 1 and 2, page 6), this decantate may be discarded.

8. Wash a precipitate as follows: add the water or other washing liquid to the precipitate in the test tube, mix thoroughly by stirring the contents of the tube with a glass stirring rod, centrifuge, and decant. *Failure to wash precipitates thoroughly is one of the main sources of error in qualitative analysis.*

9. If a precipitate or solution is to be preserved from one laboratory period to the next, the test tube in which it is kept should be stoppered. Stoppering prevents contamination and also keeps solutions from evaporating and precipitates from drying out. Test tubes should be labeled so that their contents can be correctly identified.

10. If no precipitate is formed with cold HCl, the absence of the ions of silver and mercury (I) is definitely proved. However, lead may be present in small quantities, since $PbCl_2$ is appreciably soluble even in cold water.

11. The object of the silver-group precipitation is to remove from solution, as completely as possible, the Ag^+, Hg_2^{++}, and Pb^{++} ions by precipitating them as $AgCl$, Hg_2Cl_2, and $PbCl_2$. A precipitate will form when the product of the concentration of the ions that react to form the precipitate just exceeds the solubility product (see page 44). Furthermore, in any precipitation process the insoluble compound will keep precipitating until the concentrations of its ions remaining in solution reach values at which their product just equals the solubility product. When this point is reached the precipitate will be in equilibrium with its ions, which means that the rate at which the precipitate is forming is equal to the rate at which it is dissolving and dissociating into its ions. This is a true equilibrium, and the equilibrium point will be shifted by changes in the concentrations of the reacting ions in accordance with the mass law. It follows, therefore, that an excess of the group reagent ion, Cl^- in this case, is desirable, since if the concentration of Cl^- is high, the concentration of Ag^+, Hg_2^{++}, and Pb^{++} remaining in solution will be low. An inordinately large excess of the reagent may, however, form soluble complex ions, thus nullifying the usual advantage resulting from having an excess of reagent. A very large excess of HCl will actually increase the amount of lead remaining in solution. The excess chloride ions react with lead ions to form the soluble stable complex ion $PbCl_4^{--}$. This will reduce the concentration of lead ions in solution below the value required for the solubility product of $PbCl_2$. As a result some $PbCl_2$ will go back

into solution in accordance with the principles discussed on page 53. The equations for the reactions are

(a) $\qquad$ $PbCl_2 \rightleftharpoons Pb^{++} + 2\,Cl^-$,

(b) $\qquad$ $Pb^{++} + 4\,Cl^- \rightleftharpoons PbCl_4^{--}$.

Silver has a slight tendency to form the stable complex ion $AgCl_2^-$ with excess HCl.

(a) $\qquad$ $AgCl \rightleftharpoons Ag^+ + Cl^-$,

(b) $\qquad$ $Ag^+ + 2\,Cl^- \rightleftharpoons AgCl_2^-$.

12. Other soluble chlorides such as NH_4Cl could be substituted for HCl, since the reaction is one between ions.

$$Pb^{++} + 2\,Cl^- = PbCl_2 \text{ (insoluble)}.$$

13. Broad statements relating to solubilities such as the one given in the first sentence of this chapter ("The chlorides of silver, mercury(I), and lead are insoluble in cold water and cold dilute hydrochloride acid; the chlorides of all other metals are soluble.") are, for all practical purposes, true, and they serve a useful purpose in pointing out general facts which form the basis for analytical separations. The student should recognize, however, that such statements require qualification. There is actually no such thing as a completely insoluble acid, base, or salt. The term *insoluble* means that the solubility of a substance is so low that, for all practical purposes, it can be considered insoluble. The "insoluble" compound $PbCl_2$ is much more soluble than either AgCl or Hg_2Cl_2. Also there is considerable difference in the solubilities of the soluble chlorides.

14. A scheme of analysis of the kind shown in Outline 2 should be started on one of the blank pages at the end of this chapter just as soon as the analysis of a silver group solution is started. This scheme should be developed step by step and procedure by procedure as the analysis is actually carried out. Notes should be made indicating the colors of precipitates or solutions formed. The scheme will then be a progress chart showing exactly what was done and what was observed. A scheme of this sort should be developed for every group solution that is analyzed.

Separation of Lead from Silver and Mercury(I)

The silver-group precipitate is a mixture of $PbCl_2$, Hg_2Cl_2, and AgCl. It is necessary to separate each individual member of the group in order that its presence may be confirmed. Lead is separated first. $PbCl_2$ is soluble in hot water; AgCl and Hg_2Cl_2 are insoluble. This difference is the basis for the separation of lead ions from mercury(I) and silver ions.

▪ ▪ ▪ Procedure 2: Separation of lead from silver
and mercury(I)

Add 15–20 drops of hot water (see Note 1) to the test tube containing the precipitate from Procedure 1, stir well until all of the precipitate is in suspension, then heat the tube by placing it in a 100-ml beaker of boiling water for about one minute. (See Note 2.) Stir frequently. Centrifuge at once and decant into another test tube immediately after centrifuging; save the decantate, which contains Pb^{++}, for Procedure 3. Wash the precipitate twice with 10-drop portions of hot water (see Note 3) and save it, in the test tube, for Procedure 4.

NOTES

1. A beaker or flask of hot distilled water should always be available on the desk. A medicine dropper to be used exclusively for hot water should be kept in this beaker or flask. A second beaker or flask and medicine dropper should be provided for cold distilled water. Additional medicine droppers should be available for transferring solutions. Use of one dropper for all operations is liable to result in contamination. Since avoidance of contamination is imperative if good results are to be obtained, it is important that all pieces of equipment be cleaned with tap water and rinsed with distilled water *directly after they have been used* and before they are put down on the desk. If this rule is followed, everything will be clean. The pieces are most conveniently rinsed by squirting them with distilled water from a medicine dropper. There is no need for special wash bottles or other equipment for dispensing distilled water. The practice of placing a clean towel, folded to approximately a 12-in. square, on the desk top during the laboratory period and keeping test tubes, stirring rods, extra medicine droppers, test-tube brush, and casseroles on this towel is highly recommended.

2. A 100-ml. beaker about three-fourths full of boiling water serves as an effective bath for heating a 3-in. test tube and its contents. Simply set the tube in the boiling water. If the beaker is fitted with a flanged aluminum cover into which three or four holes, each large enough to hold a small test tube, have been punched, the tube will be held in a more nearly vertical position and three or four tubes can be heated conveniently at one time.

The contents of a test tube can be boiled by direct heating in the open flame; however, great care must be taken, otherwise the liquid may be thrown completely out of the tube. Hold the tube well above the flame with a test tube holder and move it back and forth in such a manner that the top as well as the bottom of the liquid in the tube is heated. As a general rule, if a solution is to be boiled or evaporated, it should be transferred to a casserole.

3. Unless specified otherwise, washings are always discarded.

4. 100 ml. of water at 0°C. dissolves 0.673 g. of $PbCl_2$. 100 ml. of water at 100°C. dissolves 3.34 g. of $PbCl_2$.

5. Since $PbCl_2$ is appreciably soluble in cold dilute HCl, lead will not be completely precipitated in the silver group. The lead ions remaining in solution will be completely precipitated as lead sulfide in the next group, the copper-arsenic group.

▪ ▪ ▪ Procedure 3: Detection of lead

Cool the decantate from Procedure 2 and divide into two parts. To one part add 1 drop of 0.2 M K_2CrO_4 solution; a yellow precipitate ($PbCrO_4$) proves the presence of lead. To the second part add 1 drop of 2 M H_2SO_4; a white precipitate ($PbSO_4$), which may form slowly, is further proof of the presence of lead.

NOTES

1. The solubility product of $PbSO_4$ is 1.3×10^{-8} and of $PbCrO_4$ is 2×10^{-16}, at 20°C. Obviously, $PbCrO_4$ provides a much more sensitive test for lead than does $PbSO_4$.

2. One confirmatory test is usually all that is required to establish the presence or absence of a given ion. The reason why two confirmatory tests for lead ions are carried out is to show that one of these tests is much more sensitive than the other. A certain concentration of lead ions will give a much stronger test when treated with chromate ions than when treated with sulfate ions because lead sulfate is about 8000 times as soluble as lead chromate. Just as the two confirmatory tests for lead differ in sensitivity so may confirmatory tests for different ions differ greatly in sensitivity. The best test that is known is used for each ion.

Separation and Detection of Silver and Mercury

AgCl is soluble in NH_4OH. Hg_2Cl_2 reacts with NH_4OH to form Hg and $HgNH_2Cl$, both insoluble. This fact is the basis for the separation of silver ions from mercury(I) ions.

▪ ▪ ▪ Procedure 4: Separation and detection of mercury(I) and silver

Add 4 drops of 15 M NH_4OH to the precipitate from Procedure 2, mix thoroughly, centrifuge, and decant into another test tube, saving the decantate for testing for silver. A black or very dark gray residue ($Hg + HgNH_2Cl$) proves the presence of mercury(I). To the decantate add 16 M HNO_3, drop by drop, with constant mixing with a stirring rod, until slightly acid (see Note 1). A white precipitate ($AgCl$) proves the presence of silver.

NOTES

1. Test for the acidity or alkalinity of a solution as follows: Place a piece of litmus paper on the clean towel or drape it over the edge of a beaker. Withdraw the stirring rod used for stirring the solution and touch the end of it to the piece of litmus paper.

2. AgCl dissolves in NH_4OH as follows.

$$AgCl + 2 NH_4OH = Ag(NH_3)_2^+ + Cl^- + 2 H_2O.$$

3. When the solution containing the complex ion, $Ag(NH_3)_2^+$, is acidified with nitric acid AgCl is precipitated in accordance with the equation

$$Ag(NH_3)_2^+ + Cl^- + 2 H^+ = AgCl + 2 NH_4^+.$$

4. Formation of the complex diamminesilver ion, $Ag(NH_3)_2^+$, is an example of a type of reaction that will be encountered in connection with the detection of other ions. Similar complexes are $Cu(NH_3)_4^{++}$, $Co(NH_3)_6^{+++}$, $Ni(NH_3)_6^{++}$, $Zn(NH_3)_4^{++}$, and $Cd(NH_3)_4^{++}$. (See discussion, chapter 2, page 24.)

5. If the $PbCl_2$ is not completely removed from the precipitate of AgCl and Hg_2Cl_2, it is converted by the NH_4OH into the finely divided insoluble white basic salt, $Pb(OH)Cl$, which may give a turbid decantate. The basic salt will dissolve in HNO_3 and will not interfere with the confirmatory test for silver.

6. NH_4OH reacts with Hg_2Cl_2 to produce a mixture of black finely divided mercury (Hg) and white mercury(II) amido chloride ($HgNH_2Cl$) according to the equation

$$Hg_2Cl_2 + 2 NH_4OH = Hg + HgNH_2Cl + NH_4^+ + Cl^- + 2 H_2O.$$

The compound, $HgNH_2Cl$, may be considered a derivative of $HgCl_2$ in which the amino group (NH_2) has replaced one atom of chlorine, thus:

7. Mercury(I) exists in solution as the stable diatomic ion, Hg_2^{++}. Therefore, the precipitate of mercury(I) chloride is Hg_2Cl_2 rather than $HgCl$.

8. The dissolving of AgCl by NH_4OH and the failure of AgCl to be

dissolved by HNO_3 may be interpreted in terms of the general rules given on page 53. The detailed equations for the reactions are

(a) $$AgCl \rightleftharpoons Ag^+ + Cl^-$$

(b) $$Ag^+ + 2NH_3 \rightleftharpoons Ag(NH_3)_2^+.$$

EQUATIONS

Lead

$$Pb^{++} + 2Cl^- = PbCl_2$$

$$PbCl_2 \rightleftharpoons Pb^{++} + 2Cl^-$$

$$Pb^{++} + SO_4^{--} = PbSO_4$$

$$Pb^{++} + CrO_4^{--} = PbCrO_4$$

Silver

$$Ag^+ + Cl^- = AgCl$$

$$AgCl + 2NH_4OH = Ag(NH_3)_2^+ + Cl^- + 2H_2O$$

$$Ag(NH_3)_2^+ + Cl^- + 2H^+ = AgCl + 2NH_4^+$$

Mercury

$$Hg_2^{++} + 2Cl^- = Hg_2Cl_2$$

$$Hg_2Cl_2 + 2NH_4OH = Hg + HgNH_2Cl + NH_4^+ + Cl^- + 2H_2O$$

QUESTIONS

1. Using the scheme of analysis as a guide, write net equations for all reactions that take place in the precipitation and analysis of the silver group.

2. You are asked to make up a water solution of an unknown which will contain lead, silver, mercury(I), copper, manganese, barium, and sodium ions, all in the same solution. What salt (sulfate, nitrate, carbonate, acetate, chloride) of each of the metals would you use to obtain a clear solution containing all seven of the above ions?

3. What reagent could be used in place of HCl as the group reagent for the silver group?

4. Cold dilute H_2SO_4 was accidentally used in place of cold concentrated HCl as the group reagent for the silver group in the analysis of an unknown solution. A white precipitate formed. Explain.

5. A solution of Na_2CO_3 in water was accidentally used in place of HCl as the group reagent for the silver group in the analysis of an unknown solution. A heavy precipitate formed. Explain.

6. State the fact upon which each of the following is based:

(a) The separation of silver, lead, and mercury(I) ions from all other cations.

(b) The separation of lead ions from silver and mercury(I) ions.

(c) The separation of silver ions from mercury(I) ions.

7. In the analysis of an unknown solution, what difficulty, if any, would arise if:

(a) Hot concentrated HCl were used instead of cold HCl in the precipitation of the silver group.

(b) The precipitate of AgCl and Hg_2Cl_2 were not washed free from $PbCl_2$.

(c) The silver-group precipitate (AgCl, Hg_2Cl_2 and $PbCl_2$) were washed too long with cold water.

(d) A large excess of concentrated HCl were used in the silver-group precipitation.

(e) Not enough HNO_3 were added in the confirmatory test for silver.

8. Using the scheme of analysis as a guide give the formula for a chemical substance which will:

(a) Form a precipitate with KCl solution and also with $CuCl_2$.

(b) Form a precipitate with HCl and also with H_2SO_4.

(c) Form a precipitate with NH_4Cl solution and also with K_2CrO_4.

(d) Form a precipitate with HCl and also with HNO_3.

(e) Form a precipitate with HCl but not with HNO_3.

(f) Form a precipitate with $AgNO_3$ solution but not with $Bi(NO_3)_3$.

(g) Form a precipitate with $Hg_2(NO_3)_2$ solution but not with $Hg(NO_3)_2$.

(h) Form a precipitate with $Ag(NH_3)_2Cl$ solution but not with $AgNO_3$.

(i) Readily dissolve $PbCl_2$ but not AgCl.

(j) Readily dissolve $ZnCl_2$ but not $PbCl_2$.

(k) Readily dissolve AgCl but not Hg_2Cl_2.

(l) Readily dissolve $HgCl_2$ but not Hg_2Cl_2.

(m) Readily dissolve $Pb(NO_3)_2$ but not $PbSO_4$.

(n) Form a precipitate with Na_2CrO_4 but not with $NaNO_3$.

9. By means of what single reagent could you distinguish between the following? (Tell what happens to each substance.)

(a) *Solutions:*

$AgNO_3$ and $Zn(NO_3)_2$.	H_2SO_4 and HCl.
K_2CrO_4 and KNO_3.	H_2SO_4 and HNO_3.
HCl and HNO_3.	$Hg(NO_3)_2$ and $Hg_2(NO_3)_2$.
$Pb(NO_3)_2$ and $Hg(NO_3)_2$.	$Ag(NH_3)_2Cl$ and $AgNO_3$.

(b) *Solids:*

Hg_2Cl_2 and $HgCl_2$. $\qquad$ AgCl and $ZnCl_2$.

$PbCl_2$ and Hg_2Cl_2. $\qquad$ AgCl and Hg_2Cl_2.

$PbSO_4$ and $Pb(NO_3)_2$. $\qquad$ $PbCrO_4$ and K_2CrO_4.

10. An unknown solution, which was known to contain only cations of the silver group, gave no precipitate when heated to boiling and treated with hot concentrated HCl but gave a white precipitate when cooled and treated with cold concentrated HCl. What conclusions can be drawn?

11. In the analysis of an unknown solution that was known to contain only cations of the silver group, the white precipitate obtained by adding cold HCl to the unknown solution partly dissolved in hot water. The residue dissolved completely in NH_4OH. What cations were present? Absent?

12. The white precipitate obtained when cold HCl was added to an unknown solution was completely insoluble in both hot water and NH_4OH. What conclusions can be drawn?

13. The white precipitate obtained when cold HCl was added to an unknown solution was completely insoluble in hot water and completely soluble in NH_4OH. What conclusions can be drawn?

14. A student was given a Silver group unknown and was told, correctly, that it contained only one cation. He treated the unknown with 6 M HCl as directed in the scheme of analysis and obtained a white precipitate. He washed this precipitate twice with cold water. He then treated the washed precipitate with one reagent. By observing what happened when this one reagent was added he was able to decide, within a few seconds, what cation was present in his unknown. What one reagent did he add to the precipitate? What would he have observed on addition of the one reagent to the washed precipitate if the unknown solution contained, as the one cation, Ag^+? Hg_2^{++}? Pb^{++}?

15. Give, in detail, the reactions that take place when solid AgOH, which is insoluble in water, is dissolved by NH_4OH.

16. Ag_3AsO_4 is soluble in HNO_3 but insoluble in $HC_2H_3O_2$. Explain, giving the ionic equations for all reactions involved.

17. Is each of the following four facts consistent with each of the other three?

(a) The solubility product for AgI is less than the solubility product for AgCl.

(b) AgCl is more soluble in water than is AgI.

(c) AgCl is soluble in 15 M NH_4OH; AgI is not dissolved by 15 M NH_4OH.

(d) When solid AgCl is shaken with a solution of 1 M KI the solid AgCl is dissolved and a precipitate of AgI is formed.

18. Suppose you were to calculate the solubility product for AgCN from its solubility in water on the assumption that only Ag^+ and CN^- ions are present, not realizing that the stable $Ag(CN)_2^-$ complex ion is formed. Would this calculated value be greater than, less than, or equal to the true value of the $[Ag^+]$ $[CN^-]$ product?

19. A student, thinking the formula of mercury(I) chloride was HgCl, calculated its solubility product from the weight of the compound present in a liter of solution. He assumed the reaction occurring when the salt dissolved was $2\ HgCl \rightleftarrows Hg_2^{++} + 2\ Cl^-$. The correct formula is Hg_2Cl_2 and the correct reaction is $Hg_2Cl_2 \rightleftarrows Hg_2^{++} + 2\ Cl^-$. Was his calculated value of the solubility product equal to, less than, or greater than the true value?

20. The solubility product of AgSCN, which is pale amber in color, is 1×10^{-12}. The solubility product of $Al(OH)_3$ is 5×10^{-33}. When a dilute solution of NaSCN is added to a beaker containing AgCl the precipitate changes in color from white to pale amber. The saturated solution formed when solid $Fe(OH)_3$ is shaken with water is less basic than the saturated solution formed when $Al(OH)_3$ is shaken with water. The water solution in equilibrium with solid Ag_3PO_4 has 4 times the concentration of Ag^+ as the water solution in equilibrium with solid AgCl. On the basis of the above facts list the following in the order of their decreasing molar solubility in water: $Al(OH)_3$, AgSCN, AgCl, $Fe(OH_3$, Ag_3PO_4.

Silver-group report

$G - Ag^+$

Silver-group report

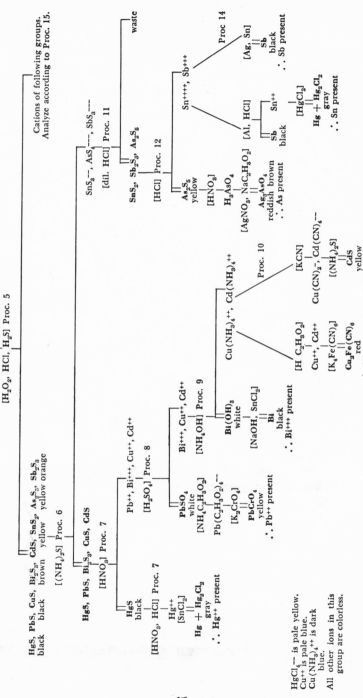

Solution containing Pb^{++}, Hg^{++}, Bi^{+++}, Cu^{++}, Cd^{++}, Sn^{++}, Sn^{++++}, As^{+++}, H$_2$AsO$_3^-$, AsO$_4^{---}$, Sb^{+++}, Al^{+++}, Cr^{+++}, Fe^{++}, Fe^{+++}, Mn^{++}, Zn^{++}, Ni^{++}, Co^{++}, Ca^{++}, Ba^{++}, Mg^{++}, K$^+$, Na$^+$ and NH$_4^+$

[H$_2$O$_2$, HCl, H$_2$S] Proc. 5

HgS, PbS, CuS, Bi$_2$S$_3$, CdS, SnS$_2$, As$_2$S$_5$, Sb$_2$S$_5$
black black brown yellow yellow orange

[(NH$_4$)$_2$S] Proc. 6

HgS, PbS, Bi$_2$S$_3$, CuS, CdS
brown

[HNO$_3$] Proc. 7

HgS, PbS, Bi$_2$S$_3$, CuS, CdS
black

[HNO$_3$] Proc. 7

HgS
black

[HNO$_3$, HCl] Proc. 7

Hg^{++}
[SnCl$_2$]

Hg + Hg$_2$Cl$_2$
gray
∴ Hg^{++} present

Pb^{++}, Bi^{+++}, Cu^{++}, Cd^{++}

[H$_2$SO$_4$] Proc. 8

PbSO$_4$
white

[NH$_4$C$_2$H$_3$O$_2$]$^{--}$
Pb(C$_2$H$_3$O$_2$)$_4$

[K$_2$CrO$_4$]

PbCrO$_4$
yellow
∴ Pb^{++} present

Bi^{+++}, Cu^{++}, Cd^{++}

[NH$_4$OH] Proc. 9

Bi(OH)$_3$
white

[NaOH, SnCl$_2$]

Bi
black
∴ Bi^{+++} present

Cu(NH$_3$)$_4^{++}$, Cd(NH$_3$)$_4^{++}$

Proc. 10

[H C$_2$H$_3$O$_2$]

Cu^{++}, Cd^{++}

[K$_4$Fe(CN)$_6$]

Cu$_2$Fe(CN)$_6$
red
∴ Cu^{++} present

[KCN]

Cu(CN)$_2^-$, Cd(CN)$_4^{--}$

[(NH$_4$)$_2$S]

CdS
yellow
∴ Cd^{++} is present

SnS$_3^{--}$, AsS$_4^{---}$, SbS$_3^-$

[dil. HCl] Proc. 11

SnS$_2$, Sb$_2$S$_3$, As$_2$S$_5$

[HCl] Proc. 12

As$_2$S$_5$
yellow

[HNO$_3$]

H$_3$AsO$_4$

[AgNO$_3$, NaC$_2$H$_3$O$_2$]

Ag$_3$AsO$_4$
reddish brown
∴ As present

Sn^{++++}, Sb^{+++}

[Al, HCl]

Sb
black

Sn^{++}

[HgCl$_2$]

Hg + Hg$_2$Cl$_2$
gray
∴ Sn present

[Ag, Sn] Proc 14

Sb
black
∴ Sb present

waste

Cations of following groups.
Analyze according to Proc. 15.

HgCl$_4^{--}$ is pale yellow.
Cu^{++} is pale blue.
Cu(NH$_3$)$_4^{++}$ is dark blue.
All other ions in this group are colorless.

OUTLINE 3: THE ANALYSIS OF THE COPPER-ARSENIC GROUP

87

CHAPTER FOUR

The copper-arsenic group

THE SULFIDES of lead, mercury(II), bismuth, copper, cadmium, arsenic, antimony, and tin are insoluble in dilute HCl. The sulfides of all metals of the following groups are soluble in HCl. Upon this fact is based the separation of the cations of the copper-arsenic group from the cations of the following groups.

■ ■ ■ Procedure 5: Precipitation of the copper-arsenic group

(A) Place 4 drops of the "known" or "unknown" solution, or the decantate from Procedure 1, in a casserole and add 2 drops of 3% H_2O_2 and 2 drops of 2 M HCl. Carefully boil down to a volume of 1 or 2 drops. (See Note 1.) Allow to cool. Then add 6 drops of 6 M HCl. Carefully evaporate the contents of the casserole down to a pasty mass, being very particular not to bake the residue. Cool, and then, *if H_2S gas is to be used as the precipitating reagent,* proceed as directed in (B) below; *if thioacetamide solution is to be used as the precipitating reagent* proceed as directed in (C) below.

(B) *Follow this procedure if H_2S gas is used as the precipitating reagent.* To the residue in the cool casserole add exactly 4 drops of

88

2 M HCl. Swish the acid around until all the residue is dissolved; if necessary stir the mixture and warm slightly. Transfer the solution to a 3-in. test tube, heat carefully until it begins to show signs of effervescence, then treat with H_2S **under the hood** for 20–30 seconds. (See Note 2.) Dilute with 10 drops of hot water and treat with H_2S for another 20–30 seconds. Then add 1 drop of 1 M $NH_4C_2H_3O_2$ and treat with H_2S for 20–30 more seconds, being sure that the H_2S gas is bubbled all the way to the bottom of the solution. Finally, add 25 more drops of cold water and treat with H_2S for another 20–30 seconds. Centrifuge; then test for complete precipitation, by first noting the appearance of the solution and then passing H_2S into the top $\frac{1}{4}$ in. of the supernatant liquid, being careful not to disturb the precipitate. If precipitation is not complete add 5 more drops of cold water and treat with H_2S for another 20–30 seconds. When tests with H_2S show that precipitation is complete, wash down, with 2 or 3 drops of water, any precipitate on the walls of the test tube, centrifuge, and decant into a casserole. Boil the decantate, which contains the cations of the following groups, for 1 minute and save it for Procedure 15. (See Note 4.) Wash the precipitate twice with 15-drop portions of hot water and analyze according to Procedure 6. If the wash water peptizes the precipitate (causes it to be converted to a colloidal suspension which will not settle when centrifuged) add 10 drops of 1 M $NH_4C_2H_3O_2$, mix well and heat nearly to boiling before centrifuging.

(C) *Follow this procedure if thioacetamide solution is used as the precipitating reagent.* To the residue in the cool casserole add exactly 4 drops of 2 M HCl. Swish the acid around until all of the residue is dissolved; if necessary, stir the mixture and warm slightly. Then transfer the solution to a 3-in. test tube, add 4 drops of 1 M thioacetamide solution (see Note 3), mix thoroughly, and heat in the boiling water bath for 4 minutes (see Note 4). Add 8 drops of hot water, 8 drops of 1 M thioacetamide and 1 drop of 1 M $NH_4C_2H_3O_2$, mix well, and heat in the boiling water bath for 4 minutes. Add 4 more drops of hot water and 8 more drops of 1 M thioacetamide, mix well and heat in the boiling water bath for 4 minutes. Centrifuge and decant into a test tube; save both the precipitate and the decantate. Test the decantate for complete precipitation by adding 2 drops of 1 M thioacetamide, mixing well, and allowing to stand for 1 minute; if a precipitate forms, indicating that precipitation is not complete, add 2 drops of hot water and 2 more drops of 1 M thioacetamide, mix well and heat in the boiling water bath for 2 minutes. When a test shows that precipitation is complete, transfer the decantate to a casserole. Boil this decantate, which contains the cations of the groups that follow, for 1 minute and save it for Procedure 15. (See Note 5.)

All precipitates obtained in the original precipitation and the successive tests for complete precipitation should be combined by flushing the latter into the test tube containing the original precipitate with a few drops of water. Wash the precipitate three times with mixtures of 10 drops of hot water and 10 drops of 1 M $NH_4C_2H_3O_2$ and analyze according to Procedure 6. In this and all future washing operations be sure that the precipitate and washing liquid are well mixed by vigorous agitation with a stirring rod.

NOTES

1. Evaporate the solution in the casserole as follows: Hold the casserole in your hand and pass it back and forth over the top of the flame. At the end of every two or three back-and-forth passes tilt the casserole slightly so that the solution will run to its lower edge. In the course of the back-and-forth pass the solution is swished around over the bottom of the casserole. Be very careful not to overheat to the point where the residue begins to bake. If brown areas develop on the bottom of the casserole, indicating baking, swish the remaining solution around until the brown area is removed. When only two or three drops of liquid remain, remove from above the flame and let the heat of the casserole complete the evaporation. Baking the residue must be avoided; baking may sublime off the chlorides of arsenic, mercury, and tin.

2. A solution is treated with H_2S gas as follows. Attach to the rubber outlet tube at the source of H_2S a clean glass bubbling tube. This bubbling tube is made by drawing down a glass tube of suitable diameter to a fairly fine constricted end. The over-all length of the bubbling tube should be about 5 in. Insert the end of the bubbling tube from which H_2S is escaping into the surface of the solution in the test tube and then gradually bring it down to the bottom of the solution. The constricted tube will deliver a stream of very fine bubbles; large bubbles would tend to throw the solution out of the small test tube. If the tip of the bubbling tube is brought suddenly all the way to the bottom of the solution the sudden rush of gas may throw the solution out of the test tube. A very rapid rate of H_2S bubbling should be avoided.

An ordinary Kipp generator, placed in a hood where it is accessible to a group of students, is a very satisfactory source of H_2S. A trap, in the form of a bottle or flask, should be placed between the generator valve and the point where the bubbling tube is attached.

One of the most satisfactory sources of H_2S is the commercial mixture of sulfur, hydrocarbon mix, and asbestos of which "Aitch Tu Ess" is an example. This mixture can be purchased in bulk or in small capsules; for class use bulk purchase is recommended. It is used for generation of H_2S as follows. Set up under the hood a generator as illustrated. Fill the 6-in.

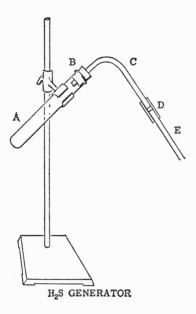

H$_2$S GENERATOR

pyrex tube A one-half to three-quarters full of H_2S-generating mixture. Insert the rubber stopper B to which is attached the delivery tube C, the rubber connecting tube D, and the clean bubbling tube E. When heat is applied to A, H_2S gas will be generated and will issue from the tip of E, which is inserted into the solution to be treated. The heating should be gentle, just strong enough to give a fairly rapid evolution of H_2S bubbles. The burner with which A is being heated can be held in one hand, while the test tube containing the solution being treated can be held in the other hand. Do not heat so strongly that sulfur is distilled over. The evolution of H_2S will cease when heating is stopped. The tube E should be removed from the solution being treated as soon as heating is stopped to avoid solution being drawn from the test tube up into E by the contracting gas.

The tube E should be removed and cleaned after each series of precipitations. The tube A, containing unexpended mixture, together with the attachments B, C, and D, can be kept in the student's desk when not in use. When the mixture no longer yields H_2S on heating, tube A can be replaced by a new tube of mixture, or the expended residue in tube A can be replaced by new mixture.

The setup described is intended for use by one or two students. If a larger tube is used at A the generator will serve several students.

H$_2$S is a poison. Therefore, all H$_2$S treatment should be carried out under a good hood.

3. The organic compound, thioacetamide, CH$_3$CSNH$_2$, hydrolyzes in water, particularly at higher temperatures, to yield H$_2$S according to the equation

$$CH_3CSNH_2 + 2 H_2O = CH_3COOH + NH_3 + H_2S.$$

It therefore serves as a convenient source of H$_2$S. The hydrolysis is so slight at room temperature that a 1 M solution of the compound, when preserved in a stoppered bottle, undergoes very little deterioration. At temperatures of about 80°C. the hydrolysis is sufficient so that a 1 M solution yields a solution saturated with H$_2$S.

4. Care should be taken so that the tube is not heated to the point where excessive frothing results in loss of solution by spillage. If the tube is grasped with a test tube holder it can be withdrawn from the boiling water if and when spillage is imminent.

5. If the solution being analyzed is a copper-arsenic group known or unknown containing only cations of the copper-arsenic group, this decantate can be discarded.

6. The group known and unknown solutions and the decantate from the silver group contain an unknown amount of acid. This acid is removed by evaporation to dryness in the first step in Procedure 5. Then a specific amount of hydrochloric acid is added. This method gives a solution of the proper acidity for the H$_2$S precipitation.

7. The sulfides, HgS, CuS, Bi$_2$S$_3$, SnS$_2$, CdS, PbS, and Sb$_2$S$_3$, are formed as a result of combination of the metallic ions (cations) with the sulfide ions produced by ionization of the weak acid, H$_2$S.

$$H_2S \rightleftharpoons 2 H^+ + S^{--}$$
$$S^{--} + Hg^{++} = HgS.$$

The net equation for the reaction is

$$Hg^{++} + H_2S = HgS + 2 H^+.$$

A particular metal sulfide will not begin to precipitate until the product of the concentrations of the cation and the sulfide ion equals the solubility product for the sulfide. The sulfide will continue to precipitate until the concentration of the cation has been reduced to a point where the product of its concentration and the sulfide ion concentration is equal to the solubility product of the sulfide. When precipitation ceases, the precipitate will be in equilibrium with its ions in solution, and the rate at which the ions in solution combine to form the precipitate will be exactly equal to the rate at which the precipitate dissolves and dissociates into its ions. Since this is a true equilibrium which obeys the mass law, it follows that the higher the concentration of sulfide ions the lower will be the concentration of cations left in solution when precipitation is complete.

The sulfide ions required for the precipitation of the copper-arsenic group sulfides, as shown in the above equations, are derived from the ionization of the weak acid H_2S, which is formed when H_2S gas is dissolved in water solution or when thioacetamide hydrolyzes. The ionization of H_2S takes place in these two stages:

$$H_2S \rightleftharpoons H^+ + HS^-,$$

$$HS^- \rightleftharpoons H^+ + S^{--}.$$

For the purposes of this discussion, however, the two stages may be combined into one equation:

$$H_2S \rightleftharpoons 2 H^+ + S^{--}.$$

If the hydrogen ion concentration (acidity) of a saturated solution of H_2S is increased by addition of HCl, the equilibrium in the above reaction is shifted to tne left, with a resulting decrease in the S^{--} ion concentration. If the concentration of the H^+ derived from the HCl is reduced by dilution while the solution is kept saturated with H_2S the concentration of the S^{--} ions in the above equilibrium will increase. That is, in a saturated solution of H_2S, the greater the H^+ concentration the smaller the S^{--} concentration and the smaller the H^+ concentration the greater the S^{--} concentration.

Not only can the concentration of H^+ ions derived from HCl be reduced by dilution but it can also be decreased, more effectively, by addition of the salt of a weak acid such as $NH_4C_2H_3O_2$. The $C_2H_3O_2^-$ ions from $NH_4C_2H_3O_2$ tie up the H^+ ions in the form of the weak acid, $HC_2H_3O_2$. (See Buffer Action, page 36.) Since the concentration of the OH^- ions is already extremely low the added NH_4^+ ions from the $NH_4C_2H_3O_2$ will have negligible effect on the condition of the solution.

To get complete precipitation of the cations of the copper-arsenic group as sulfides, the concentration of the sulfide ion, which is the group-reagent ion, should be as high as possible; to get a high S^{--} concentration, the H^+ concentration should be as low as possible. There are two factors that modify the application of this rule. The conversion of arsenites and arsenates to sulfides requires a high concentration of hydrogen ion (HCl), as will be explained in Note 8. At the other extreme, if the acidity is too low, the sulfide ion concentration will be so high that the solubility products for the sulfides of iron, zinc, manganese, cobalt, and nickel will be exceeded, and these sulfides also will be precipitated. By varying the concentration of the HCl solution from approximately 2 M to approximately 0.2 M complete precipitation of all cations of the copper-arsenic group is obtained without precipitation of the cations of the following group.

8. Arsenic is rarely if ever present in a solution as As^{+++} or

As^{+++++}. Usually it is present as arsenate (AsO_4^{---}) or arsenite ($H_2AsO_3^-$). If $AsCl_3$ or $AsCl_5$ are dissolved in water they immediately hydrolyze to give the weak acids H_3AsO_3 and H_3AsO_4 according to the equations

$$AsCl_3 + 3 H_2O = H_3AsO_3 + 3 H^+ + 3 Cl^-,$$

$$AsCl_5 + 4 H_2O = H_3AsO_4 + 5 H^+ + 5 Cl^-.$$

When arsenic is present as arsenate or arsenite, the sulfides are precipitated according to the equations

$$2 H_3AsO_4 + 5 H_2S = As_2S_5 + 8 H_2O,$$

$$2 H_3AsO_3 + 3 H_2S = As_2S_3 + 6 H_2O.$$

Some arsenate may be reduced by H_2S to arsenite.

$$H_3AsO_4 + H_2S = H_3AsO_3 + H_2O + S.$$

The H_3AsO_3 then reacts with H_2S to form As_2S_3 as noted above.

Each of these reactions is very slow. However, each is speeded up when the H^+ concentration is increased (perhaps by catalysis). Therefore, to insure complete precipitation of arsenic, the solution in the first stage of the sulfide precipitation is strongly acidic.

9. To get complete separation of tin, arsenic, and antimony from mercury, lead, bismuth, cadmium, and copper in Procedure 6 it is necessary that tin be present as $Sn(IV)$. (See Note 1, Procedure 6.) H_2O_2 is added in the first step in Procedures 5(A) and 5(B) to oxidize $Sn(II)$ to $Sn(IV)$.

$$Sn^{++} + 2 H^+ + H_2O_2 = Sn^{++++} + 2 H_2O.$$

Arsenite if present will be oxidized to arsenate.

$$H_3AsO_3 + H_2O_2 = H_3AsO_4 + H_2O.$$

Any excess H_2O_2 is destroyed when the solution is boiled.

10. Six drops of 6 M HCl are added before evaporation to dryness in order that nitrate ions (HNO_3) may be destroyed in accordance with the equation

$$2 NO_3^- + 6 Cl^- + 8 H^+ = 4 H_2O + 2 NO + 3 Cl_2.$$

Nitrate ions (HNO_3) if present, will oxidize the H_2S, S being precipitated.

$$2 NO_3^- + 3 H_2S + 2 H^+ = 4 H_2O + 2 NO + 3 S.$$

Other oxidizing agents, such as Fe^{+++} or $Cr_2O_7^{--}$, may be present in a solution to be analyzed. They will react with H_2S in acid solution as follows.

$$2 Fe^{+++} + H_2S = 2 Fe^{++} + 2 H^+ + S.$$

$$Cr_2O_7^{--} + 3 H_2S + 8 H^+ = 2 Cr^{+++} + 3 S + 7 H_2O.$$

Fe^{+++} will not be affected by evaporation with 6 M HCl. $Cr_2O_7^{--}$ will be reduced as follows.

$$Cr_2O_7^{--} + 6\,Cl^- + 14\,H^+ = 2\,Cr^{+++} + 3\,Cl_2 + 7\,H_2O.$$

11. If a solution containing members of the copper-arsenic group is diluted with water, a milky-white suspension may result because of the formation, by hydrolysis, of the insoluble white basic salts of bismuth and antimony according to the equations

$$Bi^{+++} + Cl^- + H_2O \rightleftharpoons BiOCl + 2\,H^+,$$

$$Sb^{+++} + Cl^- + H_2O \rightleftharpoons SbOCl + 2\,H^+.$$

If the milky suspension is treated with HCl, the milkiness will disappear because the equilibrium point in these two reactions will have been shifted to the left. In concentrated HCl solution antimony exists as the complex tetrachloroantimonate(III) ion, $SbCl_4^-$. This ion is quite stable.

$$SbCl_4^- \rightleftharpoons Sb^{+++} + 4\,Cl^-.$$

The hydrolysis that takes place when a strongly acid solution of antimony chloride is added to water may therefore be represented by the equation

$$SbCl_4^- + H_2O \rightleftharpoons SbOCl + 2\,H^+ + 3\,Cl^-.$$

12. It is to be noted that lead and mercury appear in the copper-arsenic group as well as in the silver group. Lead chloride is somewhat soluble in dilute HCl. For that reason lead ions are not completely precipitated in the silver group and are carried over into the copper-arsenic group. Mercury occurs in the monovalent and bivalent state. Although Hg_2Cl_2 is very insoluble in dilute HCl, $HgCl_2$ is very soluble. Therefore, mercury(II) is not precipitated in the silver group.

13. The sulfides of mercury, lead, and copper are black. SnS and Bi_2S_3 are dark brown. CdS, SnS_2, As_2S_3, and As_2S_5 are yellow. Sb_2S_3 and Sb_2S_5 are orange. Lead may first form an orange-red precipitate of PbS · $PbCl_2$; this changes to black PbS on continued H_2S treatment. Mercury first precipitates as white HgS · $HgCl_2$; this changes through yellow, orange, and brown, to black HgS on continued H_2S treatment, the intermediate colored precipitate being a mixture of HgS · $HgCl_2$ and HgS in varying proportions.

14. $CuCl_2$ is green in concentrated solution and blue in dilute solution. The chlorides of all other members of the copper-arsenic group from colorless solutions except that $BiCl_3$ and $SbCl_3$ hydrolyze as explained in Note 11. The complete absence of any green or blue color in an unknown solution shows the absence of copper.

15. The statement has been made that, as a general rule, the water-insoluble salt of a weak acid will dissolve in a strong acid. (See Chapter 2, page 53.) By this rule the metal sulfides should dissolve in HCl. The

fact that they do not dissolve means that their normal solubility in water is so very small that not even a strong acid can give a concentration of hydrogen ions sufficiently high to cause them to go into solution. Taking CuS as an example, its solubility is very low (its solubility product is 4×10^{-36}); that means that the concentration of sulfide ions in the equilibrium

$$\text{CuS} \rightleftharpoons \text{Cu}^{++} + \text{S}^{--}$$

is extremely low. The equilibrium reaction, $\text{S}^{--} + 2\,\text{H}^+ \rightleftharpoons \text{H}_2\text{S}$, which is set up when a strong acid is added to the sulfide, is not capable of giving a sulfide ion concentration lower than that which is in equilibrium with CuS and Cu^{++}. Consequently CuS does not dissolve.

On prolonged boiling with HCl, CuS will dissolve, very slowly. In this case the S^{--} ions are actually removed from solution as H_2S.

It should be noted at this point that the solubility product principle tells very little about the *rate* at which an "insoluble" substance will dissolve.

Separation of the Copper Subgroup from the Arsenic Subgroup

The sulfides of arsenic, antimony, and tin(IV) are soluble in a solution of ammonium sulfide. The sulfides of copper, lead, mercury, bismuth, and cadmium are insoluble. This fact is the basis for the separation of the copper subgroup from the arsenic subgroup.

■ ■ ■ Procedure 6: Separation of the copper subgroup from the arsenic subgroup

To the test tube containing the precipitate from Procedure 5, add 10 drops of ammonium sulfide solution. Stir the contents of the tube well; then heat for 3–4 minutes in the boiling water bath, stirring the contents meanwhile. Avoid heating the tube to the point where excessive frothing of the contents occurs. Centrifuge, decant into a test tube, and save the decantate, which may contain SnS_3^{--}, SbS_3^{---}, and AsS_4^{---}, for Procedure 11. Repeat the treatment of the precipitate with a second 10-drop portion of ammonium sulfide solution, heating the tube in the boiling water bath and stirring for 2 minutes. Centrifuge and decant, combining the second decantate with the first; save it in a stoppered test tube for Procedure 11.

Wash the precipitate twice with a mixture of 10 drops of hot water and 10 drops of 1 M $\text{NH}_4\text{C}_2\text{H}_3\text{O}_2$; analyze this precipitate, which may consist of the sulfides of mercury(II), lead, bismuth, copper, and cadmium, according to Procedure 7.

NOTES

1. $(NH_4)_2S$ will dissolve As_2S_3, As_2S_5, Sb_2S_3, and SnS_2 but it will not dissolve SnS. Therefore if tin is to go into solution in $(NH_4)_2S$ along with arsenic and antimony as the separation requires, it must be present as SnS_2. That means that it must be present as Sn(IV) during treatment with H_2S. To guarantee that tin is present as Sn(IV) the solution, before precipitation with H_2S, is boiled with H_2O_2.

2. The separation of arsenic, antimony, and tin from mercury(II), lead, bismuth, copper, and cadmium depends on the fact that As_2S_3, As_2S_5, SnS_2, and Sb_2S_3 are soluble in a solution of $(NH_4)_2S$, whereas HgS, PbS, Bi_2S_3, CuS, and CdS are insoluble. The molecular equations for the reactions that take place are

$$SnS_2 + (NH_4)_2S = (NH_4)_2SnS_3 \qquad \text{(ammonium thiostannate(IV))},$$

$$As_2S_5 + 3\,(NH_4)_2S = 2\,(NH_4)_3AsS_4 \qquad \text{(ammonium thioarsenate(V))}.$$

The compounds $(NH_4)_2SnS_3$, $(NH_4)_3AsS_3$, $(NH_4)_3AsS_4$, and $(NH_4)_3SbS_3$ are strong electrolytes and ionize to give NH_4^+ ions and, respectively, SnS_3^{--}, AsS_3^{---}, AsS_4^{---} and SbS_3^{---} ions. The formation of the latter ions can be represented by the net equations

$$As_2S_3 + 3\,S^{--} = 2\,AsS_3^{---}, \qquad \text{(trithioarsenate(III) ion)},$$

$$As_2S_5 + 3\,S^{--} = 2\,AsS_4^{---}, \qquad \text{(tetrathioarsenate(V) ion)}.$$

Since these ions are formed as a result of a reaction of an ion with a molecule they may be classed as complex ions. Their formation probably involves the following detailed reactions.

(a) $\qquad As_2S_5 \rightleftharpoons 2\,As^{+++++} + 5\,S^{--},$

(b) $\qquad\qquad\qquad As^{+++++} + 4\,S^{--} \rightleftharpoons AsS_4^{---}.$

Not only is the concentration of the As^{+++++} in equation (a) very low due to the low solubility of the sulfide, but these As^{+++++} ions have a strong tendency to hydrolyze:

$$As^{+++++} + 4\,H_2O \rightleftharpoons H_3AsO_4 + 5\,H^+.$$

That means that the concentration of As^{+++++} available for reaction (b) is extremely low; which means that the rate at which the solid sulfide dissolves in $(NH_4)_2S$ is low. To speed up the rate of this solution process the contents of the tube in Procedure 6 are kept hot.

Mercury, lead, bismuth, copper, and cadmium do not form complex thio-ions. It may be stated, therefore, that separation of the sulfides of arsenic, antimony, and tin from the sulfides of mercury, lead, bismuth, copper, and cadmium depends on the fact that the sulfides of arsenic, antimony, and tin form complex ions with sulfide ions, whereas the sulfides of the other metals in the group do not form such complex ions.

A careful examination of the formulas for the thio salts of arsenic, antimony, and tin and the molecular equations for their formation suggests why these sulfides are unique in their ability to form complex ions. $(NH_4)_2SnS_3$ is the ammonium salt of thiostannic acid, H_2SnS_3, in the sulfur system. It is the analog of the ternary salt, $(NH_4)_2SnO_3$, in the oxygen system. Any ternary salt in the oxygen system may be looked upon as having been formed as a result of the reaction of a basic oxide with an acidic oxide. The oxides of metals are basic oxides; the oxides of non-metals are acidic oxides.

Basic oxide		Acidic oxide		Salt
CaO	$+$	CO_2	$=$	$CaCO_3$
PbO	$+$	N_2O_5	$=$	$Pb(NO_3)_2$
$(NH_4)_2O$	$+$	SnO_2	$=$	$(NH_4)_2SnO_3$
$3(NH_4)_2O$	$+$	As_2O_3	$=$	$2(NH_4)_3AsO_3$

The sulfides of the elements bear the same relationship to H_2S that the oxides bear to H_2O.

CuO	H_2O
CuS	H_2S
As_2O_3	H_2O
As_2S_3	H_2S

Therefore, CuS, PbS, HgS, CdS, SnS, Bi_2S_3, and $(NH_4)_2S$ are basic sulfides in the sulfur system just as CuO, PbO, HgO, CdO, SnO, Bi_2O_3, and $(NH_4)_2O$ are basic oxides in the oxygen system. Likewise, SnS_2, As_2S_3, As_2S_5, and Sb_2S_3 are acidic sulfides in the sulfur system just as SnO_2, As_2O_3, As_2O_5, and Sb_2O_3 are acidic oxides in the oxygen system.

Just as, in the oxygen system, a basic oxide will react with an acidic oxide to form a salt, so a basic sulfide will react with an acidic sulfide to form a salt in the sulfur system. SnS_2, As_2S_3, As_2S_5, and Sb_2S_3 are acidic sulfides. $(NH_4)_2S$ is a basic sulfide. Therefore, the former would be expected to react with the latter to form the salts $(NH_4)_2SnS_3$, $(NH_4)_3AsS_3$, $(NH_4)_3AsS_4$, and $(NH_4)_3SbS_3$.

In the oxygen system one basic oxide does not ordinarily react with another basic oxide. By analogy one basic sulfide will not react with another basic sulfide. Since $(NH_4)_2S$ is a basic sulfide it would not be expected to react with the basic sulfides HgS, PbS, Bi_2S_3, CuS, CdS, and SnS.

Therefore, it seems justifiable to conclude that separation of the sulfides of arsenic, antimony, and tin (IV) from the sulfides of mercury, lead, bismuth, copper, and cadmium depends on the fact that the former, being *acidic sulfides, will dissolve in the basic sulfide,* $(NH_4)_2S$, while the latter, being *basic sulfides, will not dissolve in the basic sulfide,* $(NH_4)_2S$.

There remains the question of why SnS is basic while SnS_2 is acidic. It is generally true that, *as the oxidation number of a polyvalent element increases, it becomes more nonmetallic in character, and as an element becomes more nonmetallic in character its compounds become more acidic.* Chromium and manganese illustrate this generalization. Chromium(III) forms the cation Cr^{+++}, which is definitely metallic in character; chromium(VI) forms the anion CrO_4^{--}, which is an acid radical. Manganese(II) gives the metallic cation Mn^{++}, while manganese (VII) forms the acidic anion, MnO_4^-. Likewise the Bi^{+++} ion is metallic, while the bismuthate ion, BiO_3^-, is definitely acidic. We can conclude, therefore, that, in its divalent state tin is predominantly metallic; therefore SnS is a basic sulfide. Tin(IV), on the other hand, is nonmetallic; therefore SnS_2 is acidic. Oxidation with H_2O_2 guarantees that the tin is present in its higher oxidation state.

3. Antimony(V) does not ordinarily exist in solution, its oxidation state of 5 being very unstable.

Separation of Mercury from Lead, Bismuth, Copper, and Cadmium

The sulfides of copper, bismuth, cadmium, and lead are soluble in warm dilute HNO_3. HgS is insoluble. The separation of mercury from lead, bismuth, copper, and cadmium is based on this fact.

▪ ▪ ▪ Procedure 7: Separation and detection of mercury(II)

Add 15 drops of 3 M HNO_3 to the test tube containing the precipitate from Procedure 6, mix thoroughly, transfer to a casserole and boil gently for about 2 minutes. Replenish the HNO_3 when necessary. Transfer to a test tube, centrifuge, and decant into a test tube, saving this decantate for Procedure 8. Wash the precipitate twice with 15-drop portions of water made acidic with a drop of 3 M HNO_3. Add the first washing to the decantate in the test tube; discard the second washing.

Treat the precipitate with 6 drops of 12 M HCl and 2 drops of 16 M HNO_3, mix thoroughly and heat for 1 minute in the boiling water bath. Add 10 drops of hot water, transfer to a casserole, boil gently for about 30 seconds, and then transfer back to a test tube. Cool by holding the test tube under the water tap, then centrifuge. To the cool supernatant solution in the test tube add 2–5 drops of 0.2 M $SnCl_2$ solution. A black (**Hg**) or gray (Hg_2Cl_2 + **Hg**) precipitate proves the presence of mercury(II).

NOTES

1. The sulfides of lead, copper, bismuth, and cadmium dissolve in HNO_3 in accordance with the equation

$$3\,CuS + 2\,NO_3^- + 8\,H^+ = 3\,Cu^{++} + 3\,S + 2\,NO + 4\,H_2O.$$

The detailed reactions involved are

(a) $CuS \rightleftharpoons Cu^{++} + S^{--}$,

(b) $3\,S^{--} + 2\,NO_3^- + 8\,H^+ = 3\,S + 2\,NO + 4\,H_2O.$

Reaction (b) removes the S^{--} ions from reaction (a) and causes it to be complete to the right.

2. If the HNO_3 is too concentrated, it will dissolve some of the HgS. In addition, it may oxidize PbS to $PbSO_4$, which will remain as a residue mixed with the HgS.

3. HgS is black. The presence of a white or yellow residue after digestion with HNO_3 does not, however, eliminate the possibility of mercury being present. The insoluble white compound $Hg(NO_3)_2 \cdot 2\,HgS$ may have formed. The residue, whatever its color, should be tested for mercury.

4. HgS is insoluble in both concentrated HNO_3 and concentrated HCl, when each is used separately. However, a mixture of the two concentrated acids dissolves HgS readily and quickly. The detailed reaction is discussed on page 56.

The net equation for the over-all reaction is

$$3\,HgS + 2\,NO_3^- + 8\,H^+ + 12\,Cl^- =$$
$$3\,HgCl_4^{--} + 2\,NO + 4\,H_2O + 3\,S.$$

The $HgCl_4^{--}$ ion is largely dissociated into Hg^{++} and 4 Cl^- ions when the solution is diluted with water. The Hg^{++} ions can then be identified by means of the reactions represented in the next note.

5. The extent to which Hg^{++} is reduced by Sn^{++} depends on the relative amounts of the two kinds of ions present. If Hg^{++} is present in large excess, the reduction is mostly to Hg_2Cl_2 as follows.

$$2\,Hg^{++} + Sn^{++} + 2\,Cl^- = Hg_2Cl_2\ (white) + Sn^{++++}.$$

If more Sn^{++} ions are added, the Hg_2Cl_2 that is first formed according to the above reaction is further reduced to Hg as follows.

$$Hg_2Cl_2 + Sn^{++} = 2\,Hg\ (black) + Sn^{++++} + 2\,Cl^-.$$

If Sn^{++} ions are present in great excess the following reaction will take place.

$$Hg^{++} + Sn^{++} = Hg\ (black) + Sn^{++++}.$$

Since $SnCl_2$ solution is added as a reagent Sn^{++} ions are generally present in excess. Therefore the precipitate that is formed is dark gray or black.

These equations illustrate the fact that tin(II) compounds are strong reducing agents.

6. The solution is boiled to remove chlorine formed by oxidation of Cl^- by NO_3^-. This chlorine would oxidize Sn^{++} to Sn^{++++}.

Separation of Lead from Bismuth, Copper, and Cadmium

Lead sulfate is insoluble in water. The sulfates of bismuth, copper, and cadmium are soluble. This fact is the basis for the separation of lead ions from bismuth, copper, and cadmium ions.

▪ ▪ ▪ Procedure 8: Separation and detection of lead

Add 4 drops of 18 M H_2SO_4 to a casserole containing the decantate from Procedure 7 and evaporate carefully down to a volume of about 1 drop. At this point dense white fumes of SO_3 will form. Cool, add 15 drops of cold water, swish, and stir the contents until all material in the casserole is dissolved or suspended; then transfer it quickly to a test tube before the suspended material has a chance to settle; swish the casserole with 4 drops of cold water and transfer this washing to the same test tube. Cool under the water tap. A white precipitate ($PbSO_4$) in the form of a fine suspension shows the presence of lead. Centrifuge until the supernatant liquid is clear and decant into a test tube, saving this decantate for Procedure 9. Wash the precipitate twice with 10-drop portions of cold water. To the washed precipitate in the test tube add 4 drops of 1 M $NH_4C_2H_3O_2$ and stir for 20 seconds; then add 2 drops of 0.2 M K_2CrO_4. A yellow precipitate ($PbCrO_4$) confirms the presence of lead.

NOTES

1. $PbSO_4$ is appreciably soluble in concentrated HNO_3 due to formation of the hydrogen sulfate ion in the manner discussed in Note 2, below. For this reason, HNO_3 must be removed before $PbSO_4$ will precipitate. When a solution containing H_2SO_4, HNO_3, and water is boiled, the water and HNO_3 are first driven off because they boil at comparatively low temperatures ($100°$–$120°C.$). After they are removed, further heating results in boiling the H_2SO_4 that remains (boiling point of sulfuric acid is $338°C.$). At its boiling temperature the H_2SO_4 decomposes to a slight extent.

$$H_2SO_4 \rightleftharpoons H_2O + SO_3.$$

SO_3 fumes strongly in moist air. Therefore, formation of dense white fumes of SO_3 at the end of the evaporation gives assurance that all HNO_3 has been removed.

2. When the solution that has been boiled down with concentrated H_2SO_4 is cooled, sulfates of bismuth, copper, and cadmium may crystallize out. However, they are soluble in dilute H_2SO_4 and will dissolve when the water is added. $PbSO_4$, on the other hand, is quite soluble in concentrated H_2SO_4, forming the acid sulfate, $Pb(HSO_4)_2$.

(a) $\qquad PbSO_4 \rightleftharpoons SO_4^{--} + Pb^{++}$

(b) $\qquad\qquad SO_4^{--} + H^+ \rightleftharpoons HSO_4^-$

On dilution with water, the soluble acid sulfate is decomposed to form insoluble $PbSO_4$.

3. The precipitate of $PbSO_4$ is very finely divided. The sulfates of bismuth, copper, and cadmium form relatively large crystals.

4. Since lead is largely removed in the silver group, only very small quantities will ordinarily appear in the copper-arsenic group. For this reason, the test for lead is not as pronounced as the tests for other cations in this group.

5. $PbSO_4$ dissolves in ammonium acetate because the complex ion, $Pb(C_2H_3O_2)_4^{--}$, which is formed in the reaction, $PbSO_4 + 4\ C_2H_3O_2^- = Pb(C_2H_3O_2)_4^{--} + SO_4^{--}$, is very stable, giving, therefore, a solution with a very low concentration of lead ions. $PbCrO_4$ is less soluble than $PbSO_4$. Therefore when K_2CrO_4 is added to the solution formed by adding $NH_4C_2H_3O_2$ to $PbSO_4$, a precipitate of $PbCrO_4$ is formed even though the concentration of lead ions in the solution is very low.

Separation of Bismuth from Copper and Cadmium

Addition of NH_4OH to a solution containing bismuth, copper, and cadmium ions first precipitates the hydroxides of all three metals.

The hydroxides of copper and cadmium, however, dissolve in an excess of NH_4OH, whereas the hydroxide of bismuth does not; the separation of bismuth ions from copper and cadmium ions is based on this fact.

■ ■ ■ Procedure 9: Separation and detection of bismuth

To the decantate from Procedure 8 add 15 M NH_4OH, dropwise, with constant mixing, until it becomes distinctly alkaline. Stir for two minutes. Centrifuge and decant, saving the decantate for Procedure 10. Wash the precipitate twice with 15-drop portions of hot water. To the washed precipitate add 3 drops of 8 M NaOH and 2 drops of 0.2 M $SnCl_2$ and stir. A jet-black precipitate (**Bi**) proves the presence of bismuth.

NOTES

1. When NH_4OH is added to a solution containing copper ions, $Cu(OH)_2$ is first precipitated.

$$Cu^{++} + 2\,NH_4OH = Cu(OH)_2 \text{ (blue)} + 2\,NH_4^+.$$

An excess of NH_4OH, however, dissolves the $Cu(OH)_2$ to give a deep-blue solution in which Cu is present as the complex tetraamminecopper(II) ion, $Cu(NH_3)_4^{++}$.

$$Cu(OH)_2 + 4\,NH_4OH = Cu(NH_3)_4^{++} + 2\,OH^- + 4\,H_2O.$$

The detailed reaction whereby $Cu(OH)_2$ is dissolved by excess NH_4OH proceeds in the manner already discussed on pages 53 and 54.

(a) $\quad Cu(OH)_2 \rightleftharpoons Cu^{++} + 2\,OH^-$

(b) $\quad\quad\quad\quad Cu^{++} + 4\,NH_3 \rightleftharpoons Cu(NH_3)_4^{++}.$

Cadmium behaves in the same manner as copper, $Cd(NH_3)_4^{++}$ being formed. $Cd(OH)_2$ (white) dissolves quite slowly in excess NH_4OH; therefore the solution is stirred for two minutes to ensure complete solution of $Cd(OH)_2$. Similar complexes will be met with in the case of the ions of nickel, cobalt, and zinc. $Ag(NH_3)_2^+$ was formed in the analysis of the silver group. (See Note 2, Procedure 4.)

2. The formation of the black precipitate of bismuth results from the action of stannate(II) ions $(Sn(OH)_4^{--})$ on $Bi(OH)_3$ (white) as follows

$$2\,Bi(OH)_3 + 3\,Sn(OH)_4^{--} = 2\,Bi + 3\,Sn(OH)_6^{--}$$

The stannate(II) ions were formed when the $SnCl_2$, added as the final reagent, reacted with the excess of NaOH which had been added previously.

$$Sn^{++} + 4\,OH^- \rightleftharpoons Sn(OH)_4^{--}.$$

The reaction of stannate(II) ions with $Bi(OH)_3$ to give stannate(IV) ions $[Sn(OH)_6^{--}]$ and bismuth serves further to illustrate the reducing character of tin(II) compounds.

3. The formation of stannate(II) ions $[Sn(OH)_4^{--}]$ by the action of NaOH on $SnCl_2$ is a two-stage reaction. If NaOH is added, dropwise, to a solution of $SnCl_2$, a white precipitate of $Sn(OH)_2$ is first formed.

$$Sn^{++} + 2\,OH^- = Sn(OH)_2.$$

This white precipitate redissolves in more NaOH to form a clear colorless solution containing tetrahydroxostannate(II) ions. The following reaction is believed to take place.

$$Sn(OH)_2 + 2\,OH^- \rightleftharpoons Sn(OH)_4^{--}.$$

If the white precipitate of $Sn(OH)_2$ which first forms when NaOH is added to a solution of $SnCl_2$ is treated with an acid, HCl for instance, it dissolves to form a clear solution which can be shown to contain Sn^{++} ions. The equation for the reaction which takes place is therefore

$$Sn(OH)_2 + 2\,H^+ = Sn^{++} + 2\,H_2O.$$

A metal hydroxide such as $Sn(OH)_2$, which will dissolve in either a strong acid (HCl) or a strong base (NaOH), is said to be *amphoteric*. (See pages 41 and 42, Chapter 2.)

4. It should be pointed out that there is not complete agreement among chemists as to the composition of the stannate(II) ion. In addition to $Sn(OH)_4^{--}$ and SnO_2^{--} the formulas $Sn(OH)_3^-$ and $HSnO_2^-$ have been suggested. Since the formula of the ion may change as the concentration of the solution changes it may well be that all four of the above ions are present at one time or another. In fact, they may all be present, in equilibrium, at one time.

5. Stannate(II) ions will reduce the hydroxides of antimony, lead, copper, and cadmium to the corresponding metal. These hydroxides, however, are reduced slowly and the metallic deposit is not jet black, whereas $Bi(OH)_3$ is reduced instantly and forms a jet black deposit of metallic bismuth.

6. On standing in contact with air, stannate(II) ions are rapidly oxidized to stannate(IV) ions $(Sn(OH)_6^{--})$. The equation for the reaction is

$$2\,Sn(OH)_4^{--} + O_2 + 2\,H_2O = 2\,Sn(OH)_6^{--}.$$

Furthermore, stannate(II) decomposes in solution as follows.

$$2\,Sn(OH)_4^{--} = Sn + Sn(OH)_6^{--} + 2\,OH^-.$$

For these reasons sodium stannate(II) is not kept on the shelf as a reagent but is formed by the action of NaOH on $SnCl_2$ at the time it is to be used.

7. A reaction of the type illustrated in the second equation of Note 6, in which a compound acts as both an oxidizing agent and a reducing agent, is referred to as *disproportionation*. One mole of $Sn(OH)_4^{--}$ is reduced to Sn, the other is oxidized to $Sn(OH)_6^{--}$.

Detection of Copper and Cadmium

■ ■ ■ Procedure 10: Separation and detection of copper and cadmium

(A) *Detection of copper.* If the decantate from Procedure 9 is colorless, copper is absent and need not be tested for; if the decantate is deep blue, because of the $Cu(NH_3)_4^{++}$ ion, copper is present. Place 5 drops of this blue decantate in a test tube, add 5 M $HC_2H_3O_2$ until the deep-blue color just disappears, and then add 2 drops of 0.2 M $K_4Fe(CN)_6$. A red precipitate ($Cu_2Fe(CN)_6$) further confirms the presence of copper.

(B) *Detection of cadmium.* If copper is absent, treat the colorless decantate from Procedure 9 with 2 or 3 drops of ammonium sulfide solution, mix thoroughly, and allow to stand for about one minute. The formation of a yellow precipitate (CdS) proves the presence of cadmium. If copper is present, add 0.2 M KCN (**Caution! See Note 1.**), dropwise, to a 10-drop portion of the blue decantate until the blue color disappears. Treat the solution with 2 or 3 drops of ammonium sulfide solution, mix thoroughly, and allow to stand for about one minute. A yellow precipitate (CdS) proves the presence of cadmium. *(See Note 5 for an alternative test for cadmium which does not require the use of KCN.)* As soon as the test for cadmium has been completed (and, for "known," approved) dump the contents of the tube to which the KCN was added into the sink and flush it away with *lots of water.*

NOTES

1. **KCN is poisonous;** for that reason KCN solution is not kept on the regular reagent shelf but is dispensed by the stockroom clerk or by the laboratory instructor. A solution or precipitate containing cyanide must

never be dumped into an acid or acid solution. An acid, even a very weak one, will react with it and liberate HCN gas. **HCN gas is poisonous.** The best way to get rid of the KCN mixture is to flush it down the sink drain with *lots of water*.

2. The blue color of $Cu(NH_3)_4^{++}$ is visible when as little as 1 part of copper is present in 25,000 parts of water. The red precipitate of $Cu_2Fe(CN)_6$ will detect 1 part of copper in 1 million parts of water.

3. $Cu_2Fe(CN)_6$ is soluble in strong acids, such as HCl and H_2SO_4, but precipitates readily in the presence of a weak acid, such as acetic acid. $Cd_2Fe(CN)_6$ precipitates under the same conditions as does $Cu_2Fe(CN)_6$, but the precipitate is white.

4. When excess KCN is added to a solution containing $Cu(NH_3)_4^{++}$ and $Cd(NH_3)_4^{++}$, the complex ions $Cu(CN)_2^-$ and $Cd(CN)_4^{--}$ are formed. The $Cu(CN)_2^-$ ion is very stable and is only very slightly dissociated into Cu^+ and CN^- ions; the resulting concentration of Cu^+ is so low that no precipitate of Cu_2S forms when sulfide ions are added. The $Cd(CN)_4^{--}$ ion is less stable and is appreciably dissociated into Cd^{++} and $4\ CN^-$ ions; the resulting concentration of Cd^{++} is high enough for a precipitate of CdS to form when sulfide ions are added. (See Table 2.3, page 25.)

The reactions that take place when excess KCN is added are represented by the following equations:

$$2\ Cu(NH_3)_4^{++}\ +\ 5\ CN^-\ +\ H_2O$$
$$=\ 2\ Cu(CN)_2^-\ +\ CNO^-\ +\ 6\ NH_3\ +\ 2\ NH_4^+,$$

$$Cd(NH_3)_4^{++}\ +\ 4\ CN^-\ =\ Cd(CN)_4^{--}\ +\ 4\ NH_3,$$

$$Cd(CN)_4^{--}\ \rightleftharpoons\ Cd^{++}\ +\ 4\ CN^-.$$

5. *Alternative test for cadmium in presence of copper.* Add a pinch of solid sodium hyposulfite, $Na_2S_2O_4$ (also called sodium hydrosulfite), to a portion of the blue decantate. Heat in the boiling water bath for two minutes. A black or dark brown precipitate of free Cu is formed. Centrifuge, and decant the clear supernatant liquid into a test tube. Treat this clear liquid with H_2S gas or add 2 or 3 drops of ammonium sulfide solution, mix thoroughly, and allow to stand for about 1 minute. A yellow precipitate (**CdS**) proves the presence of cadmium.

The hyposulfite first reduces Cu(II) to Cu(I), the blue solution being decolorized. The Cu(I) is then reduced to metallic copper.

$$2\ Cu(NH_3)_4^{++}\ +\ S_2O_4^{--}\ +\ 2\ H_2O$$
$$=\ 2\ Cu^+\ +\ 2\ SO_3^{--}\ +\ 4\ NH_4^+\ +\ 4\ NH_3.$$

$$2\ Cu^+\ +\ S_2O_4^{--}\ +\ 2\ H_2O\ =\ 2\ SO_3^{--}\ +\ 2\ Cu\ +\ 4\ H^+.$$

▪ ▪ ▪ Procedure 11: Reprecipitation of the sulfides of arsenic, antimony, and tin

To the test tube which contains the decantate from Procedure 6 as a solution of AsS_4^{---}, SbS_3^{---}, and SnS_3^{--}, add 6 M HCl, with constant stirring, until the solution shows an acidic reaction when tested with litmus. (As long as each drop of 6 M HCl keeps on bringing down more precipitate, the solution is still alkaline; when no more precipitate forms, the solution is probably acidic.) A large excess of HCl must be avoided. Centrifuge and decant, discarding the decantate. Wash the precipitate three times with a mixture of 5 drops of 1 M $NH_4C_2H_3O_2$ and 5 drops of hot water and analyze according to Procedure 12. (See Note 4.)

NOTES

1. The addition of dilute HCl to the soluble thiosalts of the arsenic subgroup reprecipitates the sulfides of the three elements in accordance with the following molecular equation.

$$2 (NH_4)_3AsS_4 + 6 HCl = 6 NH_4Cl + 2 H_3AsS_4.$$

The compound H_3AsS_4 is unstable and decomposes.

$$2 H_3AsS_4 = 3 H_2S + As_2S_5.$$

$(NH_4)_3AsS_3$, $(NH_4)_2SnS_3$, and $(NH_4)_3SbS_3$ react in a similar manner. The H_3AsS_3, H_2SnS_3 and H_3SbS_3 which are formed decompose to give, respectively, As_2S_3, SnS_2 and Sb_2S_3. The net equations for the reactions are

$$2 AsS_4^{---} + 6 H^+ = As_2S_5 + 3 H_2S,$$
$$2 SbS_3^{---} + 6 H^+ = Sb_2S_3 + 3 H_2S.$$

This shows that H_2S plays the same role in the thioacid system that water plays in the oxygen acids and that As_2S_5, As_2S_3, Sb_2S_3, and SnS_2 are acid anhydrides in the sulfur acid system.

2. In reprecipitating the arsenic group, a large excess of HCl must be avoided, since SnS_2 and Sb_2S_3 are appreciably soluble in high concentrations of this acid. Also, the liquid in contact with the precipitate of SnS_2, As_2S_5, As_2S_3, and Sb_2S_3 should be decanted off at once, since the SnS_2 and Sb_2S_3 will dissolve on long standing.

3. A dark-colored decantate from Procedure 6 means that some CuS, and perhaps HgS, has been put into a state of colloidal suspension by

the $(NH_4)_2S$. If this decantate is allowed to stand for about 24 hours, the CuS and HgS will ordinarily settle out. The yellow supernatant liquid can then be decanted, leaving the CuS and HgS behind. If the decantate is to be analyzed immediately add 5 drops of 1 M $NH_4C_2H_3O_2$ to coagulate the CuS and HgS, mix thoroughly, centrifuge, and decant, discarding the precipitate.

4. The precipitate that is formed in Procedure 11 may be only sulfur. Ammonium sulfide may contain some ammonium polysulfide, $(NH_4)_2S_2$. When HCl is added to a solution containing $(NH_4)_2S_2$ sulfur is liberated according to the reaction

$$(NH_4)_2S_2 + 2 H^+ = 2 NH_4^+ + H_2S + S.$$

Separation of Arsenic from Antimony and Tin

The separation of arsenic from antimony and tin depends on the fact that arsenic sulfide is insoluble in very concentrated HCl, whereas the sulfides of tin and antimony dissolve in the HCl to form soluble chlorides.

■ ■ ■ Procedure 12: Separation of arsenic from antimony and tin

To the precipitate from Procedure 11 add 15 drops of 12 M HCl, mix thoroughly, and heat the test tube in the boiling water bath for 3–4 minutes, stirring frequently. Add 7 drops of hot water, mix well and continue heating in the boiling water bath for another 20–30 seconds. Centrifuge, and decant into a casserole. Save this decantate, which may contain antimony and tin, for Procedure 14. Wash the precipitate once with 10 drops of 6 M HCl, then three times with a mixture of 5 drops of hot water and 5 drops of 1 M $NH_4C_2H_3O_2$. Analyze the precipitate according to Procedure 13.

NOTES

1. Concentrated HCl dissolves SnS_2 and Sb_2S_3 as follows.

$$SnS_2 + 4 H^+ = Sn^{++++} + 2 H_2S,$$
$$Sb_2S_3 + 6 H^+ = 2 Sb^{+++} + 3 H_2S.$$

The Sn^{++++} and Sb^{+++} ions react with the Cl^- ions present to form the complex chloro ions, $SnCl_6^{--}$ and $SbCl_4^-$.

$$Sn^{++++} + 6 Cl^- \rightleftharpoons SnCl_6^{--},$$
$$Sb^{+++} + 4 Cl^- \rightleftharpoons SbCl_4^-.$$

2. The precipitate (As_2S_5 and As_2S_3) is first washed with 6 M HCl rather than with water, to remove all traces of Sb^{+++}. Sb^{+++} ions will react with water to form insoluble SbOCl, which will remain with the As_2S_5 and As_2S_3. The final washing with hot water is to remove all traces of HCl. Chloride, if present, will interfere with the confirmatory test for arsenic (Procedure 13) by forming a white precipitate of AgCl.

▪ ▪ ▪ Procedure 13: Detection of arsenic

Add 10 drops of 16 M HNO_3 to the test tube containing the precipitate from Procedure 12 and heat in the boiling water bath for about one minute or until the original precipitate is disintegrated and a deposit of sulfur is formed. Add 4–5 drops of water, centrifuge, and decant into a casserole, discarding any precipitate that remains in the test tube. Evaporate the solution in the casserole very carefully, to complete dryness. Allow it to cool. Add 4 drops of 0.2 M $AgNO_3$ and swish around in the casserole for about 10 seconds. Then add 0.2 M $NaC_2H_3O_2$, a drop at a time, with thorough mixing, until a maximum of 30 drops has been added. A reddish-brown or chocolate-brown precipitate (Ag_3AsO_4) proves the presence of arsenic.

NOTES

1. The As_2S_5 and As_2S_3 are dissolved by HNO_3 as follows:

$$3\,As_2S_5 + 10\,NO_3^- + 10\,H^+ + 4\,H_2O = 6\,H_3AsO_4 + 10\,NO + 15\,S,$$

$$3\,As_2S_3 + 10\,NO_3^- + 10\,H^+ + 4\,H_2O = 6\,H_3AsO_4 + 10\,NO + 9\,S.$$

2. Ag_3AsO_4 is formed in the confirmatory test for arsenic according to the equation

$$H_3AsO_4 + 3\,Ag^+ = Ag_3AsO_4 + 3\,H^+.$$

3. Ag_3AsO_4 is the salt of a weak acid and is, therefore, soluble in the strong acid, HNO_3; it is, however, insoluble in a weakly acidic or neutral solution. Evaporation to dryness should remove all the HNO_3. As a precaution against the possibility of some HNO_3 being left, $NaC_2H_3O_2$ is added to the reaction mixture. $NaC_2H_3O_2$, being the salt of a weak acid, will serve as a "buffer" for any HNO_3 that might have remained. The $C_2H_3O_2^-$ ions from the strong electrolyte, $NaC_2H_3O_2$, combine with the H^+ ions from HNO_3 to form the weak acid, $HC_2H_3O_2$. This reaction maintains the H^+ ion concentration at such a low value (makes the solution so weakly acidic) that Ag_3AsO_4 will precipitate.

4. The formation of a white precipitate (AgCl) means that the precipitate of As_2S_3 and As_2S_5 was not washed free of chloride in Procedure 12. $AgC_2H_3O_2$ (white), being sparingly soluble, may also precipitate.

▪ ▪ ▪ Procedure 14: Detection of antimony and tin

(A) *Detection of antimony.* Transfer the decantate from Procedure 12 to a casserole, boil for one minute to remove all H_2S, then add 4–5 drops of cold water and mix thoroughly. Place a drop of this solution on a clean silver coin. Place a piece of mossy tin in this drop of solution. Rapid formation of a black deposit (Sb) on the silver coin proves the presence of antimony. (See Note 7 for an alternative test for antimony.)

(B) *Detection of tin.* To the remainder of the solution in the casserole add a 1-in. piece of 26-gauge aluminum wire. Warm gently until the wire has dissolved; then boil gently for about two minutes or until the black precipitate either has all dissolved or appears not to be dissolving any more, replenishing the solution with 6 M HCl if necessary. (If no black residue remains, antimony is absent; if a black residue (Sb) remains after 2 minutes' boiling, antimony is present.) Transfer the contents of the casserole immediately to a test tube, cool, centrifuge, and decant. Immediately add 2–3 drops of 0.1 M $HgCl_2$ solution to the decantate, mix thoroughly, and allow to stand one minute; a white (Hg_2Cl_2) or gray ($Hg_2Cl_2 + Hg$) precipitate proves the presence of tin.

NOTES

1. The solution that is used in making the confirmatory test for antimony must be free from H_2S; otherwise a black stain of Ag_2S will be formed on the silver coin. Boiling the solution removes all H_2S.

2. The confirmatory test for antimony depends on the fact that when silver and tin are immersed in a solution of an electrolyte, $SbCl_3$ in this case, a miniature battery is set up. The more active metal, tin, goes into solution giving Sn^{++} ions, while Sb^{+++} ions are driven out of solution and are deposited as metallic antimony on the less active metal, silver. The following reaction takes place.

$$Sn = Sn^{++} + 2\,electrons.$$

These electrons are conducted away by the tin and cause it to become the more negative plate in the battery. Some of the electrons travel to the silver coin. The silver coin becomes, accordingly, negative too, but less negative than the tin. It is customary to say that the silver coin is the *positive pole* of a battery, tin being the *negative pole*. To say that silver is the positive pole means, actually, that it is *less negative* than the tin.

The Sb^{+++} ions in the solution are attracted by the negative electrons that have gathered on the surface of the coin. Each Sb^{+++} ion picks up three electrons from the surface of the coin; as a result, black antimony is deposited.

$$Sb^{+++} + 3\,electrons = Sb.$$

The over-all reaction is sometimes summarized as

$$3\,Sn + 2\,Sb^{+++} = 3\,Sn^{++} + 2\,Sb.$$

This equation is misleading since it suggests that a simple replacement occurs. Tin can replace antimony according to the above equation. It does not, however, do so in the test; this is shown by the fact that the antimony deposits on the silver, not on the tin.

3. The aluminum is added to reduce Sn^{++++} to Sn. The reaction is

$$4\,Al + 3\,Sn^{++++} = 4\,Al^{+++} + 3\,Sn.$$

Excess aluminum is dissolved by the HCl.

The tin then dissolves in HCl to form Sn^{++} ions.

$$Sn + 2\,H^+ = Sn^{++} + H_2.$$

The tin does not dissolve until all the aluminum has dissolved. Furthermore, since tin is not very active it dissolves less readily than the aluminum. For that reason the mixture must be boiled.

Since the tin(II) formed by the reaction of tin with HCl may eventually be oxidized by the oxygen of the air to tin(IV), the test should be completed as rapidly as possible.

4. The chemistry of the final test for tin, in which Sn^{++} reduces Hg^{++} to $Hg + Hg_2Cl_2$, is the same as that involved in the confirmatory test for mercury. (See Note 5, Procedure 7.)

5. The metallic aluminum, added to the solution containing Sn^{++++} and Sb^{+++}, replaces antimony (black) as well as tin (gray). Antimony, being less active than hydrogen, does not dissolve in HCl.

6. A flame test for tin may be carried out as follows: Fill with cold water a test tube which is clean on the outside as well as on the inside. Dip the bottom of the test tube into the solution to be tested; then hold the bottom of the test tube in a hot, nonluminous Bunsen flame. A blue coloration in the flame, which appears to cling to the wall of the test tube, proves the presence of tin. A trial flame test for tin should first be run on a sample of tin salt solution from the reagent shelf so that the characteristic blue coloration may be recognized.

7. *Alternative test for antimony.* Place 2–3 drops of the solution, one drop of which was used in making the silver coin test for antimony, in a

test tube. Add 5 M NH_4OH drop by drop with constant stirring until a litmus test shows that the solution is *just barely alkaline*. (If either antimony or tin are present a white precipitate or milky suspension, **SbOOH**, **Sn(OH)$_4$**, will form when the solution is alkaline; if no precipitate or suspension forms tin and antimony are absent.) Then add 5 M $HC_2H_3O_2$ drop by drop with constant stirring until the solution is acidic to litmus. (If a white precipitate or suspension was present in the alkaline solution it will still remain in the weakly acidic solution; this precipitate should be ignored since it will not interfere with the confirmatory test for antimony.) Add 2 drops of 2 M $Na_2S_2O_3$ (sodium thiosulfate) or a small crystal of solid $Na_2S_2O_3 \cdot 5$ H_2O, heat just to boiling and allow to stand for two minutes. An orange-red precipitate (Sb_2OS_2) proves the presence of antimony.

The thiosulfate ion, $S_2O_3^{--}$, hydrolyzes sparingly to yield H_2S.

$$S_2O_3^{--} + H_2O = SO_4^{--} + H_2S.$$

Although the concentration of S^{--} ions provided by this H_2S is not high enough to precipitate tin as SnS_2 it will precipitate antimony as Sb_2OS_2.

$$2\,\textbf{SbOOH} + 2\,H_2S = \textbf{Sb}_2\textbf{OS}_2 + 3\,H_2O.$$

QUESTIONS

1. Using the scheme of analysis as a guide, write net equations for all reactions that take place in the copper-arsenic group.

2. Upon what fact or facts is each of the following based?

(a) The separation of the cations of the copper-arsenic group from the cations of the groups that follow.

(b) The separation of the copper subgroup from the arsenic subgroup.

(c) The separation of mercury from lead, bismuth, copper, and cadmium.

(d) The separation of lead from bismuth, copper, and cadmium.

(e) The separation of bismuth from copper and cadmium.

(f) The identification of cadmium in the presence of copper.

(g) The confirmatory test for mercury.

(h) The confirmatory test for bismuth.

(i) The separation of arsenic from antimony and tin.

(j) The confirmatory test for antimony.

(k) The confirmatory test for tin.

3. What difficulties, if any, would arise under the following conditions in the precipitation of the copper-arsenic group?

(a) If HNO_3 were used in place of HCl.

(b) If H_2SO_4 were used in place of HCl.

4. Give the reason for each of the following in the Cu-As group analysis.

(a) Addition of H_2O_2 in the first procedure.

(b) Evaporation of the solution to dryness with 6 M HCl in the first procedure.

(c) Avoiding baking the precipitate in the first evaporation step.

(d) The addition of $NaC_2H_3O_2$ in the confirmatory test for arsenic.

5. Point out, in detail, what takes place in each of the following. Give the equations for the significant reactions.

(a) The confirmatory test for tin.

(b) The confirmatory test for antimony.

(c) The confirmatory test for bismuth.

(d) The confirmatory test for cadmium in the presence of copper.

(e) The confirmatory test for lead.

6. The precipitate formed in the confirmatory test for mercury (II) is sometimes white, sometimes gray, and sometimes black. Explain.

7. Point out where the following take place in the copper-arsenic group analysis and give the equations for the reactions.

(a) Three reactions in which tin is oxidized from an oxidation state of 2 to an oxidation state of 4.

(b) One reaction in which mercury is reduced from 2 to 1.

(c) One reaction in which mercury is reduced from 1 to 0.

(d) One reaction in which bismuth is reduced from 3 to 0.

(e) One reaction in which tin is reduced from 4 to 0.

(f) One reaction in which sulfur is oxidized from −2 to 0.

8. A 1 M solution of HCl in water was saturated with H_2S. This solution was then diluted with four volumes of distilled water, and the diluted solution was saturated with H_2S. How does the concentration of sulfide ions in the diluted solution compare with the concentration of sulfide ions in the original solution, both of which were saturated with H_2S? Explain.

9. Give the formula for a chemical substance that will:

(a) Form a precipitate with $SnCl_2$ solution but not with $SnCl_4$.

(b) Form a precipitate with $Pb(NO_3)_2$ solution but not with $Cu(NO_3)_2$.

(c) Form a precipitate with H_2S solution but not with HCl.

(d) Form a precipitate with $(NH_4)_3AsS_4$ solution but not with $CuCl_2$.

(e) Form a precipitate with $SnCl_2$ solution but not with $HgCl_2$.

(f) Form a precipitate with $Bi_2(SO_4)_3$ solution but not with $CuSO_4$.

(g) Form a precipitate with HNO_3 solution but not with HCl.

(h) Form a precipitate with H_2SO_4 solution but not with HNO_3.

(i) Form a precipitate with $Pb(NO_3)_2$ solution but not with NaCl.

(j) Form a precipitate with $CuCl_2$ solution but not with KCl.

(k) Dissolve As_2S_3 but not HgS.

(l) Dissolve CuS but not HgS.

(m) Dissolve Sb_2S_3 but not As_2S_5.

(n) Dissolve SnS_2 but not PbS.

(o) Dissolve $Pb(NO_3)_2$ but not PbS.

(p) Dissolve $HgCl_2$ but not Hg_2Cl_2.

(q) Oxidize $Sn(OH)_4{}^-$ to $Sn(OH)_6{}^{--}$.

(r) Reduce Hg^{++} to Hg.

(s) Reduce Bi(III) to Bi.

(t) Oxidize Sn^{++} to Sn^{+++}.

(u) Dissolve $Cu(OH)_2$ but not $Bi(OH)_3$.

(v) Oxidize Cl^- to Cl_2.

10. How would you distinguish between the following compounds by means of one reagent? (Tell what happens to each substance.)

(a) *Solids:*

CuS and SnS_2	$Cu(OH)_2$ and $Bi(OH)_3$
SnS_2 and As_2S_5	FeS and CdS
CdS and HgS	SnS and SnS_2
$PbSO_4$ and $Bi_2(SO_4)_3$	$SbCl_3$ and $PbCl_2$
Hg_2Cl_2 and $HgCl_2$	ZnS and CuS

(b) *Solutions:*

$(NH_4)_2S$ and NH_4Cl	H_2S and HCl
$CdCl_2$ and $CuCl_2$	Na_3AsO_4 and NaCl
$Pb(NO_3)_2$ and $Cd(NO_3)_2$	$SbCl_3$ and $AlCl_3$
$SnCl_2$ and $HgCl_2$	$(NH_4)_2SnS_3$ and $SnCl_2$
HNO_3 and HCl	$SnCl_2$ and $SbCl_3$
H_2SO_4 and HNO_3	H_2SO_4 and HCl

11. How do you account for the following facts?

(a) SnS_2 is soluble in $(NH_4)_2S$ while SnS is insoluble.

(b) $PbSO_4$ is soluble in a solution of $NH_4C_2H_3O_2$.

(c) $PbSO_4$ is soluble in concentrated H_2SO_4.

(d) $Sn(OH)_2$ is soluble in excess NaOH.

(e) $Cd(OH)_2$ is soluble in excess NH_4OH.

(f) Ag_3AsO_4 will not precipitate from a solution containing a small amount of HNO_3 but will precipitate from a solution containing a small amount of HNO_3 and also some dissolved $NaC_2H_3O_2$.

(g) HgS is insoluble in HNO_3 but CuS is soluble.

(h) CdS is insoluble in HCl but soluble in HNO_3.

(i) HgS is insoluble in HNO_3 but soluble in aqua regia.

(j) Sb_2S_3 and As_2S_3 are acidic in character while PbS and CuS are basic.

(k) A solution of $K_2Cr_2O_7$ is an oxidizing agent while a solution of $CrCl_3$ is not an oxidizing agent.

(l) Tin (II) compounds are reducing agents.

(m) Iron(III) compounds are oxidizing agents.

(n) Copper sulfide will precipitate when H_2S is added to a solution containing $Cu(NH_3)_4^{++}$ ions but will not precipitate when H_2S is added to a solution containing $Cu(CN)_2^-$ ions.

(o) When a piece of tin is placed in a drop of a solution of Sb^{+++} ions contained in a platinum dish, metallic antimony is deposited on the platinum dish.

12. Give the net equations to account for each of the following.

(a) When NaOH is added, drop by drop, to a solution of $SnCl_2$ a white precipitate is first formed, which disappears on further addition of NaOH to form a water-clear solution. When HCl is added, dropwise, to this water-clear solution a precipitate is formed, which disappears on further addition of HCl.

(b) When NH_4OH is added, dropwise, to a solution of $CdCl_2$, a white precipitate is first formed, which disappears on further addition of NH_4OH to form a water-clear solution; when HCl is added, dropwise, to the water-clear solution, there is first formed a white precipitate, which disappears on further addition of HCl to give a clear solution.

13. When a green solution of $CuCl_2$ is diluted with water, the color changes to a pale blue; addition of excess NH_4OH to the pale-blue solution makes it a deep blue; addition of KCN to this deep-blue solution causes it to become colorless. Account for the color changes.

14. The mixture of sulfides obtained when a copper-arsenic group unknown was completely precipitated with H_2S was completely insoluble in $(NH_4)_2S$ and completely soluble in 3 M HNO_3, sulfur being formed in the latter case. The solution obtained with HNO_3 gave a colorless solution with no precipitate or milky suspension when treated with excess NH_4OH. What conclusions can be drawn?

15. A colorless copper-arsenic group unknown solution turned milky white when diluted with water but became colorless again when acidified with HCl. Explain.

16. A colorless solution which was known to contain only cations of the copper-arsenic group gave a dark-brown precipitate in the regular H_2S precipitation. This precipitate was completely insoluble in $(NH_4)_2S$ and completely soluble in warm dilute HNO_3. What conclusions can be drawn?

17. A mixture of solid chlorides, known to contain only cations of the copper-arsenic group, dissolved readily and completely in cold water to give a clear pale-blue solution. The regular H_2S precipitation gave a brown precipitate. This precipitate was partially soluble in $(NH_4)_2S$; the residue, which did not dissolve in $(NH_4)_2S$, was completely soluble in warm dilute HNO_3. What conclusions can be drawn?

18. On being subjected to the regular H_2S precipitation, a solution known to contain only cations of the copper-arsenic group gave an orange-yellow precipitate. What conclusions can be drawn?

19. A solution known to contain only cations of the copper-arsenic group was divided into four parts which were treated as described below.

(a) One part, when diluted with water, gave a white precipitate; this precipitate dissolved on addition of HCl.

(b) The second part gave no precipitate when warmed and treated with $SnCl_2$ solution.

(c) The third part, on evaporation with H_2SO_4 to white SO_3 fumes and dilution with water, gave a finely divided white precipitate.

(d) The fourth part was treated with H_2S in the usual manner. A brownish black precipitate formed. This precipitate was partially soluble in $(NH_4)_2S$. The decantate from the $(NH_4)_2S$ treatment, on being acidified with dilute HCl, gave a precipitate which dissolved completely in 12 M HCl. What conclusions can be drawn?

20. A colorless solution known to contain only ions of the silver and copper-arsenic groups gave a white precipitate when treated with HCl. The decantate gave a dark brown precipitate in the regular treatment with H_2S. The white precipitate was completely soluble in NH_4OH solution. The dark brown precipitate was completely insoluble in $(NH_4)_2S$ and completely insoluble in HNO_3. What conclusions can be drawn?

21. A solution, A, which was known to contain only those cations of the silver and copper-arsenic groups which are listed below, when treated with excess NH_4OH gave a white precipitate, B, and a colorless supernatant liquid C. The decanted supernatant liquid C, upon addition of 6 M HCl, gave no precipitate. The white precipitate B, upon treatment with excess NaOH, dissolved completely to give a colorless solution. When this colorless solution was acidified with dilute H_2SO_4, a white precipitate, D, was formed. When $(NH_4)_2S$ was added to the decantate from D, a brown precipitate, E, was formed. The addition of concentrated HCl to the decantate from E resulted in the evolution of a gas; when this HCl solution was evaporated to dryness the addition of water to the residue gave a white precipitate.

Indicate whether each of the following cations is present, absent, or undetermined: Ag^+, Hg_2^{++}, Pb^{++}, Hg^{++}, Bi^{+++}, Cu^{++}, Cd^{++}, Sb^{+++}, Sn^{++}, Sn^{++++}.

23. A solid unknown was known to be a mixture of two or more of the following compounds: $AgNO_3$, Na_3AsO_4, $Pb(NO_3)_2$, $Cu(NO_3)_2$, $BiCl_3$, $Cd(NO_3)_2$, $Hg(NO_3)_2$, $SnSO_4$.

(a) One sample of the solid dissolved completely in cold water to give a clear blue solution; there was no precipitate of any kind in the beaker.

When 0.1 M SnSO$_4$ was added to this clear solution a precipitate formed.

(b) After a second sample of the solid contained in a beaker was treated with *hot* dilute HCl the beaker was found to contain a blue solution and a white precipitate.

(c) A third sample of the solid was found to dissolve completely in dilute H$_2$SO$_4$ to give a blue solution.

(d) After a fourth sample of the solid was treated with excess 2 M NH$_4$OH the beaker was found to contain a deep blue solution and a white precipitate.

(e) After a fifth sample of the solid was treated with excess 2 M NaOH the beaker was found to contain a colorless solution and a dark precipitate. Indicate each compound which is present, each compound which is absent, and each compound which is undetermined.

24. For each of the following pairs of solids give the formula of a single chemical reagent which will dissolve one solid but not the other. Give the formula of the predominant soluble species that is formed when the solid dissolves.

(a) PbSO$_4$ and PbCrO$_4$ (e) Sn and Sb
(b) SnS and SnS$_2$ (f) Cd(OH)$_2$ and Bi(OH)$_3$
(c) Cu$_2$S and CdS   (g) HgS and As$_2$S$_5$
(d) Ag$_3$AsO$_4$ and AgCl   (h) Pb(OH)$_2$ and Bi(OH)$_3$

25. Select from the following the most stable complex ion.

(a) Cd(CN)$_4$$^{--}$ with instability constant of 1.4×10^{-19}.
(b) Cd(NH$_3$)$_4$$^{++}$ with instability constant of 7.5×10^{-8}.
(c) Cu(NH$_3$)$_4$$^{++}$ with instability constant of 4.7×10^{-15}.
(d) HgI$_4$$^{--}$ with instability constant of 5×10^{-31}.

26. Select from the following the compound with the smallest molar solubility.

(a) Ag$_3$AsO$_4$ with Ksp of 1×10^{-23}.
(b) ZnS with Ksp of 1×10^{-23}.
(c) Hg$_2$Br$_2$ with Ksp of 1×10^{-23}.
(d) Cu$_3$(PO$_4$)$_2$ with Ksp of 1×10^{-23}.

27. In the following four statements circle the one statement that is inconsistent with, or has no connection with, the other three statements.

(a) SnS is insoluble in 4 M (NH$_4$)$_2$S, but SnS$_2$ is soluble in 4 M (NH$_4$)$_2$S.

(b) In its higher oxidation states an element is more nonmetallic, while in its lower oxidation states it is more metallic.

(c) When SnS and SnS$_2$, respectively, are treated with concentrated HNO$_3$, white SnO$_2$ is formed in each instance.

(d) SnS is predominantly basic in character, while SnS_2 is predominantly acidic in character.

28. Using the scheme of analysis for the Cu-As group as your only source of information select, in each part, the correct substance.

(a) Compound with smallest solubility product: CdS, HgS, ZnS.

(b) Most stable ion: $Cu(NH_3)_4{}^{++}$, $Cu(CN)_2{}^-$, $Cd(CN)_4{}^{--}$.

(c) Most electropositive: Sb, Sn, Ag.

(d) Most acidic sulfide: CuS, SnS, Sb_2S_3.

(e) Solution which, when saturated with H_2S gas, will contain the highest $[S^{--}]$: 1 M HCl, 2 M HCl, 3 M HCl.

(f) Reaction with the highest oxidation potential: $Ag = Ag^+ + e$, $Sb = Sb^{+++} + 3e$, $Sn = Sn^{++} + 2e$.

(g) Strongest reducing agent: Sn^{++}, $Hg_2{}^{++}$, Hg.

29. The reactions in set 1, in which M is a divalent metal, are observed to proceed substantially to completion in the direction written. On the basis of this information alone, decide whether each reaction in set 2 will proceed as written, will fail to proceed, or cannot be predicted.

Set 1:

$$MCO_3 + 2\,OH^- = M(OH)_2 + CO_3{}^{--}$$
$$M(IO_3)_2 + CO_3{}^{--} = MCO_3 + 2\,IO_3{}^-$$
$$M(NH_3)_4{}^{++} + 2\,OH^- = M(OH)_2 + 4\,NH_3$$
$$M(OH)_2 + S^{--} = MS + 2\,OH^-$$
$$M(OH)_2 + Se^{--} = MSe + 2\,OH^-$$

Set 2:

$$M(NH_3)_4{}^{++} + Se^{--} = MSe + 4\,NH_3$$
$$MS + Se^{--} = MSe + S^{--}$$
$$MS + CO_3{}^{--} = MCO_3 + S^{--}$$
$$M(IO_3)_2 + S^{--} = MS + 2\,IO_3{}^-$$
$$M(IO_3)_2 + 4\,NH_3 = M(NH_3)_4{}^{++} + 2\,IO_3{}^-$$

Copper-arsenic group report

Hg^{++}

Cu^{++}

$As\ O_4^{+++}$

Sb

Copper-arsenic group report

Copper-arsenic group report

Copper-arsenic group report

The aluminum-nickel group

ADDITION OF NH_4Cl, NH_4OH, and $(NH_4)_2S$ to a solution containing all the cations not precipitated in the preceding groups results in the precipitation of aluminum, chromium, and iron(III) as hydroxides, and manganese, nickel, cobalt, iron(II), and zinc as sulfides. Under these conditions the hydroxides and sulfides of calcium, barium, magnesium, potassium, and sodium are soluble. This solubility permits a separation of the cations of the aluminum-nickel group from those of the barium-magnesium group.

■ ■ ■ Procedure 15: Precipitation of the aluminum-nickel group in the absence of phosphates and borates

If the solution to be analyzed is an aluminum-nickel group "known" or "unknown" (see Schedule of Laboratory Work 5 and 6, page 6), follow (A) (see Note 1). If the decantate from the copper-arsenic group precipitation, Procedure 5, is to be analyzed, follow (B).

(A) Place 3 drops of the aluminum-nickel group known or unknown solution in a test tube (see Note 2). Add 4 drops of 2 M

Solution containing Al^{+++}, Cr^{+++}, Fe^{+++}, Fe^{++}, Zn^{++}, Co^{++}, Ni^{++}, Mn^{++}, Mg^{++}, Ca^{++}, Ba^{++}, Na^+, K^+, and NH_4^+

[NH_4Cl, NH_4OH] Proc. 15

$Al(OH)_3$, $Cr(OH)_3$, $Fe(OH)_3$, $Fe(OH)_2$, $Zn(NH_3)_4^{++}$, $Co(NH_3)_6^{+++}$, $Ni(NH_3)_6^{++}$, Mn^{++}, Mg^{++}, Ca^{++}, Ba^{++}, Na^+, K^+, NH_4^+
white   green   red   green   colorless   amber   blue

[$(NH_4)_2S$] Proc. 15

Mg^{++}, Ca^{++}, Ba^{++}, Na^+, K^+, NH_4^+
Analyze according to Proc. 22

FeS, CoS, NiS, MnS, ZnS
black   black   black   peach   white

[HCl, HNO_3] Proc. 16

$Al(OH)_3$, $Cr(OH)_3$, $Fe(OH)_3$,
white   green   red

[HCl, HNO_3] Proc. 16

Al^{+++} (colorless), Cr^{+++} (green), Fe^{+++} (yellow), Zn^{++} (colorless), Ni^{++} (green)
Mn^{++} (faint pink), Co^{++} (pink to wine red to blue)

[$NaOH$]

$Fe(OH)_3$ (red), $Mn(OH)_2$ (brown), $Ni(OH)_2$ (green), $Co(OH)_2$ (blue-pink) $Cr(OH)_4^-$ (green)
$Al(OH)_4^-$ (colorless), $Zn(OH)_4^{--}$ (colorless)

[H_2O_2]

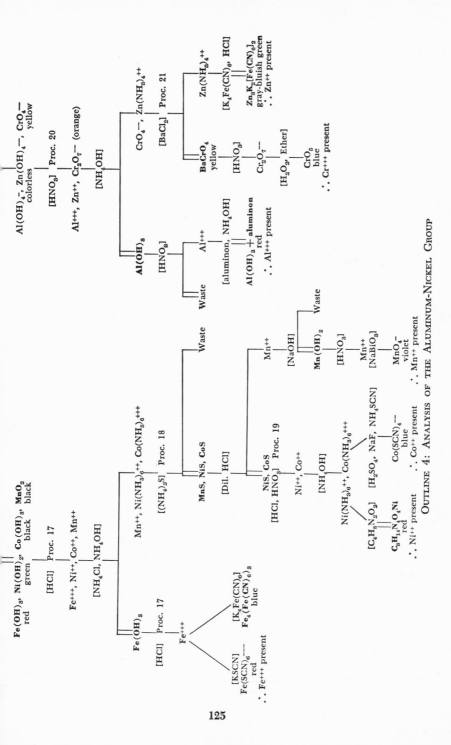

OUTLINE 4: ANALYSIS OF THE ALUMINUM-NICKEL GROUP

125

NH_4Cl, mix thoroughly, then add 15 M NH_4OH, drop by drop, with constant stirring until the solution is just alkaline; for the known solution 3 drops of NH_4OH is generally sufficient. Then add one extra drop of 15 M NH_4OH and 20 drops of hot water and mix thoroughly. Then add 8 or 9 drops of ammonium sulfide solution and mix thoroughly.

Heat the tube carefully for one or two minutes in the boiling water bath; avoid allowing the contents of the tube to overflow because of frothing. Centrifuge, and test for complete precipitation with a drop of ammonium sulfide solution. When precipitation with $(NH_4)_2S$ is complete wash down the sides of the tube with a few drops of hot water, centrifuge, and decant, saving the decantate for Procedure 23 (see Note 3). Wash the precipitate three times with mixtures of 10 drops of hot water and 10 drops of 1 M $NH_4C_2H_3O_2$, and analyze according to Procedure 16.

(B) Place the decantate from Procedure 5 in a casserole and evaporate down carefully to a volume of 8 to 10 drops. Transfer to a test tube, centrifuge, and decant into another test tube, discarding the precipitate. Treat the decantate in the test tube according to the directions beginning with the second sentence of Method (A), above.

NOTES

1. If phosphates, borates, fluorides, oxalates, silicates, or tartrates are present in an unknown to be analyzed and if this unknown also contains calcium, barium, or magnesium ions as well as cations of the aluminum-nickel group, a special series of procedures, different from those presented in this chapter, must be used. However, since the combination of ions just mentioned is rare and will not ordinarily be encountered in solutions being analyzed, the average analysis is carried out most successfully by using a more general procedure of the type presented in this chapter.

Fluorides, oxalates, silicates, and tartrates are not among the anions discussed in this book; therefore they will not be present in solutions ordinarily submitted for analysis in this course.

If an unknown solution to be analyzed does, in fact, contain the combination of ions listed at the beginning of this note, the student should be referred to the basic acetate method in one of the reference textbooks listed at the end of Chapter 2.

2. If the aluminum-nickel group unknown is issued in the form of a finely divided solid, proceed as follows: Place in a test tube as much of the solid as can be carried on $\frac{1}{4}$ in. of the tip of the spatula. Add 3–4 drops of 6 M HCl, warm gently, and then add 5–6 drops of hot water. Mix

thoroughly and heat carefully until a clear solution is obtained, replenishing the water and acid if necessary. Proceed with the analysis of this solution as directed in the second sentence of Procedure 15A.

If the solid unknown is not finely divided when received, the entire sample should first be pulverized in a clean mortar.

3. If the substance being analyzed is an aluminum-nickel group "known" or "unknown," this decantate can be discarded.

4. NH_4Cl is added, in the precipitation of the aluminum-nickel group, to prevent the precipitation of magnesium as $Mg(OH)_2$; if $Mg(OH)_2$ were to precipitate, the subsequent analysis of the group would be more complicated; hence it is desirable to carry magnesium over to the next group.

$Mg(OH)_2$ will precipitate if a solution contains enough Mg^{++} ions and enough OH^- ions so that the two, when they combine, will give more than enough $Mg(OH)_2$ to form a saturated solution; the extra $Mg(OH)_2$, over and above what will ordinarily dissolve in the solution, will precipitate. A solution contains enough Mg^{++} and OH^- to form a saturated solution, and thence a precipitate, when the product of the concentration of the Mg^{++} ions and the OH^- ions, squared, exceeds the solubility product for $Mg(OH)_2$.

Ammonium hydroxide is a weak base; it may be represented as ionizing according to equation (a).

(a) $$NH_4OH \rightleftharpoons NH_4^+ + OH^-.$$

Even though ammonium hydroxide is a weak base, it ionizes to give enough OH^- ions to form a precipitate with the concentration of Mg^{++} present in the usual known or unknown solution. Therefore, when NH_4OH alone is added to a water solution of an unknown containing Mg^{++}, $Mg(OH)_2$ is precipitated.

NH_4Cl is a salt and hence a strong electrolyte. Consequently, NH_4Cl in solution provides an abundance of NH_4^+ ions. If NH_4Cl is present in a solution also containing ammonium hydroxide, the NH_4^+ ions from NH_4Cl will shift the equilibrium point in equation (a) to the left. This shift will greatly reduce the concentration of OH^- ions and will give a condition represented by equation (b).

(b) $$NH_4OH \rightleftharpoons NH_4^+ + \text{oh-.}$$

There are not enough OH^- ions present in equation (b) to form a precipitate of $Mg(OH)_2$ with the Mg^{++} ions present in the average solution. In other words, NH_4Cl prevents the precipitation of $Mg(OH)_2$ by NH_4OH; it reduces the concentration of the OH^- to such a low value that the product of the concentration of the Mg^{++} ions and the OH^- ions is less than the solubility product for $Mg(OH)_2$.

The decrease of the ionization of NH_4OH by ammonium ions from NH_4Cl is an example of the common ion effect.

NH_4Cl also prevents the precipitation of $Mn(OH)_2$ by NH_4OH, and in exactly the same way. However, MnS is quite insoluble, so that manganese precipitates as MnS when $(NH_4)_2S$ is added. MgS is soluble and does not precipitate.

The hydroxides of aluminum, chromium, and iron(III) are so insoluble that they precipitate even in the presence of the low concentration of OH^- ions represented in equation (b). The hydroxides of cobalt, nickel, and zinc are likewise so insoluble that they, too, will precipitate in the presence of the OH^- in (b); they, however, redissolve in excess NH_4OH in a fashion to be discussed in Note 9.

The behavior of iron(II) in the presence of NH_4^+ and OH^- is complicated by the fact that $Fe(II)$ is readily oxidized by air to $Fe(III)$. The net result is that a green precipitate, probably $Fe(OH)_2 \cdot Fe(OH)_3$, is formed when NH_4OH is added to Fe^{++}. This green precipitate gradually darkens as more $Fe(OH)_2$ is oxidized to $Fe(OH)_3$.

$$4\,Fe(OH)_2 + O_2 \text{ (air)} + 2\,H_2O = 4\,Fe(OH)_3.$$

5. The colors of the precipitates in this group are

$Fe(OH)_3$	Brownish red	CoS	Black
$Cr(OH)_3$	Grayish green	MnS	Peach
$Al(OH)_3$	White	NiS	Black
$Fe(OH)_2$	Green	ZnS	White
FeS	Black		

Careful observation of the colors of the precipitate formed, first when NH_4OH is added and later when $(NH_4)_2S$ is added, may give definite information about the presence or absence of certain ions.

If NH_4Cl and NH_4OH give no precipitate then aluminum, chromium, iron(II) and iron(III) ions are definitely absent; if a white precipitate forms the presence of aluminum is indicated; a green precipitate indicates iron or chromium and a brownish-red precipitate indicates iron.

If the addition of $(NH_4)_2S$ gives no further precipitation, cobalt, nickel, manganese, and zinc ions are absent. If a white precipitate is formed zinc is probably present; manganese, which forms a peach colored sulfide, is probably absent, and cobalt and nickel, whose sulfides are black, are definitely absent.

The formation of a black precipitate on addition of $(NH_4)_2S$ may be due to the conversion of red $Fe(OH)_3$ to black FeS according to the equation

$$2\,Fe(OH)_3 + 6\,NH_4^+ + 3\,S^{--} = 2\,FeS + 6\,NH_4OH + S.$$

If NH_4OH and $(NH_4)_2S$ were added together instead of being added separately, the hydroxides and sulfides would immediately precipitate together; it would then obviously be impossible to make the observations of color noted above.

6. The decantate from the copper-arsenic group is boiled down before the aluminum-nickel group is precipitated in order to drive off all H_2S and to precipitate any sulfides of the copper-arsenic group that may have gone into the decantate. If the H_2S were not removed, the sulfides and hydroxides of the aluminum-nickel group would all precipitate together when NH_4OH was added. As a result the desirable valuable observation of colors of precipitates referred to in Note 5 could not be made.

7. NH_4Cl, being a strong electrolyte, helps coagulate any hydroxides or sulfides, thereby preventing them from becoming colloidal. Similarly, the addition of $NH_4C_2H_3O_2$ to the washing water at various points in the analysis prevents peptization of the precipitate being washed.

8. A large excess of NH_4OH tends to cause dispersion of the precipitated sulfides and hydroxides, making them difficult to settle out. If a very large excess of NH_4OH has been added the mixture should be boiled for one minute before centrifuging.

9. The behavior of zinc, nickel and cobalt ions on being treated with NH_4OH is the same as that already noted for copper and cadmium ions (See Note 1, Procedure 9). The hydroxides of the three metals are first formed. Excess of NH_4OH dissolves these hydroxides with the formation of $Zn(NH_3)_4^{++}$, $Ni(NH_3)_6^{++}$, and $Co(NH_3)_6^{+++}$.

$Zn(NH_3)_4^{++}$ is colorless, $Ni(NH_3)_6^{++}$ is pale violet-blue and $Co(NH_3)_6^{+++}$ has a characteristic deep amber color.

It will be noted that $Co(II)$ has been oxidized to $Co(III)$. This results from the fact that, in alkaline solution, $Co(II)$ is a fairly strong reducing agent and is slowly oxidized to $Co(III)$ by atmospheric oxygen. The reaction can be represented in either of two ways (b_1 or b_2).

(a) $\qquad Co^{++} + 2 NH_4OH^- = Co(OH)_2 + 2 NH_4^+$

(b_1) $\quad 4 Co(OH)_2 + O_2 + 2 H_2O = 4 Co(OH)_3,$

$\quad Co(OH)_3 + 6 NH_4OH = Co(NH_3)_6^{+++} + 3 OH^- + 6 H_2O.$

(b_2) $\quad Co(OH)_2 + 6 NH_4OH = Co(NH_3)_6^{++} + 2 OH^- + 6 H_2O,$

$\quad 4 Co(NH_3)_6^{++} + O_2 + 2 H_2O = 4 Co(NH_3)_6^{+++} + 4 OH^-.$

10. Ammonium sulfide reacts with $Zn(NH_3)_4^{++}$, $Ni(NH_3)_6^{++}$ and $Co(NH_3)_6^{+++}$ to form ZnS, NiS, and CoS as follows.

$$S^{--} + Ni(NH_3)_6^{++} = NiS + 6 NH_3.$$

$$3 S^{--} + 2 Co(NH_3)_6^{+++} = 2 CoS + S + 12 NH_3.$$

MnS and FeS are formed by direct combination of the two ions involved.

$$Mn^{++} + S^{--} = MnS.$$

FeS may also be formed by reduction of Fe(III) as mentioned in Note 5.

11. If $(NH_4)_2S$ is added to a cold neutral solution containing aluminum, chromium, and iron(III) ions, $Al(OH)_3$, $Cr(OH)_3$, and Fe_2S_3 will be precipitated.

$$2 Fe^{+++} + 3 S^{--} = Fe_2S_3,$$

$$2 Al^{+++} + 3 S^{--} + 6 H_2O = 2 Al(OH)_3 + 3 H_2S,$$

$$2 Cr^{+++} + 3 S^{--} + 6 H_2O = 2 Cr(OH)_3 + 3 H_2S.$$

At higher temperatures Fe_2S_3 is hydrolyzed, brownish-red $Fe(OH)_3$ being precipitated.

$$Fe_2S_3 + 6 H_2O = 2 Fe(OH)_3 + 3 H_2S.$$

(FeS will be formed, as explained in Note 5.)

12. Ammonium sulfide is a salt and is therefore completely ionized and provides a high concentration of S^{--} ions. This high concentration of sulfide ions insures complete precipitation of zinc, manganese, cobalt, nickel and iron(II) as sulfides.

Separation of the Aluminum Subgroup from the Nickel Subgroup

The hydroxides of aluminum, chromium, and zinc are amphoteric and are therefore soluble in NaOH. In contrast, the hydroxides of iron, manganese, cobalt, and nickel are not amphoteric; they are not soluble in NaOH. Upon this fact is based the separation of the cations of the aluminum subgroup (Al^{+++}, Cr^{+++}, and Zn^{++}) from the cations of the nickel subgroup (Fe^{+++}, Mn^{++}, Co^{++}, and Ni^{++}).

■ ■ ■ Procedure 16: Separation of the aluminum subgroup from the nickel subgroup

Treat the precipitate from Procedure 15 with 10 drops of 12 M HCl, mix thoroughly, transfer to a casserole and boil gently for half a minute. If the precipitate is not completely dissolved add 3 drops of 16 M HNO_3, mix thoroughly and boil until a clear solution is obtained. Add 10 drops of cold water, transfer to a test tube, centrifuge to remove any precipitate of sulfur, and decant into a casserole. Make the solution strongly alkaline with 8 M NaOH and mix thoroughly. If the quantity of precipitate is so large that the product is mushy or nonfluid add 10 to 20 drops of water. Then add 2 drops of 3% H_2O_2, stir for one minute and then boil for two minutes, replenishing the water lost. Transfer to a test tube before the precipitate has had a chance to settle, and centrifuge. Decant, saving the decantate for Procedure 20. Wash the precipitate three times with hot water and analyze according to Procedure 17 or Procedure 17a.

NOTES

1. $Al(OH)_3$, $Fe(OH)_3$, $Cr(OH)_3$, MnS, FeS, and ZnS are readily soluble in HCl. NiS and CoS are not readily soluble in HCl but are soluble in aqua regia ($HCl + HNO_3$). (See Note 4, Procedure 7.)

(a) $$NiS \rightleftharpoons Ni^{++} + S^{--},$$

(b_1) $$3\,S^{--} + 2\,NO_3^- + 8\,H^+ = 3\,S + 2\,NO + 4\,H_2O,$$

(b_2) $$Ni^{++} + 4\,Cl^- \rightleftharpoons NiCl_4^{--}.$$

Aqua regia oxidizes $Fe(II)$ to $Fe(III)$.

$$3\,Fe^{++} + NO_3^- + 4\,H^+ = 3\,Fe^{+++} + NO + 2\,H_2O,$$

$$Fe^{+++} + 4\,Cl^- \rightleftharpoons FeCl_4^-.$$

2. When NaOH is added to a solution containing the members of the aluminum-nickel group, the hydroxides of all seven metals are first precipitated. The hydroxides of aluminum, chromium, and zinc are amphoteric (see Note 3, Procedure 9 and Chapter 2, page 41) and dissolve in an excess of NaOH to form the complex ions, $Al(OH)_4^-$, $Cr(OH)_4^-$, and $Zn(OH)_4^{--}$, respectively. The hydroxides of iron, manganese, cobalt, and nickel are not amphoteric and do not dissolve in excess of NaOH.

Solution		Precipitate		Solution	
Al^{+++}		$Al(OH)_3$		$Al(OH)_4^-$	(colorless)
Cr^{+++}		$Cr(OH)_3$		$Cr(OH)_4^-$	(green)
Zn^{++}		$Zn(OH)_2$		$Zn(OH)_4^{--}$	(colorless)
Fe^{+++}	+ NaOH =	$Fe(OH)_3$	+ excess NaOH =		
Mn^{++}		$Mn(OH)_2$		*Residue*	
Ni^{++}		$Ni(OH)_2$		$Fe(OH)_3$	(brownish-red)
Co^{++}		$Co(OH)_2$		$Mn(OH)_2$	(tan)
				$Ni(OH)_2$	(green)
				$Co(OH)_2$	(blue)

3. Hydrogen peroxide is added to oxidize chromate(III), $Cr(OH)_4^-$, to chromate(VI), CrO_4^{--}. The reason why it is necessary to do this is discussed in Note 1, Procedure 20. The equation for the reaction is

$$2\,Cr(OH)_4^- + 3\,H_2O_2 + 2\,OH^- = 2\,CrO_4^{--} + 8\,H_2O.$$

$Cr(OH)_4^-$ is pale green; CrO_4^{--} is yellow. Therefore, if the color of the solution changes from pale green to yellow on treatment with H_2O_2, chromium is present.

4. Hydrogen peroxide in alkaline solution oxidizes $Mn(OH)_2$ to MnO_2 and $Co(OH)_2$ to $Co(OH)_3$ as follows:

$$H_2O_2 + Mn(OH)_2 = MnO_2 + 2\,H_2O,$$

$$2\,Co(OH)_2 + H_2O_2 = 2\,Co(OH)_3.$$

MnO_2 and $Co(OH)_3$ are black; hence, a darkening of the color of the precipitated hydroxides on addition of H_2O_2 indicates the presence of manganese or cobalt.

5. Any excess H_2O_2 present in the solution must be decomposed by boiling; otherwise it will interfere with the subsequent analysis as discussed in Note 3, Procedure 20.

6. A careful observation of colors of solutions and precipitates formed in Procedure 16 may give valuable information regarding the cations present. The colors not already given in Note 2 are:

Al^{+++}	Colorless
Zn^{++}	Colorless
Mn^{++}	Colorless to faint pink
Fe^{+++}	Reddish brown to yellow
Cr^{+++}	Green
Ni^{++}	Green
Co^{++}	Reddish pink
$Al(OH)_3$	White
$Cr(OH)_3$	Grayish green
$Zn(OH)_2$	White

Pure freshly precipitated $Mn(OH)_2$ is tan, but it rapidly turns brown in contact with air because of oxidation to MnO_2 and Mn_2O_3.

The precipitate formed when NaOH is added to Co^{++} may vary in color from blue to pink to tan to light brown. $Co(OH)_2$ exists in two forms, one blue the other pink. The blue form is believed to be more finely dispersed. It changes to the coarser pink form on standing; heat speeds up the change. Air oxidizes some $Co(OH)_2$ to black $Co(OH)_3$.

A pink $CoCl_2$ solution turns blue when heated to boiling but regains its pink color when cooled. A pink solution of $CoCl_2$ turns blue when treated with concentrated HCl; the pink color is restored by dilution with water. These color changes are due to changes in the composition and structure of the complex ions present in the solution. The pink color is due to the $Co(H_2O)_6^{++}$ ion; the blue color is due to the $Co(H_2O)Cl_3^-$ and $CoCl_4^{--}$ ions. It should be noted that the ions responsible for the colors of the solutions referred to at the beginning of this note are probably all complex in a manner similar to that already noted for the cobalt ion. They will, however, be treated as simple ions.

Separation of Iron from Manganese, Nickel, and Cobalt

When NH_4Cl and excess NH_4OH are added to a solution containing iron(III), manganese, nickel, and cobalt ions the iron is precipitated as $Fe(OH)_3$ leaving Mn^{++}, $Ni(NH_3)_6^{++}$, and $Co(NH_3)_6^{+++}$ in solution.

■ ■ ■ Procedure 17: Separation and detection of iron
(see Note 1 for Procedure 17a)

Treat the precipitate from Procedure 16 with 10 drops of 12 M HCl, mix thoroughly, and heat carefully until completely dissolved. Add 10 drops of 2 M NH$_4$Cl, and then add 15 M NH$_4$OH, with constant stirring, until the solution is alkaline. Then add a 2-drop excess of 15 M NH$_4$OH. Mix thoroughly, centrifuge at once, and decant immediately into a test tube, saving this decantate for Procedure 18. Wash the precipitate three times with hot water; then dissolve it in 4–6 drops of 2 M HCl and dilute with 10 drops of water. Divide the solution into two parts. To one part add a drop of 0.2 M K$_4$Fe(CN)$_6$. A blue precipitate [$Fe_4(Fe(CN)_6)_3$] proves the presence of iron. To the second part add 0.2 M KSCN. A red color, due to the hexathiocyanatoferrate(III) ion, $Fe(SCN)_6^{---}$, proves the presence of iron.

NOTES

1. The following procedure may be used in place of procedures 17, 18, and 19, for the detection of iron, manganese, cobalt, and nickel. For convenience it will be referred to as Procedure 17a.

To the precipitate from Procedure 16 add 20 drops of 2 M H$_2$SO$_4$, mix thoroughly, and transfer to a casserole. Boil gently for 1 minute, add a drop of 3% H$_2$O$_2$, and continue boiling for 1 minute after the precipitate is completely dissolved. Add 10 drops of water, allow to cool, and divide into four approximately equal portions.

Test for iron: To one portion add 1 or 2 drops of 0.2 M KSCN. A blood-red solution, due to $Fe(SCN)_6^{---}$, proves the presence of iron.

Test for manganese: Dilute the second portion with an equal volume of water, add 2 drops of 3 M HNO$_3$, mix thoroughly, then add a few grains of solid sodium bismuthate, mix thoroughly, and allow to stand for 1 minute. Centrifuge. A pink to reddish-purple solution, due to the permanganate ion (MnO_4^-), proves the presence of manganese.

Test for nickel: Make the third portion alkaline with NH$_4$OH. If a precipitate of $Fe(OH)_3$ or $Mn(OH)_2$ forms, centrifuge and decant; to the clear decantate add 2–4 drops of dimethyl glyoxime, mix thoroughly, and allow to stand for one minute. A strawberry-red precipitate ($NiC_8H_{14}N_4O_4$) proves the presence of nickel.

Test for cobalt: Treat the fourth portion with enough solid NaF to form a saturated solution. Then add 10–20 drops of a saturated solution of ammonium thiocyanate in alcohol. A blue solution, due to $Co(SCN)_4^{--}$, proves the presence of cobalt.

Procedure 17a can be represented, schematically, as follows:

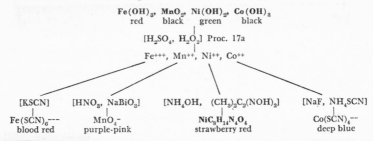

Detailed notes on the above tests will be found under Procedures 17, 18, and 19.

$Fe(OH)_3$ and $Ni(OH)_2$ dissolve readily in 2 M H_2SO_4 to give Fe^{+++} and Ni^{++}. MnO_2 and $Co(OH)_3$ are very slowly dissolved by 2 M H_2SO_4. H_2O_2 speeds up the solution process by reducing MnO_2 and $Co(OH)_3$ to MnO and $Co(OH)_2$; these latter compounds, in which Mn and Co are in their lower oxidation states, are more basic in character and as a result are readily dissolved by H_2SO_4. The net equations for the reduction by H_2O_2 and the subsequent solution by H_2SO_4 are:

$$MnO_2 + H_2O_2 = MnO + H_2O + O_2,$$

$$2\,Co(OH)_3 + H_2O_2 = 2\,Co(OH)_2 + 2\,H_2O + O_2,$$

$$MnO + 2\,H^+ = Mn^{++} + H_2O,$$

$$Co(OH)_2 + 2\,H^+ = Co^{++} + 2\,H_2O.$$

Attention has already been called to the fact that H_2O_2, in alkaline solution, *oxidizes* $Mn(OH)_2$ and $Co(OH)_2$ to MnO_2 and $Co(OH)_3$, respectively (see Note 4, Procedure 16). In Procedure 17a we find that, in strongly acid solution, H_2O_2 functions as a reducing agent and *reduces* MnO_2 and $Co(OH)_3$ to Mn^{++} and Co^{++}, respectively. It should be noted in the above equations that, when H_2O_2 functions as a reducing agent, O_2 gas is given off. In effect, the H_2O_2 molecule gives off one atom of oxygen. This atom then picks up one atom of oxygen from the compound which functions as the oxidizing agent (MnO_2 and $Co(OH)_2$ in the above equations) to form a molecule of O_2 gas.

The identification of Fe^{+++} and Co^{++} in Procedure 17a is unique in that each is identified by the use of the same reagent and each forms the same type of complex ion, $Fe(SCN)_6^{---}$ and $Co(SCN)_4^{--}$. The test for iron is carried out in dilute aqueous solution in which the red complex ion, $Fe(SCN)_6^{---}$, is very stable; the blue complex ion, $Co(SCN)_4^{--}$, is unstable in aqueous solution. As a result, cobalt ions do not interfere with the test for iron. The test for cobalt is carried out in alcoholic solution and in the presence of fluoride ions. The blue complex ion, $Co(SCN)_4^{--}$, is stable in alcoholic solution; the Fe^{+++} ions are tied up in the form of the colorless, stable complex ion, FeF_6^{---} (or, possibly, FeF^{++}, FeF_2^{+}, FeF_4^{-}, or FeF_5^{--}), and cannot, therefore, interfere with the test for cobalt.

2. MnO_2 and $Co(OH)_3$ dissolve in HCl as follows:

$$MnO_2 + 2\,Cl^- + 4\,H^+ = Mn^{++} + 2\,H_2O + Cl_2,$$

$$2\,Co(OH)_3 + 2\,Cl^- + 6\,H^+ = 2\,Co^{++} + 6\,H_2O + Cl_2.$$

$Ni(OH)_2$ and $Fe(OH)_3$ dissolve readily in HCl to give Ni^{++} and Fe^{+++}, respectively.

3. NH_4Cl prevents precipitation of $Mn(OH)_2$ by NH_4OH, as explained in Note 4, Procedure 15. However, a precipitate gradually forms if the solution is allowed to stand in contact with air. This precipitate is a mixture of brown Mn_2O_3 and black MnO_2 formed when $Mn(II)$ is oxidized by the air. To prevent this precipitation, with resulting loss of manganese, the solution is centrifuged and decanted as quickly as possible. Any Mn_2O_3 and MnO_2 that precipitate out will not interfere seriously with the confirmatory test for iron.

4. The confirmatory tests for iron are both very sensitive—so sensitive, in fact, that iron should not be reported unless both tests are strong.

Traces of iron are often introduced as impurities in the course of the manufacture of the compounds used in making up the unknown and compounds used as reagents in the analysis. Hence, the student should learn to distinguish between a weak test which indicates a trace of iron, probably as an impurity, and a strong positive test. In case of doubt, tests for iron(II) and iron(III) should be made on the original sample. (See Note 5.)

5. To test for iron in a solid, proceed as follows. Dissolve a small sample of the solid in 10–15 drops of dilute HCl. Divide the solution into three parts. Test two parts for iron(III) ions according to Procedure 17. To the third part, add a few drops of potassium ferricyanide, $K_3Fe(CN)_6$. A dark blue precipitate (Turnbull's blue) proves the presence of Fe^{++} ions.

$$3\,Fe^{++} + 2\,Fe(CN)_6^{---} = Fe_3[Fe(CN)_6]_2 \quad \text{(dark blue)}.$$

Note particularly that whereas potassium hexacyanoferrate(II) (potassium *ferro*cyanide), $K_4Fe(CN)_6$, gives a dark blue precipitate with Fe^{+++}, potassium hexacyanoferrate(III) (potassium *ferri*cyanide), $K_3Fe(CN)_6$, gives a dark blue precipitate with Fe^{++}.

Although the $Fe(SCN)_6^{---}$ ion is widely accepted as the predominant species responsible for the red color in the test for Fe^{+++}, there is little doubt that complexes with a smaller number of SCN^- ions, such as $FeSCN^{++}$. $Fe(SCN)_2^{+}$, $Fe(SCN)_4^{-}$, and $Fe(SCN)_5^{--}$ are also present. When the concentration of SCN^- is high, as is the case when 0.2 M KSCN is added in making the test, the predominant species is likely to be $Fe(SCN)_6^{---}$.

Separation of Manganese from Cobalt and Nickel

Separation of manganese from cobalt and nickel depends on the fact that when the sulfides of these three metals are treated with cold dilute HCl, MnS is dissolved immediately, whereas CoS and NiS are only very slightly affected.

▪ ▪ ▪ Procedure 18: Separation of manganese from cobalt and nickel and detection of maganese

Treat the decantate from Procedure 17 with 3 drops of $(NH_4)_2S$ solution. Centrifuge and decant, discarding the decantate. Wash the precipitate three times with hot water to which 5 drops of 2 M NH_4Cl have been added. Add 10 drops of 2 M HCl to this precipitate and stir for one minute. Centrifuge, and draw off the supernatant liquid with a medicine dropper; save this decantate in a casserole for detection of manganese. Wash the precipitate (CoS, NiS) once with 2 M HCl and twice with hot water and save for Procedure 19.

Detection of manganese. Boil the decantate, saved for the detection of manganese, gently for about half a minute, cool, make just alkaline with 8 M NaOH, and then add an excess of 1 drop of NaOH. Transfer to a test tube, centrifuge and decant, discarding the decantate, and wash the precipitate three times with hot water. Treat this precipitate with 5–6 drops of 3 M HNO_3 and a few grains of solid sodium bismuthate ($NaBiO_3$). Mix thoroughly, allow to stand for one minute, then centrifuge. A pink to reddish-purple solution due to the presence of permanganate (MnO_4^-) proves the presence of manganese.

NOTES

1. In the separation of MnS from CoS and NiS, small amounts of CoS and NiS may dissolve. These small amounts of Co^{++} and Ni^{++} do not, however, interfere with the test for manganese. If appreciable amounts of CoS dissolve, the pink color of cobalt nitrate may be mistaken for the violet of MnO_4^-.

2. The fact that nickel and cobalt do not precipitate in the copper-

arsenic group indicates that NiS and CoS are soluble in dilute HCl. However, in the analysis of the aluminum-nickel group, CoS and NiS do not dissolve in either dilute or concentrated HCl. This contradictory behavior is explained as follows: Freshly precipitated NiS and CoS exist in a form readily dissolved by dilute HCl. On standing, this soluble modification changes into a second form which is insoluble in both dilute and concentrated HCl.

3. The oxidation of Mn^{++} to MnO_4^- by sodium bismuthate ($NaBiO_3$) takes place as follows:

$$2\,Mn^{++} + 5\,HBiO_3 + 9\,H^+ = 2\,MnO_4^- + 5\,Bi^{+++} + 7\,H_2O.$$

4. Reducing agents of any kind, such as chlorides and sulfides, will interfere with the confirmatory test for manganese because they reduce the violet MnO_4^- to practically colorless Mn^{++}. For that reason:

(a) The decantate containing manganese ions is boiled to drive off all H_2S.

(b) Manganese is precipitated as $Mn(OH)_2$ and the precipitate of $Mn(OH)_2$ is washed free from chlorides.

Permanganate ion is reduced by chlorides and sulfides as follows:

$$2\,MnO_4^- + 10\,Cl^- + 16\,H^+ = 2\,Mn^{++} + 5\,Cl_2 + 8\,H_2O,$$

$$2\,MnO_4^- + 5\,H_2S + 6\,H^+ = 2\,Mn^{++} + 5\,S + 8\,H_2O.$$

5. The formation of MnO_4^- is a very sensitive test for Mn^{++}. The test may be carried out on a sample of the original solid as follows: Boil a pinch of the solid material with HCl. Filter. Precipitate the $Mn(OH)_2$ with excess NaOH and test the carefully washed precipitate for manganese as directed in Procedure 18. Cobalt interferes with this test.

6. Bismuth is predominantly metallic in character; its common oxidation number is 3 and its compounds ionize to give Bi^{+++} ions. In the compound $NaBiO_3$, bismuth has an oxidation number of 5 and has the property of a nonmetal in that it is present in the negative ion, BiO_3^-. This behavior of bismuth illustrates the rule that as the oxidation number of an element increases it becomes more nonmetallic in character.

7. The behavior of $NaBiO_3$ illustrates the rule that those compounds of polyvalent elements in which the element exists in one of its higher oxidation states very generally can act as oxidizing agents. Other compounds (oxidizing agents) that illustrate this rule are $KMnO_4$ and $K_2Cr_2O_7$.

▪ ▪ ▪ Procedure 19: Detection of nickel and cobalt

Treat the precipitate from Procedure 18 with 10 drops of 12 M HCl and 3 drops of 16 M HNO_3, mix thoroughly, and heat gently until a clear solution is obtained. Add 6 drops of water, mix well, centrifuge, and decant into a test tube, discarding the precipitate (S).

Make the decantate alkaline with 15 M NH_4OH and divide it into two parts. To one part add 4–8 drops of dimethyl glyoxime. A strawberry-red precipitate ($NiC_8H_{14}N_4O_4$) proves the presence of nickel. Make the second part acid with 2 M H_2SO_4. Saturate with NaF by adding a pinch of solid NaF. Stir for one minute. Then add 10–20 drops of a saturated solution of ammonium thiocyanate in alcohol. A blue solution, due to $Co(SCN)_4^{--}$ ions, proves the presence of cobalt.

NOTES

1. As in the case of difficultly soluble HgS, NiS and CoS are dissolved by a mixture of HCl and HNO_3, a reagent which will attack both ions that are in equilibrium with the solid sulfide.

(a) $$CoS \rightleftharpoons Co^{++} + S^{--},$$

(b_1) $$3\,S^{--} + 2\,NO_3^- + 8\,H^+ = 3\,S + 2\,NO + 4\,H_2O,$$

(b_2) $$Co^{++} + 4\,Cl^- \rightleftharpoons CoCl_4^{--}.$$

2. Dimethyl glyoxime has the chemical formula $(CH_3)_2\,C_2(NOH)_2$ and the structural formula

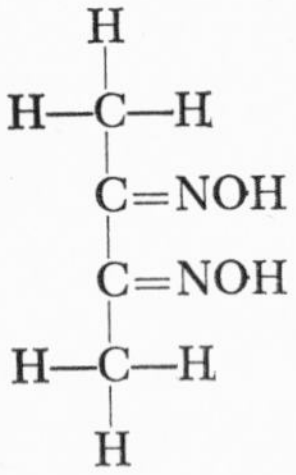

$$
\begin{array}{c}
H \\
| \\
H-C-H \\
| \\
C=NOH \\
| \\
C=NOH \\
| \\
H-C-H \\
| \\
H
\end{array}
$$

The following reaction takes place in the confirmatory test for nickel:

$$2(CH_3)_2C_2(NOH)_2 + Ni(NH_3)_6^{++} =$$
$$2\,NH_4^+ + NiC_8H_{14}N_4O_4 \text{ (red)} + 4\,NH_3.$$

Since the red compound is readily soluble in acids, the reaction must be carried out in alkaline solution. Cobalt does not interfere with this test. Iron(II) ions react with $(CH_3)_2C_2(NOH)_2$ to form a soluble red compound; however, no precipitate is formed.

3. Because of the striking similarity in the chemical behavior of cobalt and nickel, their separation offers considerable difficulty. It is most convenient to test for them in the presence of each other in the manner outlined above.

4. NaF prevents Fe^{+++}, which may be present, from forming the blood-red $Fe(SCN)_6^{---}$ and thereby interfering with the cobalt test.

The fluoride ions react with Fe^{+++} to form the stable complex ion, FeF_6^{---}. There are, accordingly, practically no Fe^{+++} ions to react with SCN^- ions.

5. The reaction of Co^{++} with SCN^- is incomplete, due to the instability of the complex ion.

$$Co^{++} + 4\,SCN^- \rightleftharpoons Co(SCN)_4^{--}.$$

An excess of SCN^- is necessary to give a good test.

6. High concentrations of Ni^{++} will give a light green solution in the test for cobalt. The cobalt blue color will, however, mask this green so there will be no interference; furthermore, the green of nickel is easily distinguished from the blue of cobalt.

7. Cobalt is oxidized to $Co(NH_3)_6^{+++}$ when treated with excess NH_4OH as already discussed in Note 9, Procedure 15. When the solution is acidified with H_2SO_4, $Co(III)$ is reduced to $Co(II)$.

$$Co(NH_3)_6^{+++} + 6\,H^+ = Co^{+++} + 6\,NH_4^+,$$
$$4\,Co^{+++} + 2\,H_2O = 4\,Co^{++} + O_2 + 4\,H^+.$$

■ ■ ■ Procedure 20: Separation and detection of aluminum

Treat the decantate from Procedure 16 with 16 M HNO_3 until slightly acid, then add 15 M NH_4OH until distinctly alkaline; continue the stirring of the ammoniacal solution for 1 minute. Centrifuge and decant, saving the decantate for Procedure 21. Because the $Al(OH)_3$ that precipitates is gelatinous, highly translucent, very finely divided, and the color of opaque, bluish-white glass, its presence, suspended in the solution, is not easy to detect. On centrifuging, however, it will appear in the bottom of the test tube as a whitish, jelly-like, opaque precipitate. Wash the precipitate three times with hot water, then dissolve it in 4–5 drops of 3 M HNO_3. (If any precipitate fails to dissolve, remove it by centrifuging and decantation.) Add 2 drops of aluminon solution, mix thoroughly, make *just barely alkaline* with 5 M NH_4OH, again mix thoroughly, then centrifuge. A cherry red precipitate (a so-called lake of $Al(OH)_3$ and adsorbed aluminon) proves the presence of aluminum.

NOTES

1. It is imperative that all chromate(III) ions $(Cr(OH)_4^-)$ be completely oxidized to chromate(VI) ions (CrO_4^{--}) in Procedure 16. Any unoxidized $Cr(OH)_4^-$ will react as follows in Procedure 20:

$$Cr(OH)_4^- + 4 H^+ \text{ (from HNO}_3) = Cr^{+++} + 4 H_2O,$$

$$Cr^{+++} + 3 NH_4OH = \mathbf{Cr(OH)_3} + 3 NH_4^+.$$

This reaction of chromate (III) ions is exactly the same as that which the aluminate ion $(Al(OH)_4^-)$ will undergo in the course of its separation.

$$Al(OH)_4^- + 4 H^+ \text{ (from HNO}_3) = Al^{+++} + 4 H_2O,$$

$$Al^{+++} + 3 NH_4OH = \mathbf{Al(OH)_3} + 3 NH_4^+.$$

It is thus evident that, if $Cr(OH)_4^-$ is not oxidized to CrO_4^{--}, $Cr(OH)_3$ will precipitate when the test for aluminum is made. It is obvious, therefore, that oxidation of $Cr(OH)_4^-$ to CrO_4^{--} by H_2O_2 is necessary if a separation of chromium from aluminum is to be accomplished. $Cr(OH)_3$ is green, but in small amounts the color is not marked, and the $Cr(OH)_3$ precipitate may be mistaken for $Al(OH)_3$.

$Cr(OH)_3$ does not form a red lake with aluminon. Excessive amounts of $Cr(OH)_3$ will, however, mask the red aluminon lake. Therefore, if much $Cr(OH)_3$ precipitates with the $Al(OH)_3$ it should be reoxidized to CrO_4^{--} with H_2O_2.

2. When HNO_3 is added in the first step in Procedure 20, a precipitate sometimes forms when the solution is just about neutral and then redissolves when more HNO_3 is added. This precipitate may be either $Al(OH)_3$ or $Zn(OH)_2$, both of which are white; in case chromium is not completely oxidized to CrO_4^{--}, $Cr(OH)_3$ (green) may precipitate. The reactions to account for the formation and disappearance of this precipitate are:

(a) When HNO_3 is added to neutrality:

$$Al(OH)_4^- + H^+ \text{ (from HNO}_3) = \mathbf{Al(OH)_3} + H_2O.$$

(b) When more HNO_3 is added:

$$\mathbf{Al(OH)_3} + 3 H^+ = Al^{+++} + 3 H_2O.$$

3. Excess H_2O_2, if present in the decantate from Procedure 16, will interfere with the separation and identification of aluminum and chromium. When HNO_3 is added in the first step in Procedure 20, the following reaction will take place:

$$2 CrO_4^{--} + 2 H^+ \rightleftharpoons Cr_2O_7^{--} + H_2O,$$

$$Cr_2O_7^{--} + 3 H_2O_2 + 8 H^+ = 2 Cr^{+++} + 3 O_2 + 7 H_2O.$$

The chromate is thus reduced to Cr^{+++}. This Cr^{+++} will then interfere with the test for aluminum, as already discussed in Note 1.

Contrast the above equation with the one given in Note 3, Procedure 16. In alkaline solution the H_2O_2 oxidizes trivalent chromium to chromate, whereas in strongly acid solution it reduces chromate to trivalent chromium.

As has already been pointed out in Note 1 of Procedure 17, O_2 is liberated when H_2O_2 functions as a reducing agent in acid solution. What happens, in net effect, is this: the H_2O_2 gives up one atom of oxygen; this atom picks up, from the oxidizing agent [$Cr_2O_7^{--}$, MnO_2, $Co(OH)_3$], the other atom of oxygen which it needs in order to pass off as O_2 gas; as a result, reduction occurs [$Cr_2O_7^{--}$ to Cr^{+++}, MnO_2 to Mn^{++}, $Co(OH)_3$ to Co^{++}].

4. When NH_4OH is added in Procedure 20, a white precipitate sometimes forms but redissolves when more NH_4OH is added. This precipitate is probably $Zn(OH)_2$. The reactions that account for its formation and redissolution are

$$Zn^{++} + 2\,NH_4OH = Zn(OH)_2 + 2\,NH_4^+,$$

$$Zn(OH)_2 + 4\,NH_4OH = Zn(NH_3)_4^{++} + 2\,OH^- + 4\,H_2O.$$

5. Since HCl may reduce chromate to Cr^{+++}, the solution is acidified with HNO_3 rather than with HCl.

6. If lead, tin, and antimony are not completely precipitated in the copper-arsenic group, they appear as insoluble hydroxides or basic salts in the final test for aluminum. The hydroxides of lead, tin, and antimony, like $Al(OH)_3$, are amphoteric. Also, their hydroxides, like $Al(OH)_3$, do not dissolve in excess NH_4OH. They do not, however, form the characteristic red lake with aluminon.

7. Aluminon is an organic dye. It is the ammonium salt of aurin tricarboxylic acid and its chemical formula is

$$(C_6H_3OHCOONH_4)_2C:C_6H_3OCOONH_4.$$

Its structural formula is

8. A lake is formed when a colored compound (a dye) combines with or is adsorbed from solution by an insoluble gelatinous precipitate. The dye, aluminon, is preferentially adsorbed by $Al(OH)_3$; this dye is not adsorbed by $Cr(OH)_3$, $Zn(OH)_2$, nor by the hydroxides of lead, tin, and antimony.

■ ■ ■ Procedure 21: Separation and detection of chromium and zinc

Follow (A) if the decantate from Procedure 20 is colorless; follow (B) if it is yellow.

(A) *Decantate is colorless; therefore chromium is absent.* Make the decantate just acid with $6M$ HCl. Then add 3–4 drops of $0.2 \ M \ K_4Fe(CN)_6$ and mix thoroughly. The resulting mixture should be acidic. A grayish-white to bluish-green precipitate $(Zn_3K_2[Fe(CN)_6]_2)$ proves the presence of zinc.

(B) *Decantate is yellow; chromium is probably present.* Add 6–7 drops of $0.2 \ M$ $BaCl_2$ to the yellow decantate, mix thoroughly, centrifuge until the supernatant liquid is clear, and decant, saving the decantate for Part (C) below. Wash the precipitate ($BaCrO_4$, mixed with some $BaSO_4$) twice with hot water, add 3 drops of $3 \ M$ HNO_3, heat gently but do not boil vigorously, and stir for about one minute. Add 10 drops of cold water, mix thoroughly, cool under the cold water tap, and then add 10 drops of ether and 1 drop of 3% H_2O_2. Mix well by vigorous stirring and allow to settle. A blue coloration of the ether layer due to chromium peroxide (CrO_5) proves the presence of chromium.

(C) Make the decantate from (B) acid with $6 \ M$ HCl. Then add 3–4 drops of $0.2 \ M$ $K_4Fe(CN)_6$ and mix thoroughly. The resulting mixture should be acidic. A grayish-white to bluish-green precipitate, $Zn_3K_2[Fe(CN)_6]_2$, proves the presence of zinc.

NOTES

1. The final test for chromium depends on the fact that in dilute acid solution $Cr_2O_7^{--}$ interacts with H_2O_2 to form a deep indigo-blue compound, chromium peroxide, CrO_5. Yellow chromate is first changed to orange dichromate ($Cr_2O_7^{--}$).

$$BaCrO_4 \ + \ 2\,H^+ \ = \ Ba^{++} \ + \ CrO_4^{--} \ + \ 2\,H^+,$$

$$2\,CrO_4^{--} \ + \ 2\,H^+ \ \rightleftharpoons \ Cr_2O_7^{--} \ + \ H_2O.$$

This change of chromate to dichromate, which always takes place when the solution is acidified, has already been referred to in Note 3, Procedure 20.

The dichromate is then converted to CrO_5 by H_2O_2.

$$Cr_2O_7^{--} + 4 H_2O_2 + 2 H^+ = 2 CrO_5 + 5 H_2O.$$

The compound CrO_5 is unstable, and decomposes on standing to form Cr^{+++}. If the concentration of HNO_3 is low, the CrO_5 decomposes very slowly; if, however, the concentration of HNO_3 is high, it decomposes so rapidly that the blue color may not be noticed. Furthermore, CrO_5 is very rapidly reduced to Cr^{+++} by excess H_2O_2. Hence high concentrations of HNO_3 and excess H_2O_2 must be avoided.

$$4 CrO_5 + 12 H^+ = 4 Cr^{+++} + 6 H_2O + 7 O_2,$$

$$2 CrO_5 + 6 H^+ + 7 H_2O_2 = 2 Cr^{+++} + 10 H_2O + 7 O_2.$$

CrO_5 is very soluble in ether; HNO_3 is not. Treating with ether partially separates the CrO_5 from the HNO_3 and concentrates it in the ether layer. Since separation from HNO_3 will increase its stability, extraction with ether preserves as well as concentrates the CrO_5.

The exact composition of the blue substance formed in the confirmatory test for chromium has been, and still is, the subject of much research, speculation, and controversy. That the composition is correctly represented by the formula CrO_5 seems pretty well proved. Other formulas that have been suggested are $HCrO_4$, $HCrO_5$, H_2CrO_5, H_2CrO_6, H_3CrO_8, and $H_6Cr_2O_{16}$.

The following structure has been proposed for CrO_5. Note that chromium has a covalence of 6, the same as in CrO_4^{--} or $Cr_2O_7^{--}$.

The oxidation number of chromium in CrO_5 can be calculated to be 10; this value is used in balancing the equations given above. It should be pointed out, however, that an oxidation number of 10 does not mean, in this instance, that ten electrons are involved in the bonding.

2. The precipitate obtained on addition of $BaCl_2$ may contain varying amounts of $BaSO_4$ because of oxidation of H_2S and S to H_2SO_4 in earlier procedures. $BaSO_4$ is white, whereas $BaCrO_4$ is light yellow. However, very finely divided $BaCrO_4$ is such a pale yellow that the precipitate may appear white even though it consists largely of $BaCrO_4$. The confirmatory test for chromium should therefore be completed as directed even if the precipitate appears white.

$BaCrO_4$, being the salt of the relatively weak acid, H_2CrO_4, is soluble in HNO_3, whereas $BaSO_4$, being the salt of a strong acid, is insoluble.

3. $Zn_3K_2[Fe(CN)_6]_2$ is insoluble in HCl; $Ba_2Fe(CN)_6$ and the hexa-cyanoferrates of other metals are soluble in HCl. Therefore, the confirmatory test for zinc is carried out in acid (HCl) solution.

Pure $Zn_3K_2[Fe(CN)_6]_2$ is grayish-white. However, because of slight contamination with iron (from the hood, ringstand, wire gauze, fingers, stirring rod, etc.), it may range in color to a pronounced bluish-green.

QUESTIONS

1. Using the scheme of analysis as a guide, write net equations for all reactions that take place in the precipitation and analysis of the aluminum-nickel group.

2. Upon what fact or facts is each of the following based?

(a) The separation of the cations of the aluminum-nickel group from the cations of the barium-magnesium group.

(b) The separation of the aluminum subgroup from the nickel subgroup.

3. Give the reason or reasons for each of the following:

(a) The addition of NH_4Cl before precipitating the aluminum-nickel group.

(b) The separate addition, first of NH_4OH, then of $(NH_4)_2S$, in the precipitation of the aluminum-nickel group.

(c) The separate addition of HCl and HNO_3, followed in each case by boiling, in dissolving the aluminum-nickel group precipitate (Procedure 16).

(d) The addition of H_2O_2 (Procedure 16).

(e) Boiling the solution before centrifuging in the separation of the aluminum subgroup from the nickel subgroup (Procedure 16).

(f) The use of dilute HNO_3 rather than concentrated HNO_3 in the confirmatory test for chromium.

(g) The use of ether in the confirmatory test for chromium.

4. In the precipitation and analysis of the aluminum-nickel group, what difficulties, if any, would arise under the following conditions?

(a) If $Cr(OH)_4^-$ were not completely oxidized to CrO_4^{--} (Procedure 16).

(b) If excess H_2O_2 were not decomposed (Procedure 16).

(c) If 1 cc. of H_2O_2 were used instead of 1 drop in the confirmatory test for chromium.

5. Write an equation or equations for a reaction occurring in the precipitation and analysis of the aluminum-nickel group in which:

(a) Fe(II) is oxidized to Fe(III).

(b) Mn(II) is oxidized to Mn(IV).

(c) Mn(II) is oxidized to Mn(VII).

(d) Mn(IV) is reduced to Mn(II).

(e) Mn(VII) is reduced to Mn(II).

(f) Cr(III) is oxidized to Cr(VI).

(g) Bi(V) is reduced to Bi(III).

(h) Co(II) is oxidized to Co(III).

(i) Fe(III) is reduced to Fe(II).

(j) CrO_5 is converted into Cr^{+++}.

(k) $Cr_2O_7^{--}$ is converted into Cr^{+++}.

(l) CrO_4^{--} is converted into $Cr_2O_7^{--}$.

(m) $Al(OH)_3$ reacts amphoteric.

(n) $Zn(OH)_4^{--}$ is converted into Zn^{++}.

(o) Ni^{++} is converted into $Ni(NH_3)_4^{++}$.

6. Give the formula for a chemical substance which will form a precipitate:

(a) With $CrCl_3$ solution but not with Na_2CrO_4.

(b) With $MnCl_2$ solution but not with $KMnO_4$.

(c) With $FeCl_3$ solution but not with $AlCl_3$.

(d) With Na_2CrO_4 solution but not with $Zn(NO_3)_2$.

(e) With $NiCl_2$ solution but not with $CrCl_3$.

(f) With $MnCl_2$ solution but not with $AlCl_3$.

(g) With $FeCl_3$ solution but not with $CoCl_2$.

(h) With $CoCl_2$ solution but not with $ZnCl_2$.

(i) With $AlCl_3$ solution but not with $ZnCl_2$.

(j) With Na_2CrO_4 solution but not with $FeCl_3$.

(k) With $AlCl_3$ solution but not with $CaCl_2$.

(l) With $NiCl_2$ solution but not with $BaCl_2$.

7. Give the formula for a reagent which will:

(a) Dissolve MnS but not NiS.

(b) Dissolve ZnS but not CuS.

(c) Dissolve $Al(OH)_3$ but not $Fe(OH)_3$.

(d) Dissolve $Ni(OH)_2$ but not $Fe(OH)_3$.

(e) Dissolve $Cr(OH)_3$ but not Bi_2S_3.

(f) Dissolve $Zn(OH)_2$ but not $Ni(OH)_2$.

(g) Dissolve Na_2CrO_4 but not $Al(OH)_3$.

8. Give the formula for a solid substance in the aluminum-nickel group which will:

(a) Dissolve readily in NH_4OH and also in NaOH.

(b) Dissolve in NaOH but not in NH_4OH.

(c) Dissolve in NH_4OH but not in NaOH.

(d) Dissolve in HCl but not in water.

(e) Dissolve in HCl and also in NaOH.

(f) Dissolve in HCl + HNO$_3$ but not in HCl.

9. How would you distinguish, by means of one reagent, between the following? (Tell what happens to each substance.)

(a) *Solutions:*

Cr^{+++} and Al^{+++}. $\qquad$ Fe^{+++} and Fe^{++}.

Cr^{+++} and Ni^{++}. $\qquad$ Fe^{+++} and CrO_4^{--}.

Mn^{++} and Zn^{++}. $\qquad$ $Zn(NH_3)_4^{++}$ and Zn^{++}.

Al^{+++} and Zn^{++}. $\qquad$ Zn^{++} and Ba^{++}.

$Al(OH)_4^-$ and $Cr(OH)_4^-$. $\qquad$ Mn^{++} and Mg^{++}.

(b) *Solids:*

ZnS and CoS. $\qquad$ $Al(OH)_3$ and $Mn(OH)_2$.

$Ni(OH)_2$ and $Cr(OH)_3$. $\qquad$ MnO_2 and $Fe(OH)_3$.

MnS and NiS. $\qquad$ $Zn(OH)_2$ and $Al(OH)_3$.

Na_2S and ZnS. $\qquad$ CuS and FeS.

10. Using as few operations as possible, how do you test for the following?

(a) Zn^{++} in a solution known to contain Ni^{++}.

(b) Mn^{++} in a solution known to contain Co^{++} and Cl^-.

(c) Al^{+++} in a solution known to contain Cr^{+++}.

(d) Fe^{++} in a solution known to contain Fe^{+++}.

(e) Ni^{++} in a solution known to contain Fe^{++}.

11. Account for each of the following facts:

(a) MnO is readily soluble in H_2SO_4; MnO_2 is not readily soluble in H_2SO_4.

(b) In the presence of fluoride ions ferric ions do not give the characteristic red coloration with thiocyanate ions.

(c) When a deep blue alcoholic solution containing $Co(SCN)_4^{--}$ ions is diluted with water the blue color disappears.

(d) When either NaOH or NH_4OH is added, drop by drop, to a solution of $ZnCl_2$ a white precipitate first appears but redissolves, on addition of more of the reagent, to give a colorless, water-clear solution. When HCl is added, dropwise, to the water-clear solution a white precipitate first appears but redissolves, when more HCl is added, to give a water-clear solution.

(e) When $(NH_4)_2S$ is added to a solution formed by dissolving solid $FeCl_3$ in water a black precipitate forms.

(f) When 5 M NH_4OH is added to a solution obtained by dissolving $MgCl_2$ in water a white precipitate of $Mg(OH)_2$ forms; when 5 M NH_4OH is added to a solution obtained by dissolving a mixture of $MgCl_2$ and NH_4Cl in water no precipitate forms.

(g) When a solution prepared by mixing 1 M NH_4OH and 1 M NH_4Cl is added to a solution containing Mn^{++} ions there is at first no visible sign of reaction. After about 20 seconds a tan coloration begins to appear; eventually a light brown precipitate forms.

(h) When 2 M H_2SO_4 is added to a solid mixture of MnO_2 and $Co(OH)_3$ there is no sign of reaction. When 2 M H_2SO_4 and some 3% H_2O_2 are added the solid mixture is quickly dissolved.

(i) $Mg(OH)_2$, which is insoluble in water, is soluble in an aqueous solution of NH_4Cl.

12. A colorless solution known to contain only cations of the aluminum-nickel group was divided into three parts which were treated as follows:

(a) To one part, NaOH was added, slowly and with constant stirring. A light-colored precipitate formed, part of which redissolved in an excess of NaOH. The solution was centrifuged and decanted. The precipitate was observed to darken on standing exposed to the air.

(b) The second part gave no precipitate on being treated with NH_4Cl and NH_4OH.

(c) The third part gave a light-colored precipitate when treated with NH_4Cl, NH_4OH, and $(NH_4)_2S$.

What conclusions can be drawn?

13. An Al-Ni group unknown solution was divided into three parts.

(a) One part was treated with NaOH and H_2O_2. A light green precipitate formed.

(b) One part was treated with NH_4Cl and excess NH_4OH. A white precipitate formed.

(c) One part was treated with a solution of $(NH_4)_2S$ in 2 M NH_4OH. A black precipitate formed.

List the cations that are shown to be absent, those shown to be present, and those that are undetermined.

14. An unknown solid is made up of one or more of the following compounds: CuS, ZnS, $AlCl_3$, $NiCl_2$, MnO. Treatment of the solid with water leaves a black residue and a colorless decantate. The residue is partially soluble in 6 M HCl; the decantate from the HCl treatment yields a tan precipitate and colorless decantate when treated with an excess of NH_4OH.

List the compounds shown to be absent, those shown to be present, and those that are undetermined.

15. On the addition of NH_4Cl and NH_4OH to a solution known to contain only cations of the aluminum-nickel group, a white flocculent precipitate forms. On addition of $(NH_4)_2S$, a black precipitate forms. The combined precipitate does not dissolve completely in HCl but dissolves completely in HCl + HNO_3. When this solution is treated with excess

NaOH, then with H_2O_2 and centrifuged, the decantate is colorless and the precipitate is light green. What conclusions can be drawn?

16. On addition of NH_4Cl and NH_4OH to a solution known to contain only cations of the aluminum-nickel group, a dark-red precipitate forms. On addition of $(NH_4)_2S$, a black precipitate forms. The combined precipitate dissolves readily and completely in HCl. The resulting green solution, having first been boiled with a few drops of concentrated HNO_3, gives a reddish-brown precipitate and a pale-green solution when treated with excess NaOH. On being treated with H_2O_2 the solution turns yellow, the precipitate undergoing no change in color. What conclusions can be drawn?

17. A solid material which was known to contain only cations of the aluminum-nickel group dissolved in HCl to give a green solution. The addition of NH_4Cl and NH_4OH gave a green precipitate, and the addition of $(NH_4)_2S$ gave a black precipitate. The total precipitate was dissolved in $HCl + HNO_3$. When the solution thus formed was treated with NaOH followed by H_2O_2, a colorless solution and a reddish-brown precipitate were formed. This precipitate was found to be soluble in either HCl, H_2SO_4, or HNO_3. What conclusions can be drawn?

18. Using the Al-Ni group scheme of analysis as your only source of information select, in each line, the correct substance.

(a) Weakest reducing agent in alkaline solution: Fe^{++}, Co^{++}, Ni^{++}.

(b) Strongest reducing agent in acid solution: Mn^{++}, Co^{++}, Ni^{++}.

(c) Most stable complex ion: $Mn(OH)_4^{--}$, $Zn(OH)_4^{--}$, $Ni(OH)_4^{--}$.

(d) Sulfide with smallest solubility product: ZnS, CoS, MgS.

(e) Amphoteric hydroxide: $Co(OH)_2$, $Zn(OH)_2$, $Ni(OH)_2$.

(f) Substance with smallest instability constant: $Fe(OH)_6^{---}$, FeF_6^{---}, $Fe(SCN)_6^{---}$.

Aluminum-nickel group report

Fe^{+++}

Co^{++}

Zn^{++}

Al^{+++}

Aluminum-nickel group report

Aluminum-nickel group report

Aluminum-nickel group report

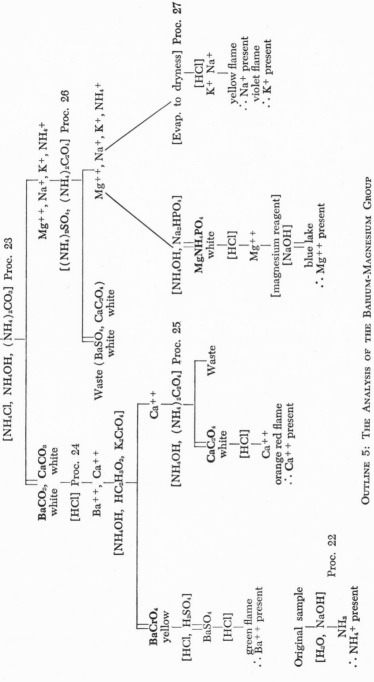

OUTLINE 5: THE ANALYSIS OF THE BARIUM-MAGNESIUM GROUP

The barium-magnesium group

AFTER REMOVAL of the preceding groups, the ions of barium, calcium, magnesium, potassium, sodium, and ammonium remain in the solution being analyzed. Barium and calcium are members of the barium subgroup. The remaining four will be called the magnesium subgroup.

Detection of Ammonium Salts

When an ammonium salt is heated with a strong base, ammonia gas is evolved. This fact is the basis for the detection of ammonium. Since NH_4Cl, as well as other ammonium salts, is added at various points in the cation analysis, the test for ammonium must be made on a sample of the original material.

■ ■ ■ Procedure 22: Detection of ammonium

Place a pellet of NaOH or 5 drops of 8 M NaOH solution in a test tube. Add 5 drops of the original solution to be tested, or a pinch of the solid to be tested. Warm gently but do not boil. The evolution of NH_3 gas, detected by its odor or by its reaction to a piece of moist red litmus held down into the mouth of the tube, proves the presence of ammonium compounds.

154

NOTES

1. Ammonia gas is evolved according to the following equation:

$$NH_4^+ + OH^- = NH_3 + H_2O.$$

2. In testing with red litmus paper do not touch the end of the tube with the paper; it may come in contact with the NaOH, which will turn it blue.

Precipitation of Calcium and Barium

The separation of barium and calcium ions from the cations of the magnesium subgroup depends on the fact that, in an alkaline solution containing excess NH_4^+ ions, calcium and barium are precipitated as $CaCO_3$ and $BaCO_3$ by $(NH_4)_2CO_3$, whereas magnesium, sodium, and potassium ions remain in solution.

■ ■ ■ Procedure 23: Precipitation of calcium and barium

If the solution to be analyzed is a barium-magnesium group known or unknown, follow Method (A), below. If the decantate from Procedure 15 is being analyzed, follow (B).

(A) First make a flame test on 2 drops of the solution to be analyzed in the manner described in Note 2 of Procedure 24. (See Note 1.) Then place 6 drops of the solution to be analyzed in a test tube and add 6 drops of cold water (see Note 2). Then add 4 drops of 2 M NH_4Cl, mix thoroughly, make alkaline with 15 M NH_4OH, and add 2 M $(NH_4)_2CO_3$ until precipitation is complete (3 to 5 drops is generally sufficient). Heat in the water bath for 1 minute, then cool. When precipitation is complete, centrifuge and decant, saving the decantate for Procedure 26. Wash the precipitate ($CaCO_3$, $BaCO_3$) three times with cold water and analyze according to Procedure 24.

(B) Place the decantate from Procedure 15 in a casserole, evaporate to a volume of 7–8 drops, transfer to a test tube, and centrifuge. Decant into a casserole, discarding any precipitate. Add 6 M HCl until the solution is slightly acidic; then evaporate to dryness and bake until absence of further sublimation indicates that all ammonium salts are driven off. Cool. Then add 12 drops of hot water and stir for 1 minute. Transfer the solution to a test tube; if the solution is clear, proceed as directed in (A) above. If the solution is not clear, then centrifuge, decant the clear supernatant liquid into a test tube, and proceed with it as directed in (A) above.

NOTES

1. A flame test performed on an original sample of the "known" solution from the barium-magnesium group will not be informative since the color of the flame will be a mixture of the colors produced by barium, calcium, sodium, and potassium. Therefore, when the barium-magnesium "known" solution is being analyzed this flame test should be omitted. However, when a barium-magnesium group "unknown" or a salt or salt mixture is being analyzed this preliminary flame test may be very helpful. Thus, if the flame test shows no coloration whatever, thereby indicating the absence of Ca^{++}, Ba^{++}, K^+, and Na^+, the separation and identification of these ions can be omitted. Likewise, the test may show the presence of K^+ and the absence of Ca^{++}, Ba^{++}, and Na^+, etc. The fact that one flame color may cover up or modify another color must not be overlooked.

By performing the flame test on a sample of the original material, the possibility of an erronous test due to contamination is greatly reduced. Contamination with Na^+ during the analytical procedures is inevitable, so a flame test for sodium should always be made on the original substance.

2. If the barium-magnesium group unknown is issued in the form of a finely divided solid, proceed as follows: Place in a test tube as much of the solid as can be carried on $\frac{1}{4}$ in. of the tip of the spatula. Add 3–4 drops of 6 M HCl, warm gently, and then add 10–12 drops of water. Mix thoroughly and heat carefully until a clear solution is obtained. Proceed with the analysis of 6 drops of this solution as directed in Procedure 23 (A).

If the solid unknown is not finely divided when received, the entire sample should first be pulverized in a clean mortar.

3. Concentrating the decantate from the Al-Ni group will remove, as sulfides or hydroxides, any cations of preceding groups that might be present.

4. The decantate from the aluminum-nickel group contains a large excess of ammonium salts. Because $CaCO_3$ and $BaCO_3$ are appreciably soluble in the presence of large amounts of these salts, the latter are removed by sublimation.

5. Since $CaCO_3$ and $BaCO_3$ are somewhat soluble in water, they must be precipitated from relatively concentrated solutions. Dissolving the residue left after baking in 12 drops of water gives a sufficiently concentrated solution.

6. If no residue remains in the evaporating dish after the ammonium salts are sublimed, then barium, calcium, magnesium, sodium, and potassium are absent.

7. NH_4Cl is added to prevent the precipitation of magnesium as $Mg(OH)_2$ or $MgCO_3$. The role of NH_4Cl in preventing the precipitation of $Mg(OH)_2$ is discussed in Note 4 of Procedure 15. The prevention of the precipitation of $MgCO_3$ is probably more involved. A possible interpretation is the following: $MgCO_3$ will not precipitate if the concentration of CO_3^{--} ions is kept sufficiently low. A high concentration of NH_4^+ ions decreases the ionization of NH_4OH, thereby producing a lowered concentration of OH^- ions in equation (a), below. Lowering the OH^- concentration causes the equilibrium in the reaction of CO_3^{--} ions [from $(NH_4)_2CO_3$] with water (hydrolysis of CO_3^{--}) as represented in equation (b) to be shifted to the right. Shifting the equilibrium in equation (b) to the right reduces the concentration of CO_3^{--} to the point where $MgCO_3$ does not precipitate.

(a) $$NH_4OH \rightleftharpoons NH_4^+ + OH^-,$$

(b) $$CO_3^{--} + H_2O \rightleftharpoons HCO_3^- + OH^-.$$

Separation of Barium from Calcium

Calcium chromate is quite soluble in dilute acetic acid. Barium chromate is relatively insoluble. Upon these facts is based the separation of barium ions from calcium ions.

▪ ▪ ▪ Procedure 24: Separation and detection of barium

Dissolve the precipitate from Procedure 23 in 3 drops of 2 M HCl. Make just alkaline with 5 M NH_4OH, then just acid with 5 M $HC_2H_3O_2$, and then add 1 drop of 5 M $HC_2H_3O_2$, 4 drops of water, and 1 drop of 0.2 M K_2CrO_4. If no precipitate forms, barium is absent; in that case analyze the solution according to Procedure 25. If a yellow precipitate ($BaCrO_4$) forms, barium is present; in that case add K_2CrO_4 until precipitation is complete. Centrifuge; save the decantate for Procedure 25. Dissolve the washed $BaCrO_4$ in 2 drops of 6 M HCl, add 2 drops of 2 M H_2SO_4, centrifuge, wash the precipitate ($BaSO_4$) three times with water, add 3 drops of 12 M HCl, mix, and make a flame test on this mixture as directed in note 2. A green flame proves the presence of barium.

NOTES

1. The solubility product of $BaCrO_4$ is 2.4×10^{-10} and of $CaCrO_4$ is 1.0×10^{-4}.

2. Directions for making a flame test: Seal a 2-in. piece of platinum wire into one end of a 5-in. piece of glass tubing. This platinum wire will serve for all subsequent flame tests. Clean the platinum wire by alternately heating it to redness and thrusting it into concentrated HCl contained in a test tube until it gives no coloration to the nonluminous flame of the Bunsen burner.

Dip the clean platinum wire into the solution to be tested; then hold it in the nonluminous flame and note any coloration.

The following ions give characteristic flame colorations: barium, green; borate, pale green; calcium, orange red; copper, green; potassium, lavender; sodium, yellow.

3. Since the chlorides of metals are in general more readily volatilized than other salts, chlorides are used in making the flame test.

4. The concentration of the acid present when barium is precipitated as $BaCrO_4$ is important. If the acid concentration is too high, $BaCrO_4$ will not precipitate. If the concentration is too low, $CaCrO_4$ may precipitate.

5. Since $CaCrO_4$ may precipitate because of faulty acid concentration, it is desirable to verify barium by means of the flame test. The brilliant green of barium is readily distinguished from the orange-red calcium flame.

6. In acid solution CrO_4^{--} ions are converted to $Cr_2O_7^{--}$ ions.

(a) $$2\,CrO_4^{--} \;+\; 2\,H^+ \;\rightleftharpoons\; Cr_2O_7^{--} \;+\; H_2O.$$

However, barium ions will precipitate $BaCrO_4$ from such a solution.

(b) $$Ba^{++} \;+\; CrO_4^{--} \;=\; \mathbf{BaCrO_4}.$$

In effect the barium ions cause equilibrium (a) to be shifted to the left. $BaCr_2O_7$ is very soluble.

7. The solution formed when $BaCrO_4$ is dissolved in HCl will contain $Cr_2O_7^{--}$ ions. These ions will cause the flame to sputter with bursts of yellow color, thereby interfering with the flame test for barium. To avoid this interference the barium is reprecipitated as $BaSO_4$, which is more insoluble than $BaCrO_4$, and the test is applied to the chromate-free solution of Ba^{++}, which is obtained when the washed $BaSO_4$ is treated with HCl. Although $BaSO_4$ is only slightly soluble in HCl, the flame test is so sensitive that even a low concentration of Ba^{++} will give a good test when no interfering substances are present.

▪ ▪ ▪ Procedure 25: Detection of calcium

Make the decantate from Procedure 24 (or, if barium is absent, the solution from Procedure 24) just alkaline with 15 M NH_4OH; then add 4–5 drops of 0.2 M ammonium oxalate, $(NH_4)_2C_2O_4$. A white precipitate (CaC_2O_4) proves the presence of calcium. Centrifuge and decant, discarding the decantate. Wash the precipitate three times with hot water, dissolve it in 6 M HCl, and run a flame test as directed in Note 2 of Procedure 24. An orange-red flame further proves the presence of calcium.

NOTE

1. Barium, if not completely removed in Procedure 24, may precipitate as white crystalline BaC_2O_4. Consequently, it is desirable to confirm calcium by the flame test.

■ ■ ■ Procedure 26: Separation and detection of magnesium

Treat the decantate from Procedure 23 with 2 drops of 0.2 M (NH_4)$_2SO_4$ and 2 drops of 0.2 M ammonium oxalate, heat to boiling, cool, centrifuge, and decant, discarding any precipitate ($BaSO_4$, CaC_2O_4). Save one half of the decantate for the detection of sodium and potassium, Procedure 27; treat the other half with 1 drop of 5 M NH_4OH and 4 drops of 0.2 M Na_2HPO_4, mix well, warm gently, and allow to stand for 1 minute. A white precipitate ($MgNH_4PO_4$) shows the presence of magnesium. (See Note 1.) Centrifuge and decant, discarding the decantate. Wash the precipitate three times with hot water, dissolve in 2–3 drops of 2 M HCl, and then add 3 or 4 drops of magnesium reagent. Then add 8 M NaOH, with constant mixing, until the solution is distinctly alkaline, and centrifuge. A blue lake (flocculent precipitate) proves the presence of magnesium.

NOTES

1. The precipitate of $MgNH_4PO_4$ sometimes forms very slowly. If a precipitate does not form at once, heat to boiling, cool, and allow to stand for 1 minute. If no precipitate forms, magnesium is absent.

2. Since $CaCO_3$ and $BaCO_3$ are slightly soluble in alkaline solution, small amounts of calcium and barium may be present in the alkaline decantate from Procedure 23. All calcium and barium must be removed before the confirmatory test for magnesium is made; otherwise they may precipitate as $Ba_3(PO_4)_2$ and $Ca_3(PO_4)_2$. Since $BaSO_4$ and CaC_2O_4 are highly insoluble, barium and calcium ions will be removed if the solution is treated with (NH_4)$_2SO_4$ and (NH_4)$_2C_2O_4$.

3. Since the oxalates of most metals are quite insoluble, the addition of (NH_4)$_2C_2O_4$ and (NH_4)$_2SO_4$ will not only remove barium and calcium

ions but will also precipitate any other cations that may have failed to precipitate completely in preceding groups. Removal of these cations is imperative, since they, like Ba^{++} and Ca^{++}, form insoluble phosphates that might be mistaken for $MgNH_4PO_4$. Magnesium oxalate is quite soluble and does not precipitate.

4. The white precipitate of magnesium ammonium phosphate is formed as follows.

$$Mg^{++} + HPO_4^{--} + NH_4OH = MgNH_4PO_4 + H_2O.$$

5. Since phosphates of other metals besides magnesium may precipitate at this point, it is necessary to show that the precipitate is a magnesium compound. The special magnesium reagent is a solution of the complex organic dye, p-nitrobenzeneazoresorcinol. In this particular test the OH^- ions, from the 8 M NaOH, react with the Mg^{++} ions to form insoluble $Mg(OH)_2$. This $Mg(OH)_2$ then combines with the dye, or possibly adsorbs it, to give a blue precipitate known as a *lake*. Nickel and cobalt hydroxides, if present, form similar blue lakes. Excess ammonium ions reduce the sensitivity of the test by interfering with the formation of the lake.

Detection of Sodium and Potassium

All cations that have been discussed up to this point form a number of highly insoluble compounds; several of them form complex ions of distinctive color. For that reason it has been comparatively easy to separate and identify them. The case of potassium and sodium is quite different. Each of these ions forms only one or two compounds that are sufficiently insoluble to make them worthy of consideration for separation and identification. Furthermore, these insoluble compounds are not *highly* insoluble; therefore, the tests which they provide are not nearly as sentitive as are the tests for the cations already discussed. The insoluble potassium compound formed in such procedure is $K_2NaCo(NO_2)_6$; the insoluble sodium compound is $NaZn(UO_2)_3(C_2H_3O_2)_9$. The insoluble potassium salt is formed with fairly low concentrations of potassium ions; the insoluble sodium salt forms only if the concentration of sodium ions is high; both salts may form slowly. The reagent used to form the insoluble compound must, in each case, be made up according to exact specifications if it is to be satisfactory; this is particularly true of the sodium reagent.

What this all adds up to is simply this: identification of sodium and potassium by precipitation tests is not very successful and, for that reason, will not be used in this book. The precipitation tests are, however, given as notes in Procedure 27.

Fortunately, sodium and potassium have very sensitive and distinctive flame tests. These flame tests will be used for their identification.

The sodium flame test is so sensitive that even a trace of sodium ion gives a characteristic fluffy yellow coloration. Traces of sodium ion get into solutions as a result of contact with glassware; sodium chloride that is continually being deposited on the surface of the skin as a result of evaporation of perspiration is transferred to the air and to anything touched by the hands. The net result is that every solution will give a positive test for sodium ion. The question to be decided is not whether sodium is absent or present, but whether it is present in small amount or large amount. The student is urged not to get discouraged by the lack of definiteness of results in the test for sodium ions in an unknown. If a more definite test were available it would be used.

The fluffy yellow sodium flame will cover up the color due to any other ion. In particular, it will completely cover the lavender color of the potassium flame. A cobalt blue glass will screen out the yellow sodium light but will not affect the potassium coloration. Potassium can therefore be detected in the presence of sodium by viewing the flame through cobalt blue glass.

▪ ▪ ▪ Procedure 27: Detection of sodium and potassium

Evaporate the remaining half of the decantate from Procedure 26 to dryness and bake in the casserole at the maximum temperature of the flame until the absence of white smoke or vapor indicates that all NH_4Cl has sublimed off. If there is no solid residue in the casserole, sodium and potassium are absent. Cool, then treat the solid residue with 2 drops of 6 M HCl, and make a flame test as directed in Note 2 of Procedure 24. A fluffy yellow flame proves the presence of sodium; a lavender flame proves the presence of potassium and the absence of sodium. In reporting the results of this test note whether the yellow flame is fairly diffuse and of short duration, indicating the presence of sodium as impurity, or if it is dense, fluffy, and of long duration, indicating the presence of sodium ions as a bona fide component of the material being tested. To aid you in making a decision, run a flame test on a sample solution of the original unknown before it has been submitted to any of the procedures. To further aid you, compare the test which you get with that given by a 0.2 M solution of NaCl.

If sodium is present observe the yellow flame through the blue cobalt glass; it may be desirable to have a fellow student thrust the platinum wire into the flame so that you can give all your attention to observing the color. A reddish-violet coloration of short duration, when viewed through the blue glass, proves the presence of potassium. In reporting the results of this test note whether the reddish-violet coloration is a small flash, indicating a trace present as impurity, or is a strong and extensive coloration of reasonable duration, indicating bona fide presence. To aid you in making a decision, perform the test on a sample of the original unknown solution and on a sample of 0.2 M KCl from the reagent shelf.

Precipitation tests for sodium and potassium may, if desired, be made on the solution remaining in the casserole in the manner described in Note 4.

NOTES

1. Ammonium salts sublime when heated and, consequently, make it difficult to detect the color of the sodium and potassium flames. Hence their removal by sublimation.

2. A violet coloration is observed when a green flame is viewed through the blue glass. Since barium, copper, and borate ions give a green coloration to the flame, they must be absent when the flame test for potassium is made.

3. The glowing of the red-hot platinum wire must not be mistaken for a potassium test. Potassium, if present, will give a violet coloration to the flame the moment the wire is introduced.

4. *Precipitation tests for sodium and potassium.* Evaporate the solution on which the flame tests for sodium and potassium have been made to dryness, allow to cool, add 3 or 4 drops of water and swish around for 2 minutes. Transfer to a test tube and, if necessary, centrifuge to give a clear supernatant liquid. Add one drop of this supernatant liquid to 2 drops of zinc uranyl acetate solution (sodium reagent), mix thoroughly, and allow to stand for 5 minutes. A pale yellow crystalline precipitate $(NaZn(UO_2)_3(C_2H_3O_2)_9)$ proves the presence of sodium. Failure of this precipitate to form does not positively prove the absence of sodium.

Transfer the remainder of the clear supernatant liquid to a test tube, add one drop of 5 M $HC_2H_3O_2$ and mix thoroughly. Then add a volume of sodium hexanitrocobaltate(III) solution, $Na_3Co(NO_2)_6$, equal to the volume of the solution in the test tube, mix thoroughly and allow to stand for 5 minutes. A yellow precipitate $(K_2NaCo(NO_2)_6)$ proves the presence of potassium. Absence of a yellow precipitate does not positively prove the absence of potassium.

It should be pointed out that ammonium ions will give a yellow precipitate ($(NH_4)_2NaCo(NO_2)_6$). Therefore ammonium salts must be completely removed by sublimation, otherwise this test is no good.

QUESTIONS

1. Using the scheme of analysis as a guide, write net equations for all reactions that take place in the precipitation and analysis of the barium-magnesium group.

2. How do you account for the fact that there are no oxidation-reduction reactions among the barium-magnesium group equations?

3. Upon what fact or facts are the following based?

(a) The separation of calcium and barium ions from magnesium, potassium, and sodium ions.

(b) The separation of barium ions from calcium ions.

(c) The confirmatory test for ammonium ions.

4. In the precipitation and analysis of the barium-magnesium group:

(a) Why add NH_4Cl and NH_4OH before precipitating $CaCO_3$ and $BaCO_3$?

(b) Why run a flame test on the original solid or solution?

(c) Why add a limited amount of dilute $HC_2H_3O_2$ before precipitating barium as $BaCrO_4$?

(d) Why convert barium and calcium to chlorides before making the flame tests?

(e) Why sublime off NH_4 salts before precipitating barium and calcium as carbonates?

(f) Why precipitate barium and calcium as carbonates from a fairly concentrated solution?

(g) Why add $(NH_4)_2SO_4$ and $(NH_4)_2C_2O_4$ to the decantate from the barium-subgroup precipitation before making the confirmatory test for magnesium?

(h) Why test for ammonium on a sample of the original material?

5. How would you distinguish between the following solids?

(a) NH_4Cl and $NaCl$. (c) $BaCl_2$ and $CaCl_2$.
(b) $MgCO_3$ and K_2CO_3. (d) $(NH_4)_2C_2O_4$ and NH_4Cl.

6. A solution known to contain only cations of the barium-magnesium group gave a white precipitate when treated with NH_4OH and $(NH_4)_2CO_3$ but gave no precipitate when treated with NH_4Cl, NH_4OH, and $(NH_4)_2CO_3$. What conclusions can be drawn?

7. How would you test for:

(a) Mg^{++} in a solution known to contain Ca^{++}?
(b) K^+ in a solution known to contain Ba^{++}?
(c) Ca^{++} in a solution known to contain Ba^{++}?
(d) Ba^{++} in a solution known to contain Mg^{++}?

8. Using the scheme of analysis for the Ba-Mg group as your only guide, select the correct answer in each line. If the scheme does not enable you to make a selection, so state.

(a) Most soluble in water: $BaCO_3$, $CaCO_3$, $MgCO_3$.
(b) Least soluble in water: $Ba(OH)_2$, $Ca(OH)_2$, $Mg(OH)_2$.
(c) Most soluble in water: BaC_2O_4, CaC_2O_4, MgC_2O_4.
(d) Least soluble in water: $Ba(OH)_2$, BaC_2O_4, $BaSO_4$.
(e) Least soluble in water: $Ca(OH)_2$, CaC_2O_4, $CaSO_4$.
(f) Least soluble in water: $BaSO_4$, $CaSO_4$, $MgSO_4$.
(g) Least soluble in water: $BaCO_3$, BaC_2O_4, $BaSO_4$.
(h) Least soluble in water: CaC_2O_4, $CaCO_3$, $CaSO_4$.
(i) Least soluble in water: $BaCrO_4$, $CaCrO_4$, $MgCrO_4$.
(j) Least soluble in water: $MgCO_3$, $MgSO_4$, MgC_2O_4.

9. Using the scheme of analysis for the Ba-Mg group as a guide select, in each of the following pairs, the substance with the smallest solubility product. If the scheme does not enable a selection to be made, so state.

(a) $MgCO_3$ and $BaCO_3$.   (g) $CaCO_3$ and CaC_2O_4.
(b) $BaSO_4$ and BaC_2O_4.   (h) $BaCO_3$ and $CaCO_3$.
(c) CaC_2O_4 and $CaSO_4$.   (i) $Ca(OH)_2$ and $Mg(OH)_2$.
(d) CaC_2O_4 and BaC_2O_4.   (j) MgC_2O_4 and CaC_2O_4.
(e) $CaSO_4$ and $BaSO_4$.   (k) $BaCrO_4$ and $CaCrO_4$.
(f) $BaCO_3$ and $BaSO_4$.   (l) $BaSO_4$ and CaC_2O_4.

10. An unknown was made up of equivalent amounts of two or more of the six solid compounds listed below. On the basis of the following information indicate whether the substance is absent, present, or impossible to determine.

$$Ba(NO_3)_2, \quad CaCl_2, \quad Na_2CrO_4, \quad K_2CO_3, \quad NH_4Cl, \quad MgSO_4.$$

(a) A white residue remained when the solid was mixed with an adequate amount of water.
(b) The mixture of residue and solution was separated.
(c) The residue was completely insoluble in dilute HCl.
(d) A sample of the solution yielded no precipitate when treated with NH_4OH.
(e) A sample of the solution gave an orange-red flame test.

11. A solid unknown contains equivalent amounts of two or more of the six compounds listed below. On the basis of the following information indicate whether a compound is present, absent, or impossible to determine.

$$Ca(NO_3)_2, \quad NaCl, \quad (NH_4)_2SO_4, \quad K_2CO_3, \quad MgC_2O_4, \quad BaCl_2.$$

(a) A white precipitate remained when the solid was dissolved in water. The precipitate and solution were separated.

(b) The precipitate from (a) was completely soluble in dilute HCl with no evolution of a gas.

(c) The solution from (a) yielded no precipitate when treated with NH_4OH.

12. An unknown solid was known to consist of equimolar quantities of two or more of the water-soluble compounds listed below. On the basis of the information given below indicate which of the following compounds are present, which are absent, which are impossible to determine.

$$BaCl_2, \quad Ca(NO_3)_2, \quad MgCl_2, \quad K_2CrO_4, \quad Na_2CO_3,$$

$$(NH_4)_2SO_4 \quad (NH_4)_2C_2O_4.$$

(a) When the solid, contained in a beaker, is treated with enough water to yield a 0.1 M solution of each substance that dissolves there remains in the beaker a white solid and a colorless solution. The white solid, S_1, is separated from the solution, S_2, by filtration.

(b) Solid, S_1, dissolves readily and completely in dilute HCl; there is no evidence of effervescence during the solution process.

(c) When a sample of solution S_2 is treated with 0.1 M $Ba(NO_3)_2$ there is formed a white precipitate which is insoluble in dilute HCl.

(d) A second sample of solution S_2 gave no precipitate when treated with NH_4OH.

13. Suppose you wish to include an additional cation among those to be separated and identified in this course. What properties of this cation and its compounds must you know in order to decide where it will fit in the total scheme of analysis?

Barium-magnesium group report

Ba^{++}

K^+

Barium-magnesium group report

The analysis of alloys

WHEN TWO or more metals are melted together and the resulting liquid is cooled until completely solidified, the solid product is called an *alloy*. Nonmetals are frequently found in alloys, sometimes as impurities, sometimes added intentionally to give certain desirable properties. The procedure outlined in this chapter, however, includes only the separation and identification of the metallic constituents of an alloy.

■ ■ ■ Procedure 28: Dissolving an alloy

Place a quantity of the alloy about $\frac{1}{10}$ the volume of a drop of water in a casserole. (See Note 1.) Add 10 drops of 16 M HNO$_3$ and 10 drops of 12 M HCl, and warm gently under a hood. If gentle heating does not cause a reaction to take place, the liquid should be boiled. Replenish the acids in the ratio of 1 drop of 16 M HNO$_3$ to 1 drop of 12 M HCl as fast as the liquid boils away, continuing the boiling until the alloy is completely dissolved or disintegrated. If the alloy dissolves but a finely divided solid, either crystalline or curdy and white, remains in the bottom of the casserole add water drop by drop with continued careful heating until the solid either is completely dissolved or becomes curdy and white. If the solid is completely dissolved the absence of silver is proved; in that case follow the directions given in (A). If a white, curdy precipitate remains in the casserole the presence of silver is indicated; in that case follow the directions given in (B).

(A) Add 12 M HCl, drop by drop, with continued boiling, until no more brown fumes of NO_2 are given off; then evaporate the solution to a volume of about 10 drops; if crystalline solid begins to form before the volume has been reduced to 10 drops discontinue the evaporation and add water, drop by drop with heating, until the solid is all dissolved; analyze 6 drops of this solution as directed in Procedure 5 (A), page 88.

(B) If a white, curdy precipitate remains after the alloy has dissolved, transfer the contents of the casserole to a test tube, centrifuge at once, and decant immediately into a casserole. Wash the precipitate twice with 10-drop portions of 2 M HCl and analyze it as directed in Procedure 2 on page 79. Treat the decantate in the casserole as directed in (A), above.

NOTES

1. Commercial alloys are usually found in the form of castings, machined articles, instrument parts, rods, plates, bolts, wire, and so on. When such an alloy is to be analyzed a small amount is filed off or a hole is drilled in the specimen, or a sample is machined on a lathe or milling machine and the filings, drillings, borings, turnings, or millings thus obtained are subjected to analysis. The alloys to be analyzed in this course will usually be issued in the form of such filings, drillings, borings, turnings, and millings. Some of the alloys are authentic commercial specimens; some are prepared solely for the purpose of giving the student experience in alloy analysis.

2. Dissolving an alloy is often a slow process requiring long boiling and numerous acid replenishings. If the alloy appears to be partly or wholly insoluble, the instructor should be consulted.

3. The mixture of HCl and HNO_3 used for dissolving the alloy is known as *aqua regia*. Its powerful solvent effect is due to the combined action of the NO_3^- ions and Cl^- ions.

The following net equations represent the reactions that are believed to take place when the metals that constitute an alloy are dissolved.

(a) *Silver forms insoluble AgCl.*

$$3\,Ag + NO_3^- + 3\,Cl^- + 4\,H^+ = 3\,\textbf{AgCl} + NO + 2\,H_2O.$$

(b) *Metals of periodic groups Ia and IIa form simple cations.*

$$3\,Ca + 2\,NO_3^- + 8\,H^+ = 3\,Ca^{++} + 2\,NO + 4\,H_2O.$$

(c) *Arsenic forms arsenic acid.*

$$3\,As + 5\,NO_3^- + 5\,H^+ + 2\,H_2O = 3\,H_3AsO_4 + 5\,NO.$$

(d) *All other metals probably form complex chloro ions.*

$$3\,Pb + 2\,NO_3^- + 12\,Cl^- + 8\,H^+ = 3\,PbCl_4^{--} + 2\,NO + 4\,H_2O.$$

The composition of the complex chloro ion formed by a specific cation generally will vary with the concentration of the Cl^- ions. For example, with increasing concentration of Cl^- ions the composition of the iron (III) complex will change from $FeCl_4^-$ to $FeCl_5^{--}$ to $FeCl_6^{---}$; it is probable that all three of these ions exist in equilibrium with each other and it is not a simple matter to decide which one predominates.

The complex chloro ion exists in equilibrium with the cation and chloride ions and is largely dissociated into these simple ions when the solution is diluted with water.

$$CuCl_4^{--} \rightleftharpoons Cu^{++} + 4\,Cl^-.$$

Therefore, the solution formed by dissolving an alloy in aqua regia can, for all practical purposes, be looked upon as a solution of the simple cations of all the metals; arsenic is present as arsenic acid.

4. Silver chloride is insoluble, and will accordingly be present in the casserole as a white curdy residue. Lead chloride is only sparingly soluble, and unless present in very small amounts, will be found in the casserole as a white crystalline precipitate.

5. Aqua regia, being a powerful oxidizing agent, will oxidize mercury to its high valence. Consequently, no Hg_2Cl_2 will precipitate, even though mercury is present in the alloy. Tin, iron, and arsenic, like mercury, will be converted to their high oxidation states.

6. Hot concentrated HNO_3, alone, will react with all the metals that are considered in this course. Antimony and tin are converted to white, insoluble Sb_2O_5 and SnO_2, respectively, whereas arsenic forms soluble arsenic acid, H_3AsO_4. The other metals are all converted to soluble nitrates.

$$2\,Sb + 10\,NO_3^- + 10\,H^+ = Sb_2O_5 + 10\,NO_2 + 5\,H_2O.$$

$$As + 5\,NO_3^- + 5\,H^+ = H_3AsO_4 + 5\,NO_2 + H_2O.$$

$$Cu + 2\,NO_3^- + 4\,H^+ = Cu^{++} + 2\,NO_2 + 2\,H_2O.$$

Less concentrated HNO_3 will yield NO rather than NO_2.

SnO_2 and Sb_2O_5 will dissolve in HCl to form $SnCl_6^{--}$ and $SbCl_4^-$, respectively.

$$Sb_2O_5 + 10\,H^+ + 12\,Cl^- = 2\,SbCl_4^- + 2\,Cl_2 + 5\,H_2O.$$

The $SnCl_6^{--}$ and $SbCl_4^-$ ions are in equilibrium with Sn^{++++} and Sb^{+++} ions.

$$SnCl_6^{--} \rightleftharpoons Sn^{++++} + 6\,Cl^-.$$

From the above facts it is obvious that an alloy can be analyzed by a plan in which concentrated HNO_3 alone serves as the initial solvent. The plan can be represented, schematically, as follows:

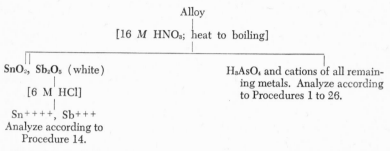

Alloy

[16 M HNO_3; heat to boiling]

SnO_2, Sb_2O_5 (white)

[6 M HCl]

Sn^{++++}, Sb^{+++}
Analyze according to
Procedure 14.

H_3AsO_4 and cations of all remaining metals. Analyze according to Procedures 1 to 26.

7. Sodium, potassium, calcium, and barium are seldom found in commercial alloys. Alloys containing high concentrations of these metals react with water to evolve hydrogen.

$$2\,Na + 2\,H_2O = 2\,Na^+ + 2\,OH^- + H_2.$$

Since ammonium exists only as a radical, there obviously is no such thing as a stable ammonium alloy.

8. The color of the solution obtained when an alloy is dissolved in aqua regia may give valuable clues as to the metals present. The following metals form colored chloride solutions: $CuCl_2$, green; $FeCl_3$, yellowish brown; $CrCl_3$, green; $NiCl_2$, green; $CoCl_2$, reddish pink or blue; $MnCl_2$, faint pink.

9. It will be noted, in the equations given in Notes 3, 6, and 7, that the metals in an alloy react exactly as if they were separate pure metals. These reactions might lead to the conclusion that an alloy is simply a mixture of metals. Some alloys are, in fact, very intimate mixtures. In a great many alloys, however, the component metals exist as compounds. In general it may be stated that most alloys are very complex in structure.

QUESTIONS

1. Show by means of outlines the complete analysis of alloys containing the following metals:

(a) Sn, Ag, Cu, Fe, Zn, Mg.
(b) Pb, Hg, Bi, Mn, Al.
(c) As, Sb, Cd, Ni, Cr.

2. Show, by appropriate equations, what happens when each of the following is dissolved in aqua regia: mercury, iron, copper, tin, arsenic, antimony, chromium, silver.

3. Show, by appropriate equations, what happens when each of the following is treated with hot concentrated HNO_3: arsenic, antimony, tin, mercury, lead, silver, iron, copper.

4. Using the simplest chemical method possible, how would you distinguish between the following metals?

(a) Tin and zinc.   (e) Lead and bismuth.
(b) Nickel and silver.   (f) Magnesium and zinc.
(c) Iron and antimony.   (g) Chromium and nickel.
(d) Arsenic and antimony.   (h) Calcium and magnesium.

5. Using the simplest method possible, how would you determine whether an alloy is brass (Cu—Zn) or bronze (Cu—Sn)?

6. An alloy showed the following behavior:

(a) It was attacked by HNO_3 to give a colorless supernatant liquid and a finely divided white residue. This residue was soluble in HCl.

(b) It was attacked by aqua regia to give a colorless solution and a white, curdy residue.

(c) It was not acted upon by water.

What conclusions can be drawn regarding its composition?

7. An alloy was found to be completely dissolved (a) by cold moderately concentrated HNO_3, (b) by cold dilute HCl, and (c) by cold dilute H_2SO_4. In each case it gave a colorless solution with no precipitate. What conclusions can be drawn regarding its composition?

8. (a) An alloy which is known to contain two or more of the eight elements listed below, but no others, is completely disintegrated (dissolved) by HNO_3 but yields a white precipitate. The precipitate and solution are separated.

Ag,   Mg,   As,   Sn,   Pb,   Cu,   Sb,   Ni.

(b) The precipitate from (a) dissolves completely in HCl but a white precipitate forms when this solution is diluted with water.

(c) The solution from (a) is green in color but changes to blue upon addition of H_2O.

(d) A precipitate is formed when HCl is added to the solution from (a); none of this precipitate dissolves when heated.

(e) The solution from (d) yields a precipitate when H_2S is added. This precipitate is partially soluble in $(NH_4)_2S$.

Indicate the elements that are present, absent and impossible to determine.

Alloy report

Alloy report

CHAPTER EIGHT

Analysis of salts and salt mixtures

TO THE STUDENT: Up to this point you have learned how to separate and identify the cations (metallic ions) and you have applied this information to the analysis of four group unknowns and an alloy. The next unknown that you will analyze will be a single salt or a mixture of salts. To analyze a salt you must identify the anions (acid radicals) as well as the cations. Consequently, before you can proceed with the analysis of your first salt or salt mixture you must learn how the anions are identified. To help familiarize you with anion identification you will perform Experiments 1, 2, 3, and 4 as described on pages 175, 177, 178, and 179. Before performing these experiments the **Summary of Steps** in the Analysis of Salts and Mixtures of Salts on page 180 should be studied.

When the four experiments have been completed, and before you start the analysis of your first salt, study carefully the **steps in the analysis** as outlined and discussed on pages 182 to 198. Once you have gained a clear picture of how the analysis of a salt is to be carried out and how the information supplied by each test can contribute to the final solution the actual operation will be relatively easy.

Experiment 1: Treatment of a solid salt of each anion with H_2SO_4. On the reagent shelf will be found solid salts of each of the 13 acids for which tests are to be made. Treat a pinch of each solid salt with concentrated sulfuric acid as directed in Procedure 33, page 192. Note exactly what happens, record your observations in the table below, and compare these observations with those given on page 191. Write the equations for the reactions that take place. Have the results of this experiment approved by your instructor before proceeding with the next experiment.

Salt	Observations	Equations
$NaNO_3$		
$NaCl$		
$NaBr$		
NaI		
ZnS		
Na_2CO_3		
Na_2SO_3		
Na_2CrO_4		
Na_2SO_4		
$NaBO_2$		
Na_3PO_4		
Na_3AsO_4		
$NaC_2H_3O_2$		

Experiment 2: Treatment of a solution of the anions with $AgNO_3$.

(A) Place 3–4 drops of a 0.2 M solution of the sodium salt of each of the anions, respectively, in 13 test tubes. Add a drop or two of 0.2 M $AgNO_3$ to each. Note the colors of the precipitates formed. Centrifuge and decant, saving the precipitate for Part (B). In the following spaces write the net equations for the formation of the precipitates obtained with $AgNO_3$. Indicate the color of each precipitate. (See Procedure 34, page 194.)

$C_2H_3O_2^-$ _____

NO_3^- _____

Cl^- _____

Br^- _____

I^- _____

S^{--} _____

CO_3^{--} _____

SO_3^{--} _____

CrO_4^{--} _____

BO_2^- _____

PO_4^{---} _____

AsO_4^{---} _____

SO_4^{--} _____

(B) Attempt to dissolve each of the precipitates obtained in (A) in 5–6 drops of 3 M HNO_3. In the spaces below write net equations for those cases in which the silver salts are *dissolved* by 3 M HNO_3. Indicate gases evolved by an upward arrow.

_____

_____

_____

_____

_____

_____

_____

List the silver salts *not dissolved* by dilute HNO_3:

_____

Taking into account the results obtained in 2(A) and 2(B), list the anions which will react with $AgNO_3$ to form precipitates in dilute nitric acid

solution. _____
Have the results of this experiment approved by your instructor before
going on with the next experiment.

Experiment 3: Treatment of a solution of the anions with BaCl₂.

(A) Place 3–4 drops of a 0.2 M solution of the sodium salt of each of
the anions, respectively, in 13 test tubes. Make each solution alkaline with
a drop of 5 M NH_4OH and then add a drop or two of 0.2 M $BaCl_2$ to
each. Note the colors of all precipitates formed. Centrifuge, decant, and
wash twice with cold water. Save each precipitate for Part (B).

In the following spaces write the net equations for the formation of the
precipitates obtained with $BaCl_2$ in alkaline (NH_4OH) solution. Indicate the color of each precipitate. (See Procedure 35, page 196.)

$C_2H_3O_2^-$ _____

NO_3^- _____

Cl^- _____

Br^- _____

I^- _____

S^{--} _____

CO_3^{--} _____

SO_3^{--} _____

CrO_4^{--} _____

BO_2^- _____

PO_4^{---} _____

AsO_4^{---} _____

SO_4^{--} _____

(B) Attempt to dissolve each of the precipitates from (A) in 4–5 drops
of 2 M HCl.

In the spaces below, write net equations for those cases in which the
barium salts are dissolved by dilute HCl. Note in which cases gases are
evolved.

_____

_____

_____

_____

_____

_____

List the barium salts that are not dissolved by dilute HCl. _____

_____

List the anions which will react with Ba++ to form precipitates in alkaline solution. _____

_____

Have the results of this experiment approved by your instructor before proceeding with the next experiment.

Experiment 4: The specific tests for the anions. Use solutions of the sodium salts of each of the 13 acids or a small amount of a solid salt of each of these acids. Carry out a specific test for each anion as directed in Procedures 36 to 48.

Note exactly what happens in each test and compare your observations with those noted in each procedure. Have each test observed and approved by your instructor. In the spaces below, write the net equations for the reactions that take place. Have these equations approved by your instructor before proceeding with the analysis of your first salt or mixture of salts.

$AsO_4{}^{---}$ _____

_____

$PO_4{}^{---}$ _____

_____

$BO_2{}^-$ or $BO_3{}^{---}$ _____

_____

$CrO_4{}^{--}$ _____

_____

$SO_4{}^{--}$ _____

_____

$SO_3{}^{--}$ _____

_____

$CO_3{}^{--}$ _____

_____

S^{--} _____

_____

I^- _____

_____

Br^- _____

_____

Cl^- _____

_____

NO_3^- _____

_____

$C_2H_3O_2^-$ _____

_____

Summary of Steps

The following summary gives the steps that will be followed and the tests that will be made in the analysis of salts and salt mixtures.

I. Examine the solid and note its distinctive and significant physical properties. (See Procedure 29, page 182.)

II. Put the solid into solution. (See Procedure 30, page 183 and the accompanying notes.) Be sure to note any observable reaction that takes place when the solid dissolves. If the solid is soluble in water and the resulting solution has a characteristic color, indicating the presence of certain cations or anions, make all possible eliminations of cations and anions. (See Solubility Rules, page 188.)

III. Determine what cations are present. This may be done either before or after the anion analysis, or simultaneously with it. (See Procedure 31, page 189.)

A. *Observe the color of the solution.* A colorless (water-clear) solution cannot contain Cu^{++}, Ni^{++}, Co^{++}, Cr^{+++}, Fe^{+++}, Fe^{++}, or Mn^{++} ions.

B. *Determine whether or not any cations can be eliminated on the basis of the solubility in water and the results of the anion analysis.* Thus, if a salt mixture is soluble in water and has been shown to contain carbonate ion, the only cations that can possibly be present are Na^+, K^+, NH_4^+. A water solution of a chromate can contain only Na^+, K^+, NH_4^+, and Mg^{++}. (See Solubility Rules, page 188.)

C. *Flame test.* (See Note 2, Procedure 24, page 158.)

D. *Blanket tests, with* Na_2CO_3, *NaOH, and* NH_4OH, *may be made if the salt is soluble in water.* (See Procedure 31, page 189.)

E. *Carry out a systematic cation analysis,* as outlined in Procedures 1 through 27, for the cations not eliminated by A, B, C and D.

IV. Determine what anions are present. This may be done either before or after the cation analysis, or simultaneously with it. (See Procedure 32, page 190.)

A. *Observe the color of the solution.* If the salt is soluble in water, and the color of the solution indicates the presence of one or more of the cations that form colored solutions, certain anions, referred to in Solubility Rules 5 and 6, can be eliminated. The colors of CrO_4^{--} and $Cr_2O_7^{--}$ ions are very distinctive; therefore, a colorless solution cannot contain these anions.

B. *Determine whether or not any anions can be eliminated on the basis of the results of the cation analysis.* If no arsenic or chromium was found in the cation analysis, arsenates and chromates cannot be present. If a salt is soluble in water and the cation analysis shows that it contains lead ion, the only anions that can be present are nitrate and acetate.

C. *Treat the solid salt with concentrated H_2SO_4.* (See Procedure 33, page 192 and the accompanying notes.)

D. *Treat a solution of the salt with silver nitrate.* (See Procedure 34, page 194 and the accompanying notes.)

E. *Treat a solution of the salt with barium chloride.* (See Procedure 35, page 196 and the accompanying notes.)

F. *Perform specific tests for the anions that have not been definitely eliminated or verified as present* by A, B, C, D, and E. The specific tests are given in the following procedures:

Arsenate,	Procedure 36, page 198.	Sulfide,	Procedure 43, page 204.
Phosphate,	Procedure 37, page 200.	Iodide,	Procedure 44, page 204.
Borate,	Procedure 38, page 201.	Bromide,	Procedure 45, page 205.
Chromate,	Procedure 39, page 201.	Chloride,	Procedure 46, page 206.
Sulfate,	Procedure 40, page 202.	Nitrate,	Procedure 47, page 207.
Sulfite,	Procedure 41, page 203.	Acetate,	Procedure 48, page 208.
Carbonate,	Procedure 42, page 203.		

The results of the analysis of salts and salt mixtures will be reported on the blanks on pages 221 to 227 in the manner illustrated on page 220.

Although the steps in the analysis of a salt are discussed, in the next few pages, in the order in which they are listed in the above summary it should be emphasized that this exact order need not always be followed when a particular salt or salt mixture is analyzed. For example, if a mixture is soluble in water it usually is advantageous to run the anion analysis before the cation analysis. On the other hand, if the mixture is insoluble in water it is usually best to do the cation analysis first. In many instances it will be a good idea to run the anion analysis and cation analysis simultaneously. In most cases it is desirable to make the treatment of the solid with concentrated sulfuric acid (Procedure 33, page 192) one of the first steps in the analysis. A flame test applied to a sample of the original solid in the manner directed in Note 2 of Procedure 24, page 158, is quickly and easily carried out and may give valuable information. If the salt is found to be soluble in water the *blanket tests* outlined in Procedure 31 on page 189 and the *preliminary tests* with $AgNO_3$ and $BaCl_2$ (Procedures 34 and 35, pages 194 and 196) should be the next steps. The wise analyst will be guided from one step to another by the behavior of the particular material being analyzed.

Steps in the Analysis

I. Examine the solid and note its distinctive and significant physical properties.

Certain metals, such as copper, nickel, manganese, chromium, cobalt, and iron form colored salts. Others form white salts. Certain anions, such as chromates, dichromates, and permanganates, have characteristic colors. It is important, therefore, to note the color of the solid, since it may give indications of the presence of one or more of the ions listed above.

The more common characteristic colors are:

CrO_4^{--}, yellow.　　　　　　　　Cr^{+++}, green to bluish grey to
$Cr_2O_7^{--}$, orange red.　　　　　　　 black.
MnO_4^-, violet-purple.　　　　　　 Cu^{++}, blue to green to brown.
Ni^{++}, green.　　　　　　　　　　Co^{++}, wine red to blue.
Fe^{+++}, reddish brown to　　　　　 Mn^{++}, pink to tan.
　yellow.　　　　　　　　　　　　Fe^{++}, grayish green.

■ ■ ■ Procedure 29: Physical examination of the sample

Examine the unknown carefully, noting the color or colors, and whether the material is crystalline or noncrystalline, homogeneous or heterogeneous. Record your observations on a report blank on pages 221–227.

NOTES

1. The information gained by the examination of the solid may not, by itself, be of much value in the analysis of a sample. However, when combined with the entire body of information, it may prove to be very valuable. The fact that a solid is green is of itself of some value; when combined with the fact that the solid is soluble in water, the fact of its green color becomes, as will be pointed out later, extremely valuable.

2. The fact that the sample is white does not prove the absence of all ions that usually form colored salts. Anhydrous copper sulfate is white, and so is ferric phosphate. The salts with characteristic colors, moreover, may be present in such small amounts as to be covered up by an excess of other salts.

II. Put the solid into solution.

Before a solid can be analyzed, it must be dissolved. The choice of solvent is made by testing the solubility of a portion of the solid in various solvents. Water is the most desirable solvent; the water solution can be used for all procedures except those which specifically call for the use of some of the solid. If the solid is insoluble in water, two separate solutions should be prepared, one for cation analysis, the other for anion analysis. The solution for cation analysis should be prepared by dissolving the solid in hydrochloric acid. The solution for anion analysis should be prepared by boiling with sodium carbonate.

▪ ▪ ▪ Procedure 30: Dissolving the solid

(A) Test a bit of the solid with 20 drops of water, first cold, then hot, to see if it will dissolve. If it is completely dissolved, prepare a stock solution by dissolving a quantity the volume of two drops of water in 5 ml. of water and use this solution for cation analysis, preliminary tests for anions, and specific tests for anions. Note the color of the solution.

(B) If the solid is not soluble in water, prepare a solution for cation analysis by dissolving in HCl or HNO_3, or, if necessary, in aqua regia (see Procedure 28). First try 6 M HCl, then 12 M HCl, followed by dilution with an equal volume of hot water; then try 16 M HNO_3, followed by dilution with water; finally try aqua regia (see Note 1).

(C) If the solid is not soluble in water prepare a solution for anion analysis as follows (see Notes 11 and 12). Place in a casserole a quantity of the solid the volume of two drops of water; then add 5 ml. of a saturated solution of Na_2CO_3 and boil gently for two minutes. Transfer to test tubes, centrifuge, and decant, discarding the precipitate (carbonates of metals) (see Note 1). A part of this decantate can be saved for making specific tests for all anions except carbonates. Transfer the remainder of the decantate to a casserole, make acidic with 3 M HNO_3, and boil gently until all CO_2 has been driven off. This solution can be used for the group tests with $AgNO_3$ and $BaCl_2$ and for the specific tests for all anions except nitrate, sulfide, sulfite, sulfate, and carbonate.

NOTES

1. If the solid is insoluble in aqua regia it will be necessary to prepare a solution for cation analysis by boiling with sodium carbonate as directed in Procedure 30(C). The metals will be precipitated as carbonates. The precipitate of the metal carbonates must therefore be saved, washed three times with hot water, and then dissolved in 6 M HCl. This series of steps gives a solution of metal chlorides.

2. The reason why a solution of a water-insoluble substance which is to be used in making the anion group tests is prepared by boiling with sodium carbonate rather than by dissolving in HNO_3 or HCl, is that all cations except sodium, potassium, and ammonium must be removed before the group test with barium chloride (Procedure 35) can be made. To illustrate the necessity of removing these metals by precipitation with Na_2CO_3 suppose that the unknown contains $Ca_3(PO_4)_2$, and suppose it is dissolved in dilute HNO_3. The solution will then contain Ca^{++} ions and PO_4^{---} ions. In making the group test with $BaCl_2$ the acid solution must first be made alkaline with NH_4OH. As soon as this is done, $Ca_3(PO_4)_2$ precipitates; there will then be no phosphate ions left in solution, and the group test with $BaCl_2$ will be negative.

If instead of being dissolved in dilute HNO_3 the above unknown is boiled with Na_2CO_3, the $Ca_3(PO_4)_2$ will react as indicated in the following equation.

$$Ca_3(PO_4)_2 + 3\,CO_3^{--} = 3\,CaCO_3 + 2\,PO_4^{---}.$$

Most of the $Ca_3(PO_4)_2$ is converted into insoluble $CaCO_3$. On centrifuging and decanting, all the calcium will be found in the precipitate as $CaCO_3$ and $Ca_3(PO_4)_2$, whereas most of the phosphate will be present in the decantate as the phosphate ion. When the decantate is now made alkaline with NH_4OH, no precipitate will form, since all the calcium ions have been removed. On addition of $BaCl_2$, a white precipitate of $Ba_3(PO_4)_2$ will form.

Insoluble salts of other metals will behave like $Ca_3(PO_4)_2$.

$$2\,AgCl + CO_3^{--} = Ag_2CO_3 + 2\,Cl^-.$$

(See page 57 for the detailed reactions that take place in these solution processes.)

The solution prepared by boiling a water-insoluble salt with sodium carbonate contains a large amount of carbonate ion added as Na_2CO_3 in preparing this solution. These CO_3^{--} ions must be destroyed, otherwise they will react with the Ba^{++} ions when the group test with $BaCl_2$ is made.

$$Ba^{++} + CO_3^{--} = BaCO_3.$$

The carbonate ions are removed by adding HNO_3 and boiling.

$$CO_3^{--} + 2\,H^+ = H_2O + CO_2.$$

This addition of HNO_3 results in the following complications when the tests for certain of the anions are made.

(a) Any carbonate present in the original unknown will be removed as CO_2 by the boiling with HNO_3.

(b) Sulfites, if present, will to some extent be either removed as SO_2 or oxidized.

$$SO_3^{--} + 2\,H^+ = H_2O + SO_2,$$

$$3\,SO_3^{--} + 2\,NO_3^- + 2\,H^+ = 3\,SO_4^{--} + 2\,NO + H_2O.$$

(c) Sulfides will to some extent either be driven off as H_2S or oxidized to sulfur.

$$S^{--} + 2\,H^+ = H_2S,$$

$$3\,S^{--} + 2\,NO_3^- + 8\,H^+ = 3\,S + 2\,NO + 4\,H_2O.$$

Therefore, the solution prepared by boiling with Na_2CO_3 followed by digestion with HNO_3 will not give dependable tests for carbonates, sulfites, sulfates, or sulfides. Furthermore, since HNO_3 was used in its preparation, this solution cannot be used in testing for nitrates.

3. Sulfides will yield a precipitate of sulfur when dissolved in nitric acid or aqua regia. This sulfur should be discarded.

$$CuS + 2\,NO_3^- + 4\,H^+ = Cu^{++} + S + 2\,NO_2 + 4\,H_2O.$$

4. The reactions that take place when a solid is dissolved in acid may give definite information about the presence or absence of certain ions. Carbonates, sulfites, and some sulfides give off CO_2, SO_2 and H_2S gas, respectively. Chromates change in color from yellow to orange-red. When effervescence occurs, the odor of the gas evolved often gives valuable clues about the anions present.

5. The evolution of chlorine gas when a solid is dissolved in concentrated HCl shows the presence of some oxidizing agent such as a nitrate, a chromate, a dioxide, or a peroxide.

$$2\,CrO_4^{--} + 6\,Cl^- + 16\,H^+ = 2\,Cr^{+++} + 3\,Cl_2 + 8\,H_2O.$$

$$MnO_2 + 2\,Cl^- + 4\,H^+ = Mn^{++} + Cl_2 + 2\,H_2O.$$

6. The evolution of I_2, Br_2, or Cl_2 when a substance is dissolved in concentrated HNO_3 shows the presence of iodides, bromides, or chlorides. (See Note 5.)

$$6\,I^- + 2\,NO_3^- + 8\,H^+ = 2\,NO + 4\,H_2O + 3\,I_2 \text{ (violet gas)}.$$

7. The evolution of brown fumes of NO_2 when a substance is dissolved in HNO_3 shows the presence of reducing agents such as sulfides, sulfites, iodides, or bromides. (See Notes 3 and 6.)

$$ZnSO_3 + 2\,NO_3^- + 2\,H^+ = Zn^{++} + SO_4^{--} + 2\,NO_2 + H_2O.$$

If a solid mixture containing a nitrate and either a chloride, bromide, iodide, sulfide, or sulfite is treated with concentrated H_2SO_4, brown fumes of NO_2 will be noted for the reason given above and in Note 6. Likewise, if a solid mixture of a halide and a chromate, dioxide, or peroxide is treated with concentrated H_2SO_4, free halogen will be formed as discussed in Note 5.

8. Many chlorides such as NaCl and $BaCl_2$, though soluble in water, are not dissolved by concentrated HCl. Hence the directions to dilute the solution with water after heating with hot concentrated acids.

9. Bismuth and antimony salts hydrolyze strongly in water to give the insoluble white basic salts:

$$Bi^{+++} + Cl^- + H_2O \rightleftharpoons BiOCl + 2\,H^+,$$

$$Sb^{+++} + Cl^- + H_2O \rightleftharpoons SbOCl + 2\,H^+.$$

The basic salts are readily dissolved by excess of acids.

10. Concentrated HNO_3, because of its powerful oxidizing property, dissolves many metallic sulfides that are unattacked by HCl. Sulfur is usually liberated (see Note 3).

11. It will not always be necessary or wise to prepare a solution of a water-insoluble mixture for anion analysis as directed in Procedure 30 (C). Suppose, for instance, that the treatment with concentrated sulfuric acid (Procedure 33) shows the absence of all anions except SO_4^{--}, PO_4^{---}, AsO_4^{---}, and BO_2^-, whereas the cation analysis shows the absence of AsO_4^{---}. Specific tests for SO_4^{--}, PO_4^{---}, and BO_2^- can then be carried out on the solid or on solutions prepared with dilute HNO_3 according to Procedure 30(B) and the group tests with $AgNO_3$ and $BaCl_2$ (Procedures 34 and 35) can be omitted entirely. The same reasoning will

hold if the sulfuric acid treatment (Procedure 33) shows the absence of all anions except CO_3^{--}, SO_4^{--}, PO_4^{---}, AsO_4^{---}, and BO_2^-.

12. A solution for use in anion analysis can be prepared by dissolving the solid mixture in nitric acid. Its use will involve the following limitations:

(a) When such a solution is treated with $AgNO_3$ in Procedure 34 the only insoluble silver salts that can precipitate are AgCl, AgBr, AgI and Ag_2S. All other silver salts are soluble in HNO_3.

(b) When such a solution is treated with $BaCl_2$ in Procedure 35 it must not first be made alkaline with NH_4OH. The only insoluble barium salt that can then precipitate is $BaSO_4$; all other barium salts are soluble in HNO_3.

Obviously, then, if such a nitric acid solution is used, SO_3^{--}, CO_3^{--}, PO_4^{---}, AsO_4^{---}, and BO_2^- must be eliminated or verified either by cation analysis, by sulfuric acid treatment (Procedure 33), or by specific tests. Since SO_3^{--} and CO_3^{--} are either eliminated or indicated by sulfuric acid treatment and AsO_4^{---} will be detected in the cation analysis, the only anions that will always require elimination or detection by specific tests are PO_4^{---} and BO_2^-.

13. Some solids must be fused with sodium carbonate in order to prepare a solution for analysis. Directions for carrying out such a fusion are given in the references listed at the end of Chapter 2.

III. Determine what cations are present.

After the sample to be analyzed has been dissolved in an appropriate solvent, the next step could be to go through a complete cation analysis according to Procedures 1–27 and follow it with a complete anion analysis according to Procedures 32–48. In many analyses that is exactly what is done. In some instances, however, observations of specific behavior may make it possible to eliminate certain cations or anions and thereby modify and shorten the over-all procedure.

Elimination of Anions and Cations on the Basis of Solubility

To illustrate such elimination suppose a salt mixture dissolves readily and completely in cold water to give a green solution. A green solution means the presence of either copper, nickel, iron(II) or chromium. The mixture cannot, therefore, contain carbonates, sulfites, phosphates, borates, chromates, arsenates or sulfides, since these anions all form insoluble salts with copper, nickel, and chromium. The preliminary test for anions involving treatment of the solution with $BaCl_2$ can be omitted, since all but one of the anions detected by this test are already eliminated.

In another illustration a salt mixture dissolves in water to give a yellow solution. This solution turns orange when HCl is added in the first step in Procedure 1. Such behavior clearly indicates the presence of a chromate. Since the chromates of all metals except magnesium, sodium, potassium, and ammonium are insoluble, there is no need to test for any cations except these four.

In another case a salt mixture dissolves readily and completely in cold water to give a water-clear solution. When HCl is added in the first step in Procedure 1, vigorous effervescence takes place, a colorless, odorless gas being evolved. Such behavior clearly indicates the presence of carbonate; and since sodium, potassium, and ammonium alone form soluble carbonates, they are the only cations that can be present.

In still another case a student first does the anion analysis on a water-soluble mixture and finds nitrates, chlorides, and phosphates. Sodium, potassium, and ammonium are the only cations whose nitrates, chlorides, and phosphates are all soluble. A complete cation analysis is therefore unnecessary in this case.

Eliminations such as those cited above require a knowledge of the solubilities of the salts of the various acids. The rules governing the solubility of the common salts are given below.

The Solubility Rules

1. The nitrates, chlorates, and acetates of all metals are soluble in water. Silver acetate is sparingly soluble.

2. All sodium, potassium, and ammonium salts are soluble in water.

3. The chlorides, bromides, and iodides of all metals except lead, silver, and mercury(I) are soluble in water. HgI_2 is insoluble in water. $PbCl_2$, $PbBr_2$, and PbI_2 are soluble in hot water. The water-insoluble chlorides, bromides, and iodides are also insoluble in dilute acids.

4. The sulfates of all metals except lead, mercury(I), barium, and calcium are soluble in water. Silver sulfate is slightly soluble. The water-insoluble sulfates are also insoluble in dilute acids.

5. The carbonates, phosphates, borates, sulfites, chromates, and arsenates of all metals except sodium, potassium, and ammonium are insoluble in water but soluble in dilute acids. $MgCrO_4$ is soluble in water; $MgSO_3$ is very slightly soluble in water.

6. The sulfides of all metals except barium, calcium, magnesium, sodium, potassium, and ammonium are insoluble in water.

7. The hydroxides of sodium, potassium, and ammonium are very soluble in water. The hydroxides of calcium and barium are moderately soluble. The oxides and hydroxides of all other metals are insoluble.

NOTES

1. Bismuth, antimony and tin salts hydrolyze in water to give the basic salts. These basic salts are soluble in dilute acids but are not soluble in water.

2. Solutions of iron(III), lead, tin, mercury(II), copper, and aluminum salts, when boiled, may hydrolyze to give precipitates of the hydroxides or basic salts of these metals.

▪ ▪ ▪ Procedure 31: Analysis for cations

Proceed as follows:

1. Make a list of those cations which can be definitely eliminated or verified on the basis of the solubility of the solid, the color of the solution, and the anion analysis (if the anion analysis has been carried out).

2. Carry out a flame test as directed in Note 2, Procedure 24, page 158.

3. If the salt is soluble in water carry out the following blanket tests:

(a) To a few drops of the water solution add Na_2CO_3 solution until it reacts basic. If no precipitate forms, all cations except Na^+, K^+ and NH_4^+ are absent. Na_3PO_4 may be substituted for Na_2CO_3 if the solution is not too acidic (see Solubility Rule 5).

(b) To a few drops of the water solution add 8 M NaOH until distinctly alkaline and stir for 1 minute. The absence of a precipitate eliminates all cations except Na^+, K^+, NH_4^+, Ba^{++}, Ca^{++}, Zn^{++}, Cr^{+++}, Al^{+++}, Pb^{++}, Sn^{++}, Sn^{++++}, Sb^{+++}, and Mg^{++}.

(c) To a few drops of the water solution add 15 M NH_4OH until distinctly alkaline and stir for 1 minute. The absence of a precipitate eliminates all cations except Na^+, K^+, NH_4^+, Ag^+, Ba^{++}, Ca^{++}, Cu^{++}, Cd^{++}, Zn^{++}, Ni^{++}, Co^{++}, and Mg^{++}.

4. Carry out a cation analysis (Procedures 1 to 27) for those cations not eliminated in Steps 1, 2, and 3. Use a solution prepared according to Procedure 30(A) or 30(B), page 183.

NOTE

1. If a solution is prepared in Procedure 30(B) by dissolving the solid in cold HCl, then Ag^+, Hg_2^{++}, and Pb^{++} must be absent, since they would form insoluble chlorides. The cation analysis will then start with Procedure 5.

IV. Determine what anions are present.

Detection of the cations was accomplished by a very logical sequence of procedures involving, first, *separation* and, second, *identification*. Detection of the anions does not proceed in quite the same way; that is, it does not consist of a methodical sequence of separations and identifications. Instead it proceeds as follows: First an effort is made to eliminate or verify certain anions on the basis of the color and solubility of the sample and the results of the cation analysis. Then the material being analyzed is submitted to a series of so-called "preliminary tests."

As a result of these observations and tests, certain of the anions may be shown definitely to be present or absent, thereby paring down the number of possibilities from thirteen to some lesser number. Next, specific tests are carried out for those anions not definitely eliminated in the preliminary tests and observations. Although this sequence of preliminary tests and specific tests is not quite as well ordered as the procedures for cation analysis, it is very logical and makes possible a rapid and systematic identification of the anions.

Only the following 13 anions will be considered: acetate, $C_2H_3O_2^-$; nitrate, NO_3^-; chloride, Cl^-; bromide, Br^-; iodide, I^-; sulfide, S^{--}; sulfate, SO_4^{--}; sulfite, SO_3^{--}; carbonate, CO_3^{--}; chromate, CrO_4^{--}; phosphate, PO_4^{---}; arsenate, AsO_4^{---}; borate, BO_2^- or BO_3^{---}. This list represents less than one-third of the anions that one might encounter in a course in general chemistry; it does, however, include the more common ones, and the methods and principles used in the identification of these 13 will serve to illustrate the methods and principles used for the identification of all others.

▪ ▪ ▪ Procedure 32: Analysis for anions

Using the solution prepared in Procedure 30(A) or 30(C), page 183, and samples of the solid unknown, make a complete anion analysis in the following order.

1. Make a list of the anions that can be eliminated on the basis of the solubility of the solid (see page 187), the cation analysis, and the color of the solution (see page 182).

2. Carry out the three preliminary tests described in Procedure 33, page 192, Procedure 34, page 194, and Procedure 35, page 196. List the anions definitely eliminated by these tests. List also the anions definitely proved present by these tests.

3. Carry out specific tests (see pages 198 to 208) for those anions not definitely proved to be either absent or present by Step 1 or Step 2.

Summarize the results of the cation and anion analyses on the report blank on page 221.

Treatment of the Solid with H_2SO_4

When dry salts of each of the 13 acids are treated with concentrated sulfuric acid, certain very characteristic reactions are noted. These reactions, together with the changes that are observed, are summarized in the following table.

A. REACTIONS OF SALTS WITH COLD CONCENTRATED H_2SO_4

Anion	Observation	Equations
$C_2H_3O_2{}^-$	No evidence of reaction	
$SO_4{}^{--}$	No evidence of reaction	
$PO_4{}^{---}$	No evidence of reaction	
$BO_3{}^{---}$	No evidence of reaction	
$AsO_4{}^{---}$	No evidence of reaction	
$NO_3{}^-$	No evidence of reaction	
Cl^-	Effervescence. The gas evolved is colorless, has sharp odor, fumes in moist air, turns blue litmus red	$NaCl + H_2SO_4 = NaHSO_4 + HCl$
Br^-	Effervescence. The gas evolved is brown, has characteristic sharp odor, fumes in moist air, turns blue litmus red	$NaBr + H_2SO_4 = NaHSO_4 + HBr$ $H_2SO_4 + 2\,HBr = 2\,H_2O + SO_2 +$ $\quad Br_2$
I^-	Effervescence. Solid turns dark brown instantly, slight evolution of gas which fumes in moist air, odor of H_2S, violet fumes of iodine	$NaI + H_2SO_4 = NaHSO_4 + HI$ $H_2SO_4 + 8\,HI = H_2S + 4\,H_2O + 4\,I_2$ $H_2SO_4 + 2\,HI = 2\,H_2O + SO_2 + I_2$

Anion	Observation	Equations
S^{--}	Effervescence. Odor of H_2S gas, free sulfur deposited	$ZnS + H_2SO_4 = ZnSO_4 + H_2S$ $H_2SO_4 + H_2S = 2 H_2O + SO_2 + S$
CO_3^{--}	Effervescence. Colorless, odorless gas	$Na_2CO_3 + H_2SO_4 = Na_2SO_4 + H_2O + CO_2$
SO_3^{--}	Effervescence. Colorless gas with a sharp, choking odor	$Na_2SO_3 + H_2SO_4 = Na_2SO_4 + H_2O + SO_2$
CrO_4^{--}	Color changes from yellow to orange red	$2 K_2CrO_4 + H_2SO_4 = K_2Cr_2O_7 + H_2O + K_2SO_4$

B. REACTIONS OF SALTS WITH HOT CONCENTRATED H_2SO_4

1. Sulfates, phosphates, borates, and arsenates show no reaction on being heated with H_2SO_4.

2. Nitrates give brown fumes of NO_2 when heated with H_2SO_4:

$$2 NaNO_3 + H_2SO_4 = Na_2SO_4 + 2 HNO_3.$$

When HNO_3 is heated, a part of it decomposes as follows:

$$4 HNO_3 = 2 H_2O + O_2 + 4 NO_2 \text{ (brown gas)}.$$

3. Acetates yield acetic acid when warmed with H_2SO_4. The acetic acid has the characteristic odor of vinegar.

$$2 NaC_2H_3O_2 + H_2SO_4 = Na_2SO_4 + 2 HC_2H_3O_2.$$

4. Chlorides, bromides, iodides, sulfides, carbonates, sulfites, and chromates show no additional reactions on being heated.

■ ■ ■ Procedure 33: Treatment of the solid with H_2SO_4

Place in a small test tube as much of the solid as can be carried on $\frac{1}{4}$ in. of the tip of the spatula. Add one or two drops of 18 M H_2SO_4. Notice everything that happens, particularly the color and odor of escaping gases. (Do not place your nose over the mouth of the test tube but fan any gas toward your nose held a few inches away.) Then heat, but not so strongly that the H_2SO_4 is boiled, and note what happens. Finally heat the sides of the test tube over its entire length and note whether or not brown fumes (NO_2) are formed (see Note 3). **Do not look down into the test tube! Do not point the test tube at yourself or at your neighbor!**

List all anions whose presence or absence is indicated by this test.

NOTES

1. The reactions observed when single salts are treated with concentrated H_2SO_4 are usually very definite and easy to interpret. However,

when a mixture of salts is treated with H_2SO_4, the observations may be both indefinite and misleading because the reactions of one salt may completely mask other reactions. Thus if iodides are present, their very violent reactions with H_2SO_4 may cover up the presence of all other anions. Likewise, bromides may cover up everything except iodides and chromates. However the number of instances when this test yields precise information are numerous enough to justify the short time required to carry it out.

2. If only small quantities of certain salts, such as chlorides, nitrates, acetates, and sulfides are present, treatment with sulfuric acid may show no definite reaction. Even iodide will not react with concentrated sulfuric acid if it is present as the highly insoluble compound, HgI_2. For this reason, elimination of anions made on the basis of this test should not be considered as absolutely final. Rather, the information obtained should supplement information gained in other tests.

3. Nitric acid decomposes only at relatively high temperatures. Furthermore, it is most readily decomposed by heating its vapors. Consequently, the test tube is heated over its entire length.

4. When concentrated sulfuric acid comes in contact with moisture, a strongly exothermic reaction takes place. This may result in the evolution of steam accompanied by sputtering if the sample is moist. Care should be taken not to mistake this effect for effervescence.

Treatment of a Solution of the Anions with $AgNO_3$

The silver salts of all thirteen anions except nitrate, acetate, and sulfate are insoluble in water. $AgNO_3$ is very soluble, Ag_2SO_4 is moderately soluble, and $AgC_2H_3O_2$ is sparingly soluble. The insoluble silver salts have the following characteristic colors: AgCl, white; AgBr, cream; AgI, pale yellow; Ag_2S, black; Ag_3AsO_4, chocolate brown; Ag_3PO_4, yellow; Ag_2CrO_4, brownish red; Ag_2CO_3, white; Ag_2SO_3, white; $AgBO_2$, white or light tan. (See Note 5, Procedure 34.)

AgCl, AgBr, AgI, and Ag_2S are insoluble in dilute HNO_3; Ag_2CrO_4, Ag_3AsO_4, Ag_3PO_4, Ag_2CO_3, Ag_2SO_3, and $AgBO_2$ are soluble in dilute HNO_3. Accordingly, if silver ions, in the form of a solution of silver nitrate, are added to water solutions containing the 13 anions, the 10 insoluble silver salts listed above will precipitate; $AgC_2H_3O_2$ may precipitate if the concentration of acetate ions is fairly high. If each precpitate is, in turn, treated with dilute HNO_3, all but AgCl, AgBr, AgI, and Ag_2S, will dissolve readily. If the solution containing the anions is acidified with dilute HNO_3 before addition of $AgNO_3$, only AgCl, AgBr, AgI, and Ag_2S will precipitate.

The anions whose silver salts are insoluble in nitric acid (Cl^-, Br^-, I^-, S^{--}) are commonly referred to as the Hydrochloric Acid Group of anions.

■ ■ ■ Procedure 34: Treatment of the solution of the anions with $AgNO_3$

If the salt or mixture of salts is completely soluble in water, follow (A). If the salt is not soluble in water, follow (C).

(A) *The salt or salt mixture is soluble in water* (See Note 1 for a scheme of analysis). Place 10 drops of the water solution in a test tube; then add 3–4 drops of 0.2 M $AgNO_3$. If no precipitate forms, Cl^-, Br^-, I^-, S^{--}, AsO_4^{---}, PO_4^{---}, CrO_4^{--}, CO_3^{--}, SO_3^{--}, and BO_2^- are shown to be absent. If a precipitate forms, any or all 13 anions may be present; if the precipitate is white, Br^-, I^-, S^{--}, AsO_4^{---}, PO_4^{---}, CrO_4^{--}, and, possibly, CO_3^{--}, are absent but the others may be present; if the precipitate is black, all 13 anions may be present, since black will cover up all other colors. Note the color of the precipitate and try, by means of the list given above, to decide what it is.

Centrifuge and decant, discarding the decantate. Wash the precipitate in the test tube once with cold water; then treat it with a few drops of 3 M HNO_3, and stir. If the precipitate dissolves completely, Cl^-, Br^-, I^-, and S^{--} are absent; if the precipitate is not completely dissolved, one or more of the four anions just enumerated is present. (See Note 4.) Note the appearance of the residue and try to decide what it is. Centrifuge and decant into a test tube. Save the decantate for Part (B).

(B) Make the decantate from Part (A) just alkaline with 15 M NH_4OH; then make it just acid with 5 M acetic acid and add a few drops of 0.2 M $AgNO_3$. The following precipitates will form if the required anions are present: Ag_2CrO_4, brownish red; Ag_3AsO_4, chocolate brown; Ag_3PO_4, yellow; $AgBO_2$, white or light tan; Ag_2SO_3, white.

On the basis of the observations made in (A) and (B), what anions, if any, are definitely shown to be absent? What anions are shown to be present?

(C) *The salt or salt mixture is not soluble in water.* A solution, for use in this Procedure and also in Procedure 35, must first be prepared as directed in Procedure 30(C), page 183.

Place 10 drops of this solution in a test tube, acidify with 3 M HNO_3, and then add 3–4 drops of 0.2 M $AgNO_3$. If no precipitate forms, Cl^-, Br^-, I^-, and S^{--} are absent. If a precipitate forms, it may be $AgCl$, $AgBr$, AgI, and Ag_2S. Note the color of the precipitate.

On the basis of the observations made in (C), what anions, if any, are definitely shown to be absent? What anions are shown to be present?

NOTES

1. The changes that take place in Parts (A) and (B) of Procedure 34 may be represented by the following scheme of analysis.

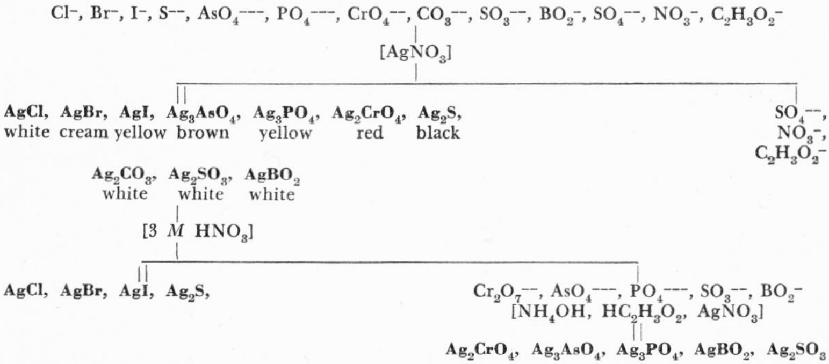

Cl^-, Br^-, I^-, S^{--}, AsO_4^{---}, PO_4^{---}, CrO_4^{--}, CO_3^{--}, SO_3^{--}, BO_2^-, SO_4^{--}, NO_3^-, $C_2H_3O_2^-$

[$AgNO_3$]

$AgCl$, $AgBr$, AgI, Ag_3AsO_4, Ag_3PO_4, Ag_2CrO_4, Ag_2S,	SO_4^{--},
white cream yellow brown yellow red black	NO_3^-,
Ag_2CO_3, Ag_2SO_3, $AgBO_2$	$C_2H_3O_2^-$
white white white	

[3 M HNO_3]

$AgCl$, $AgBr$, AgI, Ag_2S,	$Cr_2O_7^{--}$, AsO_4^{---}, PO_4^{---}, SO_3^{--}, BO_2^-
	[NH_4OH, $HC_2H_3O_2$, $AgNO_3$]
	Ag_2CrO_4, Ag_3AsO_4, Ag_3PO_4, $AgBO_2$, Ag_2SO_3

$AgC_2H_3O_2$ (white), being sparingly soluble, may precipitate when $AgNO_3$ is added if the acetate ion concentration is quite high. (See Note 5.)

2. In the presence of HNO_3, Ag_2CrO_4 will not precipitate on addition of $AgNO_3$ unless the concentration of CrO_4^{--} ions is very high. Once Ag_2CrO_4 has precipitated, however, it is only slowly dissolved by HNO_3.

3. $AgBO_2$, Ag_2CO_3, Ag_2SO_3, Ag_2CrO_4, Ag_3PO_4 and Ag_3AsO_4 are salts of weak acids. Therefore, they dissolve in the strong acid HNO_3 in the manner discussed on page 53.

(a) $Ag_2SO_3 \rightleftharpoons 2 Ag^+ + SO_3^{--}$

(b) $SO_3^{--} + 2 H^+ \rightleftharpoons H_2SO_3 \rightleftharpoons H_2O + SO_2$

Because H_2CO_3 is very unstable as well as extremely weak Ag_2CO_3 will also dissolve in the weak acid $HC_2H_3O_2$; the other five are not dissolved by $HC_2H_3O_2$ because it is such a weak acid that it does not provide a high enough concentration of H^+ ions to reduce the concentration of the anion in equation (a) below the equilibrium solubility product value.

4. The reason why Ag_2S will not dissolve in HNO_3 even though it is the salt of a weak acid is discussed on page 54.

5. Although Ag_2CO_3 is white the precipitate formed when $AgNO_3$ is added to a solution of CO_3^{--} ions darkens quickly. The reason is that Ag_2CO_3 is unstable and tends to decompose to form black Ag_2O. Ag_2CO_3 (white) $= Ag_2O$ (black) $+ CO_2$.

Treatment of a Solution of the Anions with BaCl₂

$BaCl_2$, $BaBr_2$, BaI_2, BaS, $Ba(C_2H_3O_2)_2$, and $Ba(NO_3)_2$ are soluble in water and in alkaline solution; $BaSO_4$, $BaSO_3$, $BaCO_3$, $BaCrO_4$, $Ba_3(AsO_4)_2$, $Ba_3(PO_4)_2$, and $Ba(BO_2)_2$ are insoluble. $BaSO_4$ is insoluble in strong acids, such as dilute HNO_3 or dilute HCl; the other water-insoluble barium salts are salts of weak acids and are therefore soluble in dilute HNO_3 or dilute HCl. These facts are the basis for the use of barium chloride as a reagent for the elimination of anions.

$BaCrO_4$ is yellow; the other barium salts are white.

The anions whose barium salts are insoluble in water and alkaline solution (SO_4^{--}, SO_3^{--}, CO_3^{--}, CrO_4^{--}, BO_2^-, AsO_4^{---}, PO_4^{---}) are commonly referred to as the Sulfuric Acid Group of anions.

The anions that do not fall in either the Hydrochloric Acid Group or Sulfuric Acid Group (NO_3^-, $C_2H_3O_2^-$) are commonly referred to as the Nitric Acid Group of anions.

▪ ▪ ▪ Procedure 35: Treatment of a solution of the anions with BaCl₂

(See Note 1 for a scheme of analysis.) If the salt or salt mixture is soluble in water, use the water solution; if the salt is not soluble in water, use the solution prepared as directed in Procedure 30(C), page 183. Place 4–5 drops of this solution in a test tube, make just alkaline with 5 M NH_4OH, and mix thoroughly. If any precipitate forms (hydroxides of metals), centrifuge and decant into a clean test tube, discarding the precipitate. Treat the decantate or solution with 2–3 drops of 0.2 M $BaCl_2$. Formation of a precipitate shows the presence of one or more of the following anions: SO_3^{--}, SO_4^{--}, CO_3^{--}, CrO_4^{--}, BO_2^-, PO_4^{---}, AsO_4^{---}. A yellow precipitate proves the presence of chromate; a white precipitate proves the absence of chromate. Make the mixture acid with 2 M HCl and stir well. If the precipitate dissolves completely, the absence of sulfate is proved. If the precipitate is not completely dissolved by HCl, the presence of sulfate is proved.

On the basis of the observations made in this procedure what anions, if any, are definitely shown to be absent? What anions are shown to be present?

NOTES

1. The changes that take place in Procedure 35 may be represented by the following scheme of analysis:

$$Cl^-, Br^-, I^-, S^{--}, AsO_4^{---}, PO_4^{---}, CrO_4^{--}, CO_3^{--}, SO_3^{--}, BO_2^-, SO_4^{--}, NO_3^-, C_2H_3O_2^-$$

$$[NH_4OH]$$

Metal hydroxides | $Cl^-, Br^-, I^-, S^{--}, AsO_4^{---}, PO_4^{---}, CrO_4^{--}, CO_3^{--},$ $SO_3^{--}, BO_2^-, SO_4^{--}, NO_3^-, C_2H_3O_2^-$

$$[BaCl_2]$$

$BaCrO_4$, $BaSO_4$, $BaCO_3$, $BaSO_3$, | $Cl^-, Br^-, I^-, S^{--}, NO_3^-, C_2H_3O_2^-$
yellow   white   white   white

$Ba(BO_2)_2$, $Ba_3(AsO_4)_2$, $Ba_3(PO_4)_2$
white   white   white

$$[HCl]$$

$BaSO_4$ | $Cr_2O_7^{--}, BO_2^-, AsO_4^{---}, PO_4^{---}, SO_3^{--}$
                     (CO_2 and SO_2 gases escape)

2. Since barium borate precipitates very slowly, absence of a precipitate in the group test for the sulfuric acid group does not positively eliminate borates. A specific test for borates should always be made.

3. Although boron may be present as either the metaborate (BO_2^-), the orthoborate (BO_3^{---}), or the tetraborate ($B_4O_7^{--}$), it is largely precipitated as the metaborate, $Ba(BO_2)_2$.

$$Ba^{++} + 2\,BO_2^- = Ba(BO_2)_2.$$

$$Ba^{++} + 2\,BO_3^{---} + 4\,H^+ = Ba(BO_2)_2 + 2\,H_2O.$$

$$2\,Ba^{++} + B_4O_7^{--} + H_2O = 2\,Ba(BO_2)_2 + 2\,H^+.$$

4. See Note 2, page 184 for the reactions that take place and the complications that arise when a solution is prepared by boiling a solid with a solution of Na_2CO_3. The detailed reactions that take place in the solution process are discussed on page 57.

5. Because all the water-insoluble barium salts except $BaSO_4$ are soluble in strong acids, it is imperative that the solution not be acid when $BaCl_2$ is added. Accordingly, the solution is first made alkaline with NH_4OH. This will precipitate, as insoluble hydroxides, those cations whose hydroxides are insoluble in the presence of excess NH_4OH.

Specific Tests for Anions

Information gained in the course of the cation analysis, together with information gained from observation of the solubility of the solid in water, may show the presence or absence of certain anions. The three preliminary tests may also show the absence of certain anions and the presence of others. For each salt mixture, however, there usually are several anions whose presence or absence is not established by any of the procedures noted above. Specific tests must then be carried out for each. These specific tests are discussed in Procedures 36 to 48.

These specific tests are independent of the cation analysis and, in general, can be made whether or not the tests for cations are carried out. They make it possible to test for nitrate in a fertilizer or for phosphate in a baking powder without going through the systematic cation analysis.

The order in which the specific tests for the anions should be performed is governed by the following facts. Arsenates, if present, will interfere with the test for phosphates and must be removed before the test for the phosphate ion can be made. Sulfites, if present, will interfere with the test for carbonates and must be removed before the carbonate test can be made. Sulfide, bromide, and iodide ions will interfere with the test for chloride. Iodide ions will interfere with the test for bromide. Consequently, the test for sulfite must be made before the test for the carbonate ion, the test for arsenate must be made before the test for the phosphate ion, and the halides and sulfide must be tested for in the order: sulfide, iodide, bromide, chloride. The order of performance of the tests for sulfate, borate, chromate, nitrate, and acetate is not important.

■ ■ ■ Procedure 36: Test for the arsenate ion (AsO_4^{---})

(To be omitted if the cation analysis has proved the absence of arsenic.) Place 6–8 drops of the solution in a small test tube and add Na_2CO_3 solution, drop by drop and with constant stirring, until no more precipitation of metal carbonates takes place and the solution is no longer acidic. If a precipitate has formed, centrifuge and decant into a clean test tube, discarding any precipitate. Make the decantate acid with 2 M HCl and boil to expel all CO_2. Then make just alkaline with 5 M NH_4OH. If any precipitate forms, centrifuge and decant into a clean test tube, discarding the precipitate. Add 4–5 drops of magnesia mixture and mix thoroughly. If no precipitate forms, arsenate is absent. If a white precipitate forms, it may be $MgNH_4AsO_4$ or $MgNH_4PO_4$, or both. Centrifuge and decant, and wash the precipitate three times with hot water. Add to the precipitate a drop of 0.2 M $AgNO_3$ solution. A chocolate-brown precipitate (Ag_3AsO_4) proves the presence of arsenate. A yellow precipitate (Ag_3PO_4) proves the presence of phosphate and, at the same time, proves the absence of arsenate.

NOTES

1. The precipitate formed by magnesia mixture is not sufficient confirmation of the arsenate ion, since phosphates, when present, precipitate as $MgNH_4PO_4$, which looks exactly like the $MgNH_4AsO_4$. The addition of $AgNO_3$ makes it possible to distinguish the arsenate from the phosphate. $AgNO_3$ reacts with both $MgNH_4AsO_4$ and $MgNH_4PO_4$, but Ag_3AsO_4 is chocolate brown and Ag_3PO_4 is light yellow.

2. Magnesium ammonium arsenite ($MgNH_4AsO_3$) is soluble and is not precipitated when magnesia mixture is added to a solution containing an arsenite. The decantate left after the removal of the $MgNH_4AsO_4$ may contain AsO_3^{---}. If this decantate is made acid with HCl, and H_2S is passed into the solution, any AsO_3^{---} present will be precipitated as yellow As_2S_3.

3. Magnesia mixture is a solution containing Mg^{++}, OH^-, and excess NH_4^+. $MgCl_2$, NH_4OH, and NH_4Cl are common sources of these ions. The important reactions involved in the test for arsenate are

$$Mg^{++} + NH_4^+ + AsO_4^{---} = MgNH_4AsO_4,$$

$$MgNH_4AsO_4 + 3\,Ag^+ = Ag_3AsO_4 + Mg^{++} + NH_4^+.$$

4. The addition of Na_2CO_3 will precipitate out, as carbonates, all cations except sodium, potassium, and ammonium. These cations, if not removed as carbonates, will precipitate as insoluble arsenates, when the solution is made alkaline with NH_4OH. The arsenate ion would thus be lost. Traces of these cations not removed as carbonates may precipitate on addition of NH_4OH.

5. If an unknown substance contained arsenate, the cation analysis of that substance would give a positive test for arsenic in Procedure 13. If no positive test for arsenic was obtained in the cation analysis, arsenate could not have been present. Therefore, if arsenic has already been shown

to be absent in the cation analysis, the test for the arsenate ion may be omitted. Performance of the test for arsenate will, however, serve as a check on the cation analysis.

■ ■ ■ Procedure 37: Test for the phosphate ion (PO_4^{---})

(A) *If arsenates are absent.* Place 4–5 drops of the solution in a test tube, acidify with 3 M HNO_3, add 3–4 drops of ammonium molybdate solution $[(NH_4)_2MoO_4]$, mix thoroughly, and heat almost to boiling for 2 minutes. Formation of a finely divided yellow precipitate $[(NH_4)_3PO_4 \cdot 12 MoO_3]$ confirms the presence of the phosphate ion.

(B) *If arsenates are present.* Place a small bit of the solid or a few drops of the solution in a test tube, add 7–8 drops of 12 M HCl, and heat just to boiling. Treat with H_2S for about 20 seconds or add 4 drops of 1 M thioacetamide and heat in the boiling water bath for 2 minutes. Add 10 drops of water, mix thoroughly, centrifuge, and decant into a casserole, discarding the precipitate (As_2S_5). Evaporate to dryness but do not bake. Cool, and then add 5 drops of water and 5 drops of 3 M HNO_3. Stir thoroughly and transfer to a test tube. If necessary, centrifuge and decant, discarding the precipitate. Treat the decantate with 3–4 drops of ammonium molybdate solution, mix thoroughly, and heat almost to boiling for 2 minutes. A yellow precipitate $[(NH_4)_3PO_4 \cdot 12 MoO_3]$ proves the presence of phosphate.

NOTES

1. Both phosphates and arsenates react with ammonium molybdate to form insoluble yellow precipitates, ammonium phosphomolybdate $[(NH_4)_3PO_4 \cdot 12 MoO_3]$ and ammonium arsenomolybdate $[(NH_4)_3AsO_4 \cdot 12 MoO_3]$. As a consequence, arsenates must be removed before the confirmatory test for phosphates can be made.

2. The formation of the yellow precipitate, $(NH_4)_3PO_4 \cdot 12 MoO_3$, takes place as follows:

$$PO_4^{---} + 12 MoO_4^{--} + 24 H^+ + 3 NH_4^+ =$$
$$(NH_4)_3PO_4 \cdot 12 MoO_3 + 12 H_2O.$$

Precipitation takes place most readily at a temperature of 60°C. in the presence of excess HNO_3.

3. Arsenates, if present, are removed as As_2S_5 by precipitation with H_2S.

$$2\,AsO_4^{---} + 5\,H_2S + 6\,H^+ = As_2S_5 + 8\,H_2O.$$

■ ■ ■ Procedure 38: Test for the borate ion
$(BO_3^{---}$ or $BO_2^-)$

Place a small quantity of the solid material in a casserole, add 3–4 drops of 18 M H_2SO_4, and stir thoroughly. Then add 10–12 drops of methyl alcohol (CH_3OH, methanol) and again mix thoroughly; then set fire to the mixture. *Do not stir after the mixture has taken fire.* If it burns with a green flame the instant that it takes fire, the borate ion is present. A green flame that does not appear until 20 or 30 seconds after the mixture has taken fire, or unless the mixture is stirred while on fire, is due to copper or barium and should be ignored.

NOTES

1. Copper and barium do not interfere with the borate test because their salts are not volatilized when the mixture *first takes fire.*

2. There are three boric acids: orthoboric (H_3BO_3, the boracic acid of commerce), metaboric (HBO_2), and tetraboric ($H_2B_4O_7$). All three of these boric acids form stable salts.

3. All borates react with H_2SO_4 to form orthoboric acid, H_3BO_3.

$$BO_2^- + H^+ + H_2O = H_3BO_3,$$

$$B_4O_7^{--} + 2\,H^+ + 5\,H_2O = 4\,H_3BO_3,$$

$$BO_3^{---} + 3\,H^+ = H_3BO_3.$$

In the presence of sulfuric acid, H_3BO_3 reacts with alcohol to form the volatile ester, methyl borate, $(CH_3)_3BO_3$.

$$3\,CH_3OH + H_3BO_3 = (CH_3)_3BO_3 + 3\,H_2O.$$

The methyl borate burns with a characteristic green flame, forming solid B_2O_3 (boric acid anhydride):

$$2\,(CH_3)_3BO_3 + 9\,O_2 = 6\,CO_2 + 9\,H_2O + B_2O_3.$$

■ ■ ■ Procedure 39: Test for the chromate (VI) ion
(CrO_4^{--})

(To be omitted if no chromium was found in the complete cation analysis.) Place two drops of the solution in a test tube, add 10 drops of water and make just acid with 3 M HNO_3. Add 5–6 drops of ether and 1 drop of 3% H_2O_2, stir well, and then allow to settle. A blue coloration of the ether layer confirms the presence of the chromate ion.

NOTES

1. The blue coloration in the ether layer is due to the presence of chromium peroxide, CrO_5.

$$2\,CrO_4{}^{--} \ + \ 2\,H^+ \ \rightleftarrows \ Cr_2O_7{}^{--} \ + \ H_2O,$$

$$Cr_2O_7{}^{--} \ + \ 4\,H_2O_2 \ + \ 2\,H^+ \ = \ 2\,CrO_5 \ + \ 5\,H_2O.$$

See Note 1, Procedure 21, for further details concerning this reaction.

2. If a chromate is carried through the complete cation analysis it is, in part at least, reduced to Cr^{+++} when the solution is evaporated down with 6 M HCl in Procedure 5 and is completely reduced to Cr^{+++} when the sulfides of the copper-arsenic group are precipitated in Procedure 5.

$$2\,CrO_4{}^{--} \ + \ 2\,H^+ \ \rightleftarrows \ Cr_2O_7{}^{--} \ + \ H_2O,$$

$$Cr_2O_7{}^{--} \ + \ 6\,Cl^- \ + \ 14\,H^+ \ = \ 2\,Cr^{+++} \ + \ 7\,H_2O \ + \ 3\,Cl_2,$$

$$Cr_2O_7{}^{--} \ + \ 3\,H_2S \ + \ 8\,H^+ \ = \ 2\,Cr^{+++} \ + \ 3\,S \ + \ 7\,H_2O.$$

The resulting Cr^{+++} ions remain in the decantate from Procedure 5 and are subsequently precipitated as $Cr(OH)_3$ in Procedure 15. A positive test for chromium is then obtained in Procedure 21.

The fact that a positive test for chromium was obtained in Procedure 21 does not mean, however, that the particular salt mixture contained chromate. The chromium may have been present as Cr^{+++}.

▪ ▪ ▪ Procedure 40: Test for the sulfate ion ($SO_4{}^{--}$)

Place a few drops of the solution in a test tube, acidify with 6 M HCl, and then add a drop of 0.2 M $BaCl_2$. A white precipitate (**$BaSO_4$**) proves the presence of sulfate.

NOTES

1. Sulfites are slowly oxidized to sulfates by atmospheric oxygen. Consequently, sulfites commonly show a positive test for sulfates.

$$2\,SO_3{}^{--} \ + \ O_2 \ = \ 2\,SO_4{}^{--},$$

$$Ba^{++} \ + \ SO_4{}^{--} \ = \ \mathbf{BaSO_4} \ (\text{white}).$$

▪ ▪ ▪ Procedure 41: Test for the sulfite ion (SO_3^{--})

Place 7–8 drops of the solution in a test tube, acidify with 6 M HCl, add 2–3 drops of 0.2 M $BaCl_2$, and mix thoroughly. If a precipitate ($BaSO_4$) forms, remove it by centrifuging and decanting. To the clear decantate add a drop of 3% H_2O_2. The formation of a white precipitate ($BaSO_4$) proves the presence of sulfite.

NOTES

1. H_2O_2 oxidizes the sulfite to sulfate.

$$SO_3^{--} + H_2O_2 = SO_4^{--} + H_2O.$$

The barium ions in solution react with these sulfate ions to form insoluble $BaSO_4$.

Any sulfate ions in the original solution are removed, as barium sulfate, when the $BaCl_2$ is first added.

▪ ▪ ▪ Procedure 42: Test for the carbonate ion (CO_3^{--})

(A) *When sulfites are absent.* Place a small amount of the solid in a test tube. Then add a few drops of 2 M HCl. Test the escaping gas for CO_2 by holding a drop of barium hydroxide solution, suspended from the tip of a medicine dropper, a short distance down into the mouth of the test tube. The "clouding" of the drop, due to the formation of a white precipitate of barium carbonate ($BaCO_3$), proves the presence of carbonate.

(B) *When sulfites are present.* Place a small amount of the solid in a test tube and add an equal amount of solid Na_2O_2. Then add 3–4 drops of water and mix thoroughly. Then proceed as directed in the second sentence of (A).

NOTES

1. Carbonates react with acids to evolve CO_2 gas. This CO_2 reacts with $Ba(OH)_2$ solution to form a white precipitate of $BaCO_3$.

Carbonate of a metal + nH^+ = Metal cation^{+n} + H_2O + CO_2.

$$CO_2 + Ba^{++} + 2OH^- = BaCO_3 \text{ (white)} + H_2O.$$

2. Sulfites evolve SO_2 gas when treated with acids. The SO_2 gas will react with $Ba(OH)_2$ solution to form a white precipitate of $BaSO_3$. Sulfites must therefore be removed or destroyed before the test for carbonates is carried out. Sodium peroxide oxidizes sulfites to sulfates.

$$SO_3^{--} + Na_2O_2 + H_2O = SO_4^{--} + 2\,Na^+ + 2\,OH^-.$$

■ ■ ■ Procedure 43: Test for the sulfide ion (S^{--})

Place a small quantity of the solid in a test tube and add 10 drops of 6 M HCl. Hold a strip of filter paper moistened with 0.2 M $Pb(C_2H_3O_2)_2$ solution over the mouth of the test tube so that any gas that is being evolved will come in contact with the lead acetate. A brownish-black or silvery black stain (**PbS**) on the paper confirms the presence of sulfides.

If no blackening of the lead acetate occurs after 1 minute heat the tube gently; if still no reaction occurs add a small amount of granulated zinc to the contents of the tube. If the lead acetate is not darkened, the sulfide ion is absent; if it is darkened, sulfide is present.

NOTES

1. The reactions that take place in the test for sulfides are

$$\text{sulfide of metal} + n\text{H}^+ = \text{metal cation}^{+n} + H_2S.$$

$$Pb^{++} + H_2S = \textbf{PbS} + 2\,H^+.$$

2. The sulfides of nickel and cobalt and the metals of the silver and copper-arsenic groups are not soluble in dilute HCl. When zinc is added, however, hydrogen is liberated.

$$Zn + 2\,H^+ = Zn^{++} + 2\,H.$$

The hydrogen reduces the sulfides, H_2S being evolved.

$$\textbf{HgS} + 2\,H = Hg + H_2S.$$

■ ■ ■ Procedure 44: Test for the iodide ion (I^-)

Place 5 drops of the solution in a test tube and acidify with 5 M $HC_2H_3O_2$. Then add 2 drops of 0.2 M KNO_2. A reddish-brown coloration, due to liberation of iodine, proves the presence of iodide. If the brown color is very faint, add a few drops of carbon tetrachloride, (CCl_4), shake, then allow to settle. A violet coloration in the CCl_4

layer shows the presence of iodine. (See Note 1 for an alternative test for iodide.)

NOTES

1. *Alternative test for iodide ion.* Place 5 drops of the solution in a test tube, acidify with 3 M HNO_3, and add a drop of 0.2 M $Fe(NO_3)_3$. A reddish-brown coloration, due to free iodine, proves the presence of iodide. If the solution is shaken with CCl_4 the iodine will concentrate in the CCl_4 layer and will give it a violet coloration.

2. Nitrite ions and ferric ions will both oxidize iodides but will not oxidize either bromides or chlorides. For that reason, both the regular test and the alternative test can be carried out in the presence of bromides and chlorides. The reactions that take place in the two tests are

$$2\,NO_2^- + 2\,I^- + 4\,H^+ = 2\,NO + I_2 + 2\,H_2O.$$

$$2\,Fe^{+++} + 2\,I^- = 2\,Fe^{++} + I_2.$$

▪ ▪ ▪ Procedure 45: Test for the bromide ion (Br⁻)

(Iodides will interfere with this test.) Place 5 drops of the solution in a test tube; add 5 drops of chlorine water. A brown coloration, due to liberated bromine, shows the presence of bromide. If the solution is shaken with a few drops of CCl_4, the brown color will concentrate in the lower CCl_4 layer. (See Note 1 for an alternative test for bromides.)

NOTES

1. *Alternative test for bromide ion.* (Iodides will interfere with this test.) Place 5 drops of the solution in a test tube, acidify with 3 M HNO_3, add a drop of 0.02 M $KMnO_4$ and mix thoroughly. Decolorization of the permanganate and formation of a brown coloration, due to free bromine, shows the presence of bromide. If the solution is shaken with CCl_4 the bromine will concentrate in the CCl_4 layer.

2. Bromide ions are oxidized by chlorine and by permanganate ions according to the following reactions.

$$Cl_2 + 2\,Br^- = 2\,Cl^- + Br_2,$$

$$2\,MnO_4^- + 10\,Br^- + 16\,H^+ = 2\,Mn^{++} + 5\,Br_2 + 8\,H_2O.$$

The violet color of MnO_4^- will disappear, due to formation of colorless Mn^{++}. Persistence of the violet MnO_4^- color is a sign that all bromide ions have been oxidized. Iodide ions will also be oxidized by both chlorine and MnO_4^-, as follows:

$$Cl_2 + 2I^- = 2Cl^- + I_2.$$

$$2MnO_4^- + 10I^- + 16H^+ = 2Mn^{++} + 5I_2 + 8H_2O.$$

3. Iodide ions, if present, must be removed before the test for bromide ions is carried out. The iodide ions can be removed by either of the following methods. *Method A:* Acidify the solution with 3 M HNO_3 and add 0.2 M KNO_2, dropwise, with constant stirring, until there is no further increase in the depth of the brown color. Extract once with 5 drops of CCl_4, discarding the CCl_4 layer. Boil the water layer carefully until the iodine has been largely driven off. Test the colorless, or near-colorless, water solution for bromides as directed above. *Method B:* Acidify the solution with 3 M HNO_3 and add 0.2 M $Fe(NO_3)_3$ dropwise, with constant stirring, until there is no further increase in the depth of the brown color. Extract once with 5 drops of CCl_4. Boil the water layer until the iodine has been largely driven off. Test the near-colorless water solution for bromides as directed above.

■ ■ ■ Procedure 46: Test for the chloride ion (Cl^-)

(Sulfides, bromides, and iodides will interfere with this test.) Place 5–6 drops of the solution in a test tube, acidify with 3 M HNO_3, and add a drop of 0.2 M $AgNO_3$. A white, curdy precipitate ($AgCl$) proves the presence of chlorides.

NOTES

1. Since Ag_2S, $AgBr$, and AgI also are insoluble in acid solution, this test is not conclusive unless S^{--}, Br^-, and I^- are definitely shown to be absent. Chromate ions, if present in high concentrations, may also interfere.

Interference from chromate ions can be eliminated by dilution with 3 M HNO_3.

Sulfide ions can be removed by boiling the solution with 2 M H_2SO_4 until the escaping vapors give no test for H_2S gas with filter paper moistened with lead acetate solution.

Iodide and bromide ions can be removed as described in Note 2.

2. *Separation and detection of chlorides, bromides, and iodides in the presence of one another.* Place 15 drops of the solution in a casserole, add 15 drops of 5 M $HC_2H_3O_2$ and 30 drops of water, and mix thoroughly. Then add a small quantity of solid potassium peroxydisulfate ($K_2S_2O_8$) and heat. A brown coloration, due to the liberation of iodine, proves the presence of iodide.

Boil the solution until all of the iodine is removed, replenishing the liquid with water. Test for complete oxidation of iodide by adding a pinch of $K_2S_2O_8$ and 2 drops of 5 M $HC_2H_3O_2$. When iodide is completely removed, add 15 drops of 2 M H_2SO_4 and another small quantity of $K_2S_2O_8$ and heat to boiling. A brown coloration, due to bromine, proves the presence of bromides.

Boil the solution until all of the bromine is driven off, replenishing the liquid with water. Test for complete oxidation of bromide by adding a pinch of $K_2S_2O_8$ and 2 drops of 2 M H_2SO_4. When removal of bromide is complete, cool the solution, acidify with 3 M HNO_3, and add 2–3 drops of 0.2 M $AgNO_3$. A white precipitate ($AgCl$) proves the presence of chlorides.

This separation depends on the fact that, in acetic acid solution, $K_2S_2O_8$ will oxidize iodide but will not oxidize bromide or chloride.

$$2\,I^- + S_2O_8^{--} = 2\,SO_4^{--} + I_2.$$

In a more strongly acid solution it will oxidize iodide and bromide but will not oxidize chloride.

$$2\,Br^- + S_2O_8^{--} = 2\,SO_4^{--} + Br_2.$$

For additional methods for detecting the halides in the presence of one another, the student is referred to the textbooks listed at the end of Chapter 2.

■ ■ ■ Procedure 47: Test for the nitrate ion (NO_3^-)

(In the absence of iodides, bromides, and chromates.) Place 2 drops of the water solution, or the supernatant liquid obtained by treating the solid with hot water, in a test tube and carefully add 10 drops of 18 M H_2SO_4. Mix thoroughly and cool. Carefully add 3–4 drops of 0.2 M $FeSO_4$ solution, allowing the latter to float on top of the sulfuric acid solution. Allow to stand for one or two minutes. A brown coloration at the junction of the two layers due to the presence of the complex nitrosyliron(II) ion, $Fe(NO)^{++}$, proves the presence of nitrate.

NOTES

1. The test for the nitrate ion is based upon the fact that, in the presence of concentrated H_2SO_4, Fe^{++} reduces NO_3^- to NO.

$$3\,Fe^{++} + NO_3^- + 4\,H^+ = 3\,Fe^{+++} + NO + 2\,H_2O.$$

$$NO + Fe^{++}\ (\text{excess}) \rightleftharpoons Fe(NO)^{++}\ (\text{brown}).$$

The NO formed combines with excess Fe^{++} ions to form the characteristic brown complex ion, $Fe(NO)^{++}$. This complex ion is unstable at higher temperatures; hence, the test must be made at room temperatures.

2. Iodides and bromides react with concentrated H_2SO_4 to liberate I_2 and Br_2.

$$SO_4^{--} + 8\,I^- + 10\,H^+ = H_2S + 4\,I_2 + 4\,H_2O,$$

$$SO_4^{--} + 2\,I^- + 4\,H^+ = SO_2 + I_2 + 2\,H_2O,$$

$$SO_4^{--} + 2\,Br^- + 4\,H^+ = SO_2 + Br_2 + 2\,H_2O.$$

Chromate(VI) ions, if present, will be reduced by Fe^{++} to green Cr^{+++}.

$$2\,CrO_4^{--} + 2\,H^+ \rightleftharpoons Cr_2O_7^{--} + H_2O,$$

$$Cr_2O_7^{--} + 6\,Fe^{++} + 14\,H^+ = 2\,Cr^{+++} + 6\,Fe^{+++} + 7\,H_2O.$$

The colors of I_2, Br_2, and Cr^{+++} will interfere with detection of the brown color of $Fe(NO)^{++}$. Consequently, I^-, Br^-, and CrO_4^{--} must be removed as follows. Place 4 drops of the water solution in a test tube and add 0.2 M $Pb(C_2H_3O_2)_2$ until precipitation is complete. Centrifuge and decant, discarding the precipitate ($PbCrO_4$). Treat the decantate with silver sulfate solution until precipitation is complete. Centrifuge and decant, into a casserole, discarding the precipitate (AgI, $AgBr$, $PbSO_4$). Evaporate the solution down to a volume of about 2 drops, add 2 drops of water, and transfer to a test tube. Test this solution for nitrate according to Procedure 47.

3. Since all nitrates are soluble in water, the nitrate ions will be contained in the supernatant liquid obtained by digesting the solid material with water, even though the solid may not be completely soluble.

■ ■ ■ Procedure 48: Test for the acetate ion $(C_2H_3O_2^-)$

Place a small amount of the solid in a test tube, add 2–3 drops of 18 M H_2SO_4, and mix thoroughly. (See Note 1.) Add 4 drops of ethyl alcohol (C_2H_5OH, ethanol) and again mix thoroughly. Heat the tube in the boiling water bath for about 1 minute. Carefully smell the odor of the escaping fumes. A fruity odor, due to ethyl acetate ($C_2H_5C_2H_3O_2$, ethylethanoate), proves the presence of acetate. If the test is doubtful, place a pinch of the solid in a test tube, heat strongly, and note whether or not there is any charring of the material. Charring is indicated by the escape of fumes that have the sharp penetrating odor of burned hair or singed feathers; also, the solid darkens in color. Charring shows the presence of acetate.

NOTES

1. If sulfites, carbonates, iodides, bromides, chlorides, or sulfides are present, the mixture should be warmed gently for some time after addition of the sulfuric acid and before addition of the alcohol. This heating will drive off all SO_2, CO_2, I_2, Br_2, HCl, and H_2S. If they are not driven off their odors will mask the characteristic odor of the ethyl acetate. Care should be taken that the heating is not so intense that $HC_2H_3O_2$ is distilled off.

2. When an acetate is treated with concentrated H_2SO_4, acetic acid (ethanoic acid) is liberated. This acetic acid reacts with ethyl alcohol to form the volatile ester, $C_2H_5C_2H_3O_2$; the characteristic fruity odor of the latter compound makes possible its identification.

$$C_2H_3O_2^- + H^+ = HC_2H_3O_2,$$

$$C_2H_5OH + HC_2H_3O_2 = C_2H_5C_2H_3O_2 + H_2O.$$

3. The presence of acetate is shown in the preliminary treatment with sulfuric acid (Procedure 33), in which it gives the characteristic odor of vinegar (acetic acid).

4. Charring on heating is characteristic of the salts of organic acids. Since acetic acid is the only organic acid among the 13, the incidence of charring when the solid is heated is proof of the presence of acetate.

QUESTIONS

SIMPLE SOLUBILITY

1. From the following list of soluble salts, select (a) 10 pairs which, when brought together in solution, will not react to form a precipitate. (b) 10 pairs which, when brought together in solution, will form a precipitate. Give the formula of the precipitate in each case and write the net equation for its formation: $Pb(NO_3)_2$, Ag_2SO_4, $MgCrO_4$, BaS, $FeCl_3$, NiI_2, $ZnBr_2$, Na_3PO_4, K_2CO_3, $(NH_4)_3AsO_4$, $NaBO_2$, $Al_2(SO_4)_3$, $Bi(NO_3)_3$, $MnCl_2$, $(NH_4)_2SO_3$, CaS.

2. Give the formula of an acid whose:

(a) Barium salt is insoluble in water but whose copper salt is soluble.
(b) Copper salt is insoluble in water but whose calcium salt is soluble.
(c) Lead salt is insoluble in water but whose zinc salt is soluble.
(d) Silver salt is insoluble in water but whose copper salt is soluble.
(e) Mercury(I) (mercurous) salt is insoluble in water but whose mercury(II) (mercuric) salt is soluble.
(f) Manganese salt is insoluble in water but whose potassium salt is soluble.

(g) Nickel salt is insoluble in water but whose magnesium salt is soluble.

3. A mixture of barium and silver salts was readily and completely soluble in cold water. What anions are not present in this mixture?

4. An unknown salt or mixture of salts is completely soluble in water and contains carbonate and nitrate as the only anions. What cations may be present?

5. An unknown salt or mixture of salts is completely soluble in water and contains Cu^{++}, Ag^+, and Na^+ as the only cations. What anions may be present?

SOLUBILITY PLUS OTHER CHARACTERISTICS

6. An unknown salt or mixture of salts is completely and readily soluble in cold water. On treating the above solution with dilute HCl effervescence takes place, a colorless, odorless gas being evolved. What cations may be present?

7. An unknown salt or mixture of salts is completely soluble in cold water. On being treated with dilute HCl the water solution changes in color from yellow to orange-red. What cations may be present?

8. A homogeneous powder which is known to contain only one metallic ion dissolves completely in cold water to give a pale-blue solution which turns a very deep blue when treated with NH_4OH. What anions may be present?

9. The chloride of a metal is soluble in cold water. Its hydroxide is white and is insoluble in water and in NH_4OH but dissolves readily in HCl and in KOH. What is the metal?

10. An unknown salt or salt mixture was readily and completely soluble in cold water. The resulting solution was green in color. List the anions that can be eliminated on the basis of solubility.

11. The sulfide of a metal is insoluble in water but soluble in dilute HCl. Its hydroxide is insoluble in water but soluble in both NaOH and NH_4OH. What is the metal?

12. A mixture of salts is completely soluble in water. When a solution of sodium carbonate is added to the water solution there is no sign of any reaction. What cations can be eliminated on the basis of this observation?

13. An unknown salt or mixture of salts is readily and completely soluble in cold water. On being treated with dilute HCl, effervescence takes place, a colorless gas with a very sharp, penetrating odor being evolved. What cations may be present?

14. A solid mixture of salts was known to contain sulfate and bromide as the only anions. (a) The solid dissolved readily and completely in cold water to give a clear transparent solution showing no sign of milkiness or opalescence. (b) When a sample of the water solution prepared in (a) was treated with an excess of NaOH, a clear solution with no precipitate was obtained. (c) When a sample of the water solution prepared in (a) was treated with an excess of NH_4OH, a clear solution with no precipitate was obtained. What cations may be present?

Solubility in Various Solvents

15. A yellow solid that is known to be a single salt is completely insoluble in hot water but dissolves in hot dilute HCl to give an orange-red solution. When this solution is cooled a white crystalline precipitate forms. This precipitate redissolves when the solution is heated but does not redissolve when cold water is added. What is the salt?

16. Give the symbol for a metal whose:

(a) Sulfide is insoluble in water but soluble in dilute HCl.
(b) Sulfide is insoluble in dilute HCl but soluble in concentrated HCl.
(c) Sulfide is insoluble in dilute HCl but soluble in dilute HNO_3.
(d) Hydroxide is insoluble in water but soluble in NaOH.
(e) Hydroxide is insoluble in water but soluble in NH_4OH.
(f) Hydroxide is insoluble in NH_4OH but soluble in KOH.
(g) Hydroxide is insoluble in NaOH but soluble in NH_4OH.
(h) Hydroxide is insoluble in water but is soluble in NH_4OH and also in NaOH.
(i) Hydroxide is amphoteric.
(j) Oxide is insoluble in HNO_3 but soluble in HCl.
(k) Chloride hydrolyzes in water to give an insoluble basic chloride.
(l) Sulfide is completely hydrolyzed in water.

Insoluble Salts

17. Give the simplest and best solvent that could be used to dissolve each of the following: ZnS, $MgCrO_4$, $CuSO_4$, $PbCO_3$, Na_3AsO_4, HgS, AgCl, $BiCl_3$, $NiSO_3$, $BaSO_4$.

18. A solid salt mixture contains $PbSO_4$, HgS, AgCl, $FePO_4$, and $Mg(NO_3)_2$. Describe in detail how you would prepare solutions of the solid mixture for both cation and anion analysis. Show schematically how you would proceed and what would happen. Write detailed ionic equations and net equations for all reactions that take place.

19. A solid unknown is a mixture of the following compounds: $ZnCO_3$, $Cu_3(PO_4)_2$, $Pb(BO_2)_2$, $MnSO_3$, and NiS. Write equations to show what happens when a solution is prepared as directed in Procedure 30(C).

20. In making a solution of a water-insoluble solid, why dissolve by boiling with Na_2CO_3? Why not simply dissolve the solid in HNO_3 and use this acid solution for making the group tests for anions?

TREATMENT WITH H_2SO_4

21. How would treatment with concentrated H_2SO_4 enable you to distinguish between the following pairs of dry salts?

(a) $BaSO_4$ and $Pb(NO_3)_2$ (e) $MgBr_2$ and K_3PO_4
(b) KCl and Na_3AsO_4 (f) $CaCrO_4$ and KI
(c) $MnSO_3$ and Na_2CO_3 (g) ZnS and $Ba(BO_2)_2$
(d) $NaC_2H_3O_2$ and $NaCl$ (h) KBr and KNO_3

22. Five different solid, dry, anhydrous sodium salts were treated, independently, with cold concentrated H_2SO_4. The results listed below for each salt were obtained:

(a) Effervescence. The evolved gas had a light reddish-brown color and a sharp odor and fumed strongly in moist air.

(b) No effervescence. Color of solid changed from yellow to orange.

(c) Effervescence. The evolved gas was colorless and odorless and did not fume in moist air.

(d) Effervescence. The evolved gas was colorless, had a sharp odor, and fumed strongly in moist air.

(e) Effervescence. The evolved gas was colorless and had a very sharp odor but did not fume in moist air and did not discolor a piece of filter paper that had been moistened with a solution of lead nitrate.

Identify each salt.

23. A silver salt was but slightly soluble in water. Upon heating the dry salt with concentrated H_2SO_4 there was no evidence of any reaction. Name the anions possibly present.

24. A pure single salt is white, crystalline, and completely soluble in water. When the water solution is acidified with HCl and then treated with H_2S a dark-brown precipitate forms. When H_2SO_4 is added to the water solution a white precipitate is formed. When cold concentrated H_2SO_4 is added to the dry salt nothing happens; when the H_2SO_4 is heated, however, a brown gas is given off. What is the salt?

PRELIMINARY TESTS WITH $AgNO_3$ AND $BaCl_2$

25. A mixture of salts was readily and completely soluble in cold water. Separate samples of this water solution gave no precipitate with $AgNO_3$ or with NH_4OH and $BaCl_2$. What anions could be present in this salt mixture?

26. An unknown salt or mixture of salts is completely soluble in water. The colorless solution gives a red flame test. When the water solution is treated with $AgNO_3$ nothing happens. What anions may be present?

27. An unknown was found to be completely soluble in water. Addition of solutions of Na_2HPO_4, $BaCl_2$, and $AgNO_3$ to separate portions of an aqueous solution of the unknown failed to yield any precipitate. Name the cations and anions possibly present.

28. An unknown salt or salt mixture was readily and completely soluble in cold water. Separate samples of this water solution showed the following behavior: (a) No precipitate when treated with $AgNO_3$ solution. (b) No precipitate when treated with HNO_3 and $AgNO_3$ solution. (c) No precipitate when treated with slight excess of NH_4OH and then with $BaCl_2$ solution. (d) No precipitate when acidified with HCl and then treated with $BaCl_2$ solution. What anions and what cations are eliminated in each test?

29. A white solid known to be a mixture of sodium salts showed the following behavior: (a) There was no sign of any reaction whatsoever when a sample of the solid was warmed with concentrated H_2SO_4. (b) A water solution of the solid gave a white precipitate when made acid with HCl and then treated with $BaCl_2$. (c) A water solution of the solid gave no precipitate when acidified with HNO_3 and then treated with $AgNO_3$. (d) A water solution of the solid gave a white precipitate when treated with a few drops of $AgNO_3$. What anions are shown to be absent?

30. A white solid which is known to be a single salt is completely soluble in cold water. This solution is acid to litmus. When the solid is treated with HCl nothing happens, when treated with H_2SO_4 effervescence takes place, the solid remaining colorless. On treating the water solution with NH_4OH a white precipitate is formed which redissolves when more NH_4OH is added. When $BaCl_2$ is added to the water solution nothing happens; but when $AgNO_3$ is added a white precipitate is formed. What is the solid?

31. A white, crystalline, homogeneous solid that is known to be a single salt dissolves in cold water to give a water-clear solution which reacts acid to litmus paper. Separate samples of this water solution give the following results when treated separately with the following reagents: (a) excess NaOH, no precipitate; (b) excess NH_4OH, no precipitate; (c) Na_2CO_3, white precipitate; (d) H_2S, white precipitate; (e) excess NH_4OH + $BaCl_2$, white precipitate; (f) HNO_3 + $AgNO_3$, no precipitate; (g) HCl, no sign of any reaction. What is the salt?

32. A green crystalline substance which is known to be a single salt is completely soluble in cold water. When an excess of NH_4OH is added to the water solution no precipitate is formed but a deep-blue solution results.

When H_2S is added to a water solution which has been acidified with HCl, a black precipitate forms. When $BaCl_2$ is added to the water solution nothing happens. When cold concentrated H_2SO_4 is added to the solid effervescence takes place, a colorless strongly fuming gas with a sharp odor being evolved. What could the single salt be?

33. A single salt is found to contain Zn^{++} as the only cation. The salt is insoluble in water. No visible reaction takes place in the H_2SO_4 treatment, no gas being evolved at either high or low temperatures. A white precipitate is obtained in the $BaCl_2$ preliminary test made on the solution prepared according to Procedure 30(C). What can the salt be?

34. A copper salt was found to be completely insoluble in water. The prepared solution (made by boiling some of the solid unknown with Na_2CO_3 solution, decanting and boiling the decantate with dilute HNO_3) was made slightly alkaline with NH_4OH and $BaCl_2$ was added. No precipitate resulted. Name the anions possibly present.

35. An unknown solid containing Cu^{++} as the only cation was completely insoluble in water but readily soluble in dilute HCl. The solution prepared in Procedure 30(C) gave no precipitate with either NH_4OH and $BaCl_2$ or HNO_3 and $AgNO_3$. For what anions must specific tests be made?

SPECIFIC TESTS FOR ANIONS

36. Describe the method by which you would make a specific test for:

(a) NO_3^- in an unknown that contains I^-.
(b) Borate in an unknown that contains Cu^{++}.
(c) CO_3^{--} in an unknown that contains SO_3^{--}.
(d) PO_4^{---} in an unknown that contains AsO_4^{---}.
(e) Br^- in an unknown that contains I^-.
(f) Cl^- in an unknown that contains S^{--}.
(g) SO_3^{--} in an unknown that contains SO_4^{--}.
(h) $C_2H_3O_2^-$ in an unknown that contains SO_3^{--}.
(i) NO_3^- in an unknown that contains CrO_4^{--}.
(j) AsO_4^{---} in an unknown that contains PO_4^{---}.

37. Describe the method by which you would test for:

(a) Boric acid in an eyewash.
(b) Nitrate in a solid fertilizer.
(c) Phosphate in bath salts.
(d) Carbonate in limestone.
(e) Arsenate in an insecticide.
(f) Sulfite in a bleaching solution.
(g) Iodide in table salt.

38. A solution of a salt mixture was prepared by boiling with sodium carbonate, discarding the precipitate, and digesting the decantate with dilute nitric acid. Why is the solution thus prepared not satisfactory for use in making confirmatory tests for carbonate, sulfate, sulfite, sulfide, and nitrate? Suppose a solution for anion analysis were prepared by boiling with sodium carbonate and discarding the precipitate, the digestion with nitric acid being omitted. Would such a solution be satisfactory for making confirmatory tests for carbonate, sulfite, sulfate, sulfide, and nitrate? List the anions for whose confirmatory tests such a solution would be satisfactory.

39. A white solid is completely soluble in cold water. Its water solution is neutral to litmus. No change takes place when the solid is warmed with concentrated H_2SO_4. There is no change when the water solution is treated with H_2SO_4 and $FeSO_4$. Which of the following substances may the solid be: KNO_3, $AlCl_3$, Na_2CO_3, Na_2SO_4, $NaBr$, $BaSO_4$, K_2CrO_4, KCl, NiS, $Cr_2(SO_4)_3$?

40. A salt mixture which was readily and completely soluble in cold water showed the following behavior: (a) One sample of the water solution gave a yellow precipitate when acidified with HNO_3 and treated with ammonium molybdate. (b) Another sample of the water solution gave a dark-brown coloration when treated with a mixture of concentrated H_2SO_4 and ferrous sulfate. (c) A sample of the solid effervesced when treated with cold concentrated H_2SO_4. The evolved gas did not fume in moist air but had a very sharp, penetrating odor. What anions are definitely shown to be present? What cations may be present?

41. A single salt is known to contain magnesium as the only cation. Effervescence takes place when the solid is treated with cold concentrated H_2SO_4, a brown gas being evolved. The $AgNO_3$ test on the water solution yields a cream colored precipitate. When H_2SO_4 and $FeSO_4$ are added to the water solution a brown ring forms at the junction of the two liquids. What is the salt?

GENERAL QUESTIONS

42. How distinguish, by means of simple tests, between the following solids?

(a) $BaSO_4$ and $Pb(NO_3)_2$. (g) $Cr(NO_3)_3$ and $Cd(NO_3)_2$.
(b) KCl and ZnS. (h) $CoCl_2$ and $AlCl_3$.
(c) $MnSO_3$ and Na_2CO_3. (i) $NiCO_3$ and KBr.
(d) $AgBr$ and $FeCl_3$. (j) $BaCl_2$ and $PbCO_3$.
(e) $HgCO_3$ and $(NH_4)_3PO_4$. (k) Mn and Zn.
(f) $Bi_2(CrO_4)_3$ and $CuSO_4$. (l) $BaSO_4$ and $PbSO_4$.

43. By means of what simple test would you be able to distinguish between the following solutions? State what happens to each solution that enables you to make the distinction.

(a) K_3AsO_4 and $CdSO_4$.

(b) Na_3PO_4 and Na_3AsO_4.

(c) $Cu(NO_3)_2$ and $Ni(NO_3)_2$.

(d) KNO_3 and KBr.

(e) $Ca(OH)_2$ and $Ca(HCO_3)_2$.

(f) Fe^{++} and Fe^{+++}.

(g) $CdCl_2$ and $ZnCl_2$.

(h) $1\ M\ Na_2SO_3$ and $1\ M\ Na_2CO_3$.

44. A solid is known to be made up of a mixture of equivalent amounts of 2 or more of the solids listed below.

$$CuSO_4, \quad AgNO_3, \quad (NH_4)_2SO_4, \quad PbCl_2, \quad Ba(NO_3)_2,$$

$$K_2CrO_4, \quad Cr(NO_3)_2, \quad Zn(NO_3)_2, \quad Na_2CO_3.$$

When water is added to the mixture there is formed a white precipitate, B, and a solution, C; solution C shows an acidic reaction toward litmus paper. The precipitate B is insoluble in $2\ M\ H_2SO_4$ but is dissolved by $6\ M$ NaOH; there was no evidence of any reaction when B was treated with $2\ M\ H_2SO_4$. When the solution C is treated with an excess of $6\ M$ NaOH there is formed a colorless solution which smells strongly of ammonia. On the basis of this information indicate whether each solid is absent, present, or impossible to determine. (Solubility products: $BaSO_4 = 1 \times 10^{-10}$; $PbSO_4 = 1 \times 10^{-8}$; $AgCl = 1.56 \times 10^{-10}$; $BaCO_3 = 5 \times 10^{-9}$; $BaCrO_4 = 2.4 \times 10^{-14}$; $PbCrO_4 = 2 \times 10^{-14}$; $PbCO_3 = 4 \times 10^{-14}$)

45. Treatment of a solid unknown with $0.3\ M$ HCl gives a black precipitate, A, and a solution, B. The precipitate, A, after washing, dissolves in hot dilute HNO_3 leaving a small amount of brownish-yellow residue. The solution, B, treated with excess NaOH, gives a green solution and no precipitate. Indicate which of the following substances are definitely present, which are definitely absent, and which are undetermined.

$$ZnS, \quad PbCl_2, \quad FeCl_3, \quad CrCl_3, \quad KHSO_4, \quad HgS.$$

46. A solution known to contain only Na^+ and K^+ as cations was treated in the following manner. To one portion of the solution $AgNO_3$ was added; a yellow precipitate resulted. $BaCl_2$, when added to the second part of the solution, gave a white precipitate which dissolved in HCl. A third part of the solution decolorized a $KMnO_4$ solution. A fourth portion of the solution gave a brown coloration when treated with a mixture of concentrated H_2SO_4 and $FeSO_4$ solution. Indicate which of the following anions are definitely present in the solution, which are definitely absent, and which are undetermined.

$$Cl^-, \quad I^-, \quad SO_4^{--}, \quad PO_4^{---}, \quad NO_3^-, \quad AsO_4^{---}.$$

47. An unknown mixture of dry salts was known to consist of equivalent amounts of two or more of the substances listed below.

$$AgNO_3, \ ZnCl_2, \ K_2CO_3, \ MgSO_4, \ Ba(C_2H_3O_2)_2, \ NH_4NO_3.$$

When the solid was treated with an amount of water sufficient to yield a 0.4 N solution of any salt that dissolved there was formed a precipitate A and a solution B.

The precipitate A was washed with water. One sample of this washed precipitate was found to be completely soluble in dilute HNO_3. Another sample of the precipitate yielded a precipitate and a clear supernatant liquid when treated with dilute HCl.

The solution B yielded a precipitate when treated with excess NH_4OH. On the basis of the above information, indicate whether a particular substance is present, absent, or impossible to determine.

48. The following formulas represent salts, each of which may or may not be present in an unknown salt mixture. Those salts which are in the mixture are present in approximately equivalent amounts.

$$CuSO_4, \ FeSO_4, \ AgNO_3, \ (NH_4)_2SO_4, \ ZnSO_4,$$

$$Ba(NO_3)_2, \ Na_2CO_3, \ Na_2CrO_4, \ PbCl_2, \ Cr_2(SO_4)_3.$$

Upon treating the unknown with hot water a white solid is left, which is separated and found to be insoluble in 3 M H_2SO_4 but soluble in 6 M NaOH. The hot water decantate is tested with indicator and found to be faintly acid. Addition of 6 M NaOH to the decantate gives a colorless solution with an odor of ammonia, and a green precipitate. On the basis of the observations given, indicate whether a certain salt is present, absent, or undetermined.

49. An unknown mixture of dry salts was known to consist of equivalent amounts of two or more of the substances listed below:

$$Fe_2(SO_4)_3, \ ZnCO_3, \ Ag_3BO_3, \ NaI, \ MgCO_3, \ Ba(NO_2)_2, \ PbBr_2.$$

A sample of the solid unknown dissolved completely in cold, dilute HCl.

When cold water was added to the solid unknown there was formed a dark, yellow-brown solution and a solid residue. The solid residue was separated from the solution; this solution was then extracted with CCl_4; the CCl_4 layer became deeply colored.

A sample of the solid dissolved completely in dilute HNO_3. This HNO_3 solution was boiled for one minute and was then cooled and treated with an *excess* of NH_4OH; a dark precipitate formed. This dark precipitate was removed and the solution which remained was treated with *excess* NaOH; a white precipitate formed.

On the basis of the above information indicate whether a particular substance is present, absent or impossible to determine.

50. A solid unknown is known to contain equivalent amounts of two or more of the following substances: $Pb(NO_3)_2$, $(NH_4)_2CO_3$, $MgBr_2$, Na_3PO_4, $FeCl_3$, $Bi_2(SO_4)_3$.

The solid was readily and completely soluble in cold, dilute HCl.

When a sample of the solid was treated with cold water a clear, colorless solution was formed.

When a sample of the solid was treated with cold, concentrated H_2SO_4 there was formed a brown gas which fumed in moist air.

When the solution formed by dissolving the solid in dilute HCl was boiled for one minute, cooled, and then treated with NH_4Cl and excess NH_4OH there was no precipitate; however, on further treatment with excess NaOH a white precipitate formed.

Indicate whether each of the above substances is present, absent, or indeterminate.

51. A solid unknown is known to contain one or more of the following substances: MgI_2, K_2CrO_4, $ZnCO_3$, $CaCl_2$, $Fe_2(SO_4)_3$, $AgNO_3$, $NiBr_2$, Na_3AsO_4.

The solid was completely soluble in water.

When a sample of the water solution was treated with excess NH_4OH there was formed a clear, colorless solution, with no precipitate.

When a sample of the water solution was treated with excess NaOH a dark precipitate formed.

Indicate whether each of the above substances is present, absent, or indeterminate.

52. You are given the following facts:

a) A cation, M^{++}, forms the insoluble compounds, MS(black), $MCrO_4$(yellow), MSO_3(white), and MSe(green).

b) All four of the above compounds are soluble in the acid, HX.

c) None of the above compounds are soluble in the acid, HY.

d) MSO_3 and $MCrO_4$ are soluble in the acid, HZ; MS and MSe are insoluble in the acid, HZ.

e) When a mixture of MS and MSe is treated with NH_4OH the MS dissolves but the MSe is not affected.

f) When 1 M NaI is added to solid MSO_3 the precipitate changes in color from white to red.   When 1 M NaI is added to solid $MCrO_4$ nothing is observed to take place.

On the basis of these facts arrange the four insoluble compounds in the order of increasing solubility products.

53. A student prepared the following five solutions and placed each solution in a separate unlabeled beaker.

1) 0.1 M $ZnCl_2$.

2) A solution 0.1 M in $Al(OH)_4^-$ and containing also Na^+ and OH^-.

3) A solution 0.1 M in SnS_3^{--} and containing also NH_4^+.

4) A solution 0.3 M in $Ag(NH_3)_2^+$ and 0.1 M in AsO_4^{---} and containing also NH_3.

5) A solution 0.1 M in Sn^{++}, 0.1 M in Bi^{+++}, 1.0 M in Cl^- and 0.5 M in H^+.

While he was gone from the laboratory the 5 unlabeled beakers were moved and were placed in a disordered group at the end of the desk. In order to identify the solution in each beaker the student proceeded as follows:

He took the five disordered beakers and labeled them A, B, C, D, and E. He then tested the solution in each beaker and found that:

Solution A, when treated, drop by drop, with 3 M HNO_3, gave a brown precipitate which dissolved in excess HNO_3 to form a clear solution.

Solution B, when treated, drop by drop, with 12 M HCl, gave a yellow precipitate which dissolved in excess HCl to form a clear solution.

Solution C, when treated, drop by drop, with 5 M NH_4OH, gave a white precipitate which dissolved in excess NH_4OH to form a clear solution.

Solution D, when treated with 6 M $NaOH$, gave a white precipitate which quickly turned black.

Solution E, when treated, drop by drop, with 6 M HCl, gave a white precipitate which dissolved in excess HCl to form a clear solution.

What is the composition of each of the solutions, A, B, C, D, and E?

54. A solid unknown which is readily soluble in dilute HCl but insoluble in water is known to contain CrO_4^{--}. How would you determine whether or not it also contains Cr^{+++}?

55. A solid unknown which is insoluble in water but soluble in dilute HCl is known to contain Cr^{+++}. How would you determine whether or not it also contains CrO_4^{--}?

56. Using reactions employed in qualitative analysis, how could you form the following in the laboratory?

(a) Metallic bismuth, starting with Bi_2S_3.

(b) $FeCl_3$, starting with $Fe_2(SO_4)_3$.

(c) Metallic mercury, starting with $Hg(NO_3)_2$.

(d) Metallic antimony, starting with Sb_2S_3.

(e) $KMnO_4$, starting with $MnCl_2$.

(f) CrO_5, starting with $Cr(NO_3)_3$.

(g) ZnS, starting with $ZnCO_3$.

(h) Hg_2Cl_2, starting with HgS.

(i) Na_2SnO_3, starting with metallic tin.

(j) $CuCO_3$, starting with $CuSO_4$.

(k) $SnCl_2$, starting with $Sn_3(PO_4)_4$.

Recording and reporting analyses

THE FORM used in recording and reporting analyses of salts and salt mixtures is illustrated by the example on this page. All solids analyzed will be reported in this manner on the pages in this chapter provided for this purpose.

REPORT OF THE ANALYSIS OF SAMPLE NO. I   DATE: *4/6/61*

I. **Physical Examination:** *White, crystalline, heterogeneous.*

II. **Solubility:** *Soluble in cold water. Colorless solution. No gases evolved.*

III. **Analysis for Cations**

(a) Cations eliminated by the color of the solution: Cu^{++}, Fe^{+++}, Co^{++}, Ni^{++}, Cr^{+++}. CrO_4^{--} *also absent.*

(b) Cations eliminated by the anion analysis: *None. Cation analysis performed before anion analysis.*

(c) Cations eliminated by solubility: *None.*

(d) Results of flame test: Na^+ *present;* K^+ *absent.*

(e) Results of blanket tests: *Tests with NaOH and with* NH_4OH *showed absence of all cations except* Na^+, K^+, NH_4^+, Ba^{++}, Ca^{++}, Mg^{++}, *and* Zn^{++}.

(f) Results of cation analysis: Zn^{++} *and* Na^+ *present.*

IV. Analysis for Anions

Anions eliminated by color of solution: CrO_4^{--}.

Anions eliminated in cation analysis: AsO_4^{---}, CrO_4^{--}.

Anions eliminated by solubility: SO_3^{--}, CO_3^{--}, PO_4^{---}, BO_3^{---}, S^{--}, CrO_4^{--}, AsO_4^{---}.

Results of H_2SO_4 treatment: *Effervescence; gas was colorless, had sharp odor and fumed in moist air; Cl^- indicated; Br^- and I^- absent, NO_3^- probably absent.*

Results of $AgNO_3$ treatment: *White, curdy precipitate, insoluble in HNO_3. Cl^- present.*

Results of $BaCl_2$ treatment: *White precipitate, insoluble in HCl. SO_4^{--} present.*

Results of specific tests: *Specific tests made for NO_3^- and $C_2H_3O_2^-$. NO_3^- and $C_2H_3O_2^-$ absent.*

V. Summary

Cations present: Zn^{++}, Na^+

Anions present: SO_4^{--}, Cl^-

DATE_____

REPORT OF THE ANALYSIS OF SAMPLE NO. _____

I. Physical Examination: _____

_____

II. Solubility: _____

_____

III. Analysis for Cations

(a) Cations eliminated by the color of the solution: _____

_____

(b) Cations eliminated by the anion analysis: _____

_____

(c) Cations eliminated by solubility: _____

_____

(d) Results of flame test: _____

_____

(e) Results of blanket tests: _____

_____

(f) Results of cation analysis: _____

_____

IV. Analysis for Anions

(a) Anions eliminated by the color of the solution: _____

(b) Anions eliminated by cation analysis: _____

(c) Anions eliminated by solubility: _____

_____

(d) Results of H_2SO_4 treatment: _____

_____

(e) Results of $AgNO_3$ treatment: _____

_____

(f) Results of $BaCl_2$ treatment: _____

_____

(g) Results of specific tests: _____

_____

V. Summary

Cations present: _____

Anions present: _____

DATE_____

REPORT OF THE ANALYSIS OF SAMPLE NO. _____

I. Physical Examination: _____
_____

II. Solubility: _____
_____

III. Analysis for Cations

(a) Cations eliminated by the color of the solution: _____
_____

(b) Cations eliminated by the anion analysis: _____
_____

(c) Cations eliminated by solubility: _____
_____

(d) Results of flame test: _____
_____

(e) Results of blanket tests: _____
_____

(f) Results of cation analysis: _____
_____

IV. Analysis for Anions

(a) Anions eliminated by the color of the solution: _____

(b) Anions eliminated by cation analysis: _____

(c) Anions eliminated by solubility: _____
_____

(d) Results of H_2SO_4 treatment: _____
_____

(e) Results of $AgNO_3$ treatment: _____
_____

(f) Results of $BaCl_2$ treatment: _____
_____

(g) Results of specific tests: _____
_____

V. Summary

Cations present: _____

Anions present: _____

DATE_____

REPORT OF THE ANALYSIS OF SAMPLE NO. _____

I. Physical Examination: _____

_____

II. Solubility: _____

_____

III. Analysis for Cations

(a) Cations eliminated by the color of the solution: _____

_____

(b) Cations eliminated by the anion analysis: _____

_____

(c) Cations eliminated by solubility: _____

_____

(d) Results of flame test: _____

_____

(e) Results of blanket tests: _____

_____

(f) Results of cation analysis: _____

_____

IV. Analysis for Anions

(a) Anions eliminated by the color of the solution: _____

(b) Anions eliminated by cation analysis: _____

(c) Anions eliminated by solubility: _____

_____

(d) Results of H_2SO_4 treatment: _____

_____

(e) Results of $AgNO_3$ treatment: _____

_____

(f) Results of $BaCl_2$ treatment: _____

_____

(g) Results of specific tests: _____

_____

V. Summary

Cations present: _____

Anions present: _____

DATE_____

REPORT OF THE ANALYSIS OF SAMPLE NO. _____

  I. Physical Examination: _____

_____

  II. Solubility: _____

_____

III. Analysis for Cations

  (a) Cations eliminated by the color of the solution: _____

_____

  (b) Cations eliminated by the anion analysis: _____

_____

  (c) Cations eliminated by solubility: _____

_____

  (d) Results of flame test: _____

_____

  (e) Results of blanket tests: _____

_____

  (f) Results of cation analysis: _____

_____

IV. Analysis for Anions

  (a) Anions eliminated by the color of the solution: _____

  (b) Anions eliminated by cation analysis: _____

  (c) Anions eliminated by solubility: _____

_____

  (d) Results of H_2SO_4 treatment: _____

_____

  (e) Results of $AgNO_3$ treatment: _____

_____

  (f) Results of $BaCl_2$ treatment: _____

_____

  (g) Results of specific tests: _____

_____

  V. Summary

Cations present: _____

Anions present: _____

DATE_____

REPORT OF THE ANALYSIS OF SAMPLE NO. _____

   I. Physical Examination: _____

_____

  II. Solubility: _____

_____

III. Analysis for Cations

 (a) Cations eliminated by the color of the solution: _____

_____

 (b) Cations eliminated by the anion analysis: _____

_____

 (c) Cations eliminated by solubility: _____

_____

 (d) Results of flame test: _____

_____

 (e) Results of blanket tests: _____

_____

 (f) Results of cation analysis: _____

_____

IV. Analysis for Anions

 (a) Anions eliminated by the color of the solution: _____

 (b) Anions eliminated by cation analysis: _____

 (c) Anions eliminated by solubility: _____

_____

 (d) Results of H_2SO_4 treatment: _____

_____

 (e) Results of $AgNO_3$ treatment: _____

_____

 (f) Results of $BaCl_2$ treatment: _____

_____

 (g) Results of specific tests: _____

_____

V. Summary

Cations present: _____

Anions present: _____

DATE_____

REPORT OF THE ANALYSIS OF SAMPLE NO. _____

I. **Physical Examination:** _____

_____

II. **Solubility:** _____

_____

III. **Analysis for Cations**

(a) Cations eliminated by the color of the solution: _____

_____

(b) Cations eliminated by the anion analysis: _____

_____

(c) Cations eliminated by solubility: _____

_____

(d) Results of flame test: _____

_____

(e) Results of blanket tests: _____

_____

(f) Results of cation analysis: _____

_____

IV. **Analysis for Anions**

(a) Anions eliminated by the color of the solution: _____

(b) Anions eliminated by cation analysis: _____

(c) Anions eliminated by solubility: _____

_____

(d) Results of H_2SO_4 treatment: _____

_____

(e) Results of $AgNO_3$ treatment: _____

_____

(f) Results of $BaCl_2$ treatment: _____

_____

(g) Results of specific tests: _____

_____

V. **Summary**

Cations present: _____

Anions present: _____

A P P E N D I X

Reagents used

ALL LIQUID reagents and known solutions should be kept on the shelves in small bottles (about 100 ml.) provided with stoppers fitted with medicine droppers. Solid reagents (except the aluminum, zinc, and tin) should be finely powdered or pulverized and should be kept in 250-ml. wide-mouth bottles provided with one-hole No. 8 rubber stoppers fitted with spatulas for dispensing the solid. The handle of the spatula is thrust through the hole of the stopper in such a way that, when the bottle is stoppered, the metal tip of the spatula will be inside the bottle and partly buried in the powdered solid.

Acids

Acetic, dilute, 5 *M.* Dilute 287 ml. of glacial acetic acid with water to 1 liter.

Hydrochloric, special concentrated, sp. gr. 1.18–1.20, 12 *M.*

Hydrochloric, concentrated, 6 *M.* Dilute 1 volume of 12 *M* HCl with 1 volume of water.

Hydrochloric, dilute, 2 *M.* Dilute 1 volume of 12 *M* acid with 5 volumes of water.

Nitric, concentrated, sp. gr. 1.42, 16 M.

Nitric, dilute, 3 M. Dilute 100 ml. of 16 M acid with water to 533 ml.

Sulfuric, concentrated, sp. gr. 1.84, 18 M.

Sulfuric, dilute, 2 M. Add 1 volume of 18 M acid to 8 volumes of water.

Bases

Ammonium hydroxide, concentrated, sp. gr. 0.90, 15 M.

Ammonium hydroxide, dilute, 5 M. Dilute 1 volume of 15 M NH_4OH with 2 volumes of water.

Barium hydroxide, saturated solution.

Sodium hydroxide, 8 M. Dissolve 356 g. of solid NaOH in water and dilute to 1 liter.

Salts

Aluminon, 1 g. of the ammonium salt of aurintricarboxylic acid in a liter of water.

Ammonium acetate, $NH_4C_2H_3O_2$, 1 M. 77 g. per liter of solution.

Ammonium carbonate, $(NH_4)_2CO_3$, 2 M. Dissolve 192 g. of the salt in a mixture of about 500 ml. of cold water and 80 ml. of 15 M NH_4OH, and dilute with water to 1 liter.

Ammonium chloride, NH_4Cl, 2 M. 107 g. per liter of solution.

Ammonium molybdate, $(NH_4)_2MoO_4$. Dissolve 20 g. of MoO_3 in a mixture of 60 ml. of distilled water and 30 ml. of 15 M NH_4OH. Add this solution slowly and with constant stirring to a mixture of 230 ml. of water and 100 ml. of 16 M HNO_3.

Ammonium nitrate, NH_4NO_3, 0.2 M. 16 g. per liter of solution.

Ammonium oxalate, $(NH_4)_2C_2O_4$, 0.2 M. 25 g. liter of solution.

Ammonium sulfide, $(NH_4)_2S$. Add one volume of the reagent grade ammonium sulfide liquid manufactured by the leading chemical companies to two volumes of water *or* saturate 5 M NH_4OH with H_2S gas.

Ammonium sulfate, $(NH_4)_2SO_4$, 0.2 M. 26 g. per liter of solution.

Ammonium thiocyanate, NH_4SCN. Saturated solution in ethyl alcohol.

Barium chloride, $BaCl_2 \cdot 2\ H_2O$, 0.2 M. 49 g. per liter of solution.

Chlorine water. Saturated solution.

Dimethylglyoxime, $(CH_3)_2C_2(NOH)_2$. Dissolve 10 g. in 1000 ml. of 95 per cent alcohol.

Hydrogen peroxide, H_2O_2, 3 per cent solution.

Iron(III) nitrate, $Fe(NO_3)_3$, 0.2 M. 48 g. per liter of solution.

Iron(II) sulfate, $FeSO_4 \cdot 7\ H_2O$, 1 M. 278 g. per liter of solution. Place clean scraps of iron in the solution and acidify with a few milliliters of 2 M H_2SO_4.

Lead acetate, $Pb(C_2H_3O_2)_2 \cdot 3\ H_2O$, 0.2 M. 78 g. per liter of solution. Add 10 ml. of 5 M acetic acid per liter of solution.

Magnesium reagent. Dissolve 0.1 g. of p-nitrobenzeneazoresorcinol (called also 4-(p-nitrophenylazo)resorcinol or 2, 4 dihydroxy-4'-nitro-azobenzene) in 1000 ml. of 0.025 M NaOH.

Magnesia mixture. Dissolve 55 g. of $MgCl_2 \cdot 6\ H_2O$ and 140 g. of NH_4Cl in 500 ml. of water. Add 131 ml. of 15 M NH_4OH and dilute with water to 1000 ml.

Mercury(II) chloride, $HgCl_2$, 0.1 M. 27 g. per liter of solution.

Potassium chromate, K_2CrO_4, 0.2 M. 38 g. per liter of solution.

Potassium cyanide, KCN, 0.2 M. 13 g. per liter of solution.

Potassium hexacyanoferrate(III), $K_3Fe(CN)_6$, 0.2 M. 66 g. per liter of solution.

Potassium hexacyanoferrate (II), $K_4Fe(CN)_6 \cdot 3\ H_2O$, 0.2 M. 84 g. per liter of solution.

Potassium nitrite, KNO_2, 0.2 M. 17 g. per liter of solution.

Potassium permanganate, $KMnO_4$, 0.02 M. 3.2 g. per liter of solution.

Potassium thiocyanate, KSCN, 0.2 M. 19 g. per liter of solution.

Silver nitrate, $AgNO_3$, 0.2 M. 34 g. per liter of solution.

Sodium acetate, $NaC_2H_3O_2 \cdot 3 H_2O$, 0.2 M. 27 g. per liter of solution.

Sodium carbonate, Na_2CO_3. Saturated solution.

Sodium hexanitrocobaltate(III), $Na_3Co(NO_2)_6$. Dissolve 10 g. of $Co(NO_3)_2 \cdot 6 H_2O$ in a mixture of 200 ml. of distilled water and 52 ml. of 5 M $HC_2H_3O_2$. Then add 100 g. of $NaNO_2$, mix well, and allow to stand 24 hours before using.

Disodium phosphate, Na_2HPO_4, 0.2 M. 28 g. per liter of solution.

Sodium thiosulfate, $Na_2S_2O_3$, 2.0 M. 496 g. $Na_2S_2O_3 \cdot 5 H_2O$ per liter of solution.

Thioacetamide, CH_3CSNH_2, 1 M. 75 g. per liter of water solution. Prepare in small quantities as needed. Solid reagent and solutions should be refrigerated.

Tin(II) chloride, $SnCl_2 \cdot 3 H_2O$, 0.2 M. Dissolve 45 g. of the salt in 500 ml. of 6 M HCl and dilute to 1 liter. Keep in a well-stoppered bottle containing a few pieces of granulated tin.

Zinc uranyl acetate. Add 10 g. of uranyl acetate, $UO_2(C_2H_3O_2)_2 \cdot 2 H_2O$, to 5 ml. of 5 M acetic acid. Heat just short of boiling for 5 minutes or until solid is dissolved. Then dilute to 50 ml. with water, and if necessary, heat until the solid is completely dissolved. Add 30 g. of zinc acetate, $Zn(C_2H_3O_2)_2 \cdot 2 H_2O$, to 5 ml. of 5 M acetic acid and heat just short of boiling for 5 minutes. Dilute with water to 50 ml., and if necessary heat until the salt is completely dissolved. The two solutions are mixed to give a clear solution. Add about 0.2 g. of NaCl and let stand 24 hours. Decant the clear solution for use.

Organic liquids

Carbon tetrachloride, CCl_4.

Ether, diethyl, $(C_2H_5)_2O$.

Alcohol, ethyl, C_2H_5OH.

Alcohol, methyl, CH_3OH.

Solids

Aluminum wire, 26 gauge, cut to 1-in. lengths.

Borax, $Na_2B_4O_7$.

H₂S source material, bulk mixture of 5 parts by weight of asbestos shreds, 25 parts by weight of finely shredded paraffin and 15 parts by weight of finely ground sulfur. Sold commercially under the trade name, Aitch-Tu-Ess.

Zinc, granulated.

Potassium peroxydisulfate, $K_2S_2O_8$.

Sodium bismuthate, $NaBiO_3$.

Sodium fluoride, NaF.

Sodium hyposulfite (sodium hydrosulfite), $Na_2S_2O_4$.

Sodium peroxide, Na_2O_2.

Sodium thiosulfate, $Na_2S_2O_3 \cdot 5 H_2O$.

Known solutions

The silver group known solution is approximately 0.1 M with respect to silver, mercury and lead. The other three known solutions are approximately 0.2 M with respect to each metal in the group except lead, which, because of the limited solubility of $PbCl_2$, is only 0.035 M and NH_4^+, which, to increase the strength of the test, is 0.6 M.

1. Silver group. 28 g. of $HgNO_3 \cdot H_2O$, 17 g. of $AgNO_3$, and 33 g. of $Pb(NO_3)_2$ per liter of solution. Place the solid $HgNO_3 \cdot H_2O$ in a 2 liter beaker, add 50 ml. of 16 M HNO_3, then add water in 200-ml. portions with frequent stirring to give a volume of about 950 ml. Allow to stand, with frequent stirring, until the $HgNO_3 \cdot H_2O$ is dissolved. Then add the $AgNO_3$ and $Pb(NO_3)_2$ and dilute to 1 liter with water. Stir until the solids are completely dissolved.

2. Copper-arsenic group. 10 g. of $PbCl_2$, 62 g. of $Na_2HAsO_4 \cdot 7 H_2O$, 54 g. of $HgCl_2$, 46 g. of $CdCl_2 \cdot 2\frac{1}{2} H_2O$, 34 g. of $CuCl_2 \cdot 2 H_2O$, 63 g. of $BiCl_3$, 46 g. of $SbCl_3$, and 70 g. of $SnCl_4 \cdot 5 H_2O$. Place the mixture of solids in a 2-l. beaker, add 492 ml. of 12 M HCl and 330 ml. of water, to give a total volume of about one liter. Stir until all solids are dissolved, warming if necessary.

3. Aluminum-nickel group. 27 g. of $ZnCl_2$, 40 g. of $MnCl_2 \cdot 4 H_2O$, 48 g. of $NiCl_2 \cdot 6 H_2O$, 54 g. of $FeCl_3 \cdot 6 H_2O$, 48 g. of $CoCl_2 \cdot 6 H_2O$, 53 g. of $CrCl_3 \cdot 6 H_2O$, and 48 g. of $AlCl_3 \cdot 6 H_2O$. Place the mixture of solids in a 2-l. beaker, add 50 ml. of 12 M HCl, then add 740 ml.

of water, to give a total volume of about one liter. Stir until the solids are completely dissolved.

4. Barium-magnesium group. 12 g. of NaCl, 15 g. of KCl, 32 g. of NH_4Cl, 29 g. of $CaCl_2 \cdot 2 H_2O$, 49 g. of $BaCl_2 \cdot 2 H_2O$, and 41 g. of $MgCl_2 \cdot 6 H_2O$. Place the mixture of solids in a 2-l. beaker, add 10 ml. of 6 M HCl, then add 850 ml. of water to give a total volume of about 1 liter. Stir until solids are completely dissolved.

Unknown solutions

The unknown solutions should be prepared in the same concentrations as the known solutions and the same salts should be used.

Solids for Experiments 1 and 4

Zinc sulfide, potassium nitrate, borax or sodium metaborate, and the sulfate, sulfite, carbonate, chromate, chloride, bromide, iodide, acetate, phosphate, and arsenate of sodium or potassium.

Solutions for Experiments 2, 3, and 4

0.2 M solutions of the sodium, potassium, or ammonium salts of each of the 13 anions ($C_2H_3O_2{}^-$, $NO_3{}^-$, Cl^-, Br^-, I^-, S^{--}, $SO_4{}^{--}$, $SO_3{}^{--}$, $CO_3{}^{--}$, $CrO_4{}^{--}$, $BO_2{}^-$, $PO_4{}^{---}$, $AsO_4{}^{---}$).

Solutions of cations

It is desirable to have 0.2 M solutions of each of the cations available.

List of equipment needed

(This equipment can be purchased in standard semimicro size at all laboratory supply houses.)

Beakers, 50, 100, 150 ml.
Beaker cover, aluminum, for 100-ml. beaker, punched to hold $\frac{3}{8}$-in. test tubes.
Burner, standard size, with rubber tubing.
Casserole, 20 ml., $1\frac{3}{4}$-in., porcelain.
Centrifuge, four-tube, to carry 3 × $\frac{3}{8}$-in. test tubes. One centrifuge for each three to six students working in a laboratory at one time.
Cork stoppers, tapered, XXXX.

File, three-cornered, small.
Flasks, 125 ml., Erlenmeyer.
Forceps, metal.
Glass tubing, 6 mm.
Graduate, 10 ml.
Hydrogen sulfide bubbling tubes, 5 in.
Hydrogen sulfide generator (central dispensing system or desk-style
 generators). (See Note 2, page 90.)
Matches.
Medicine droppers and medicine-dropper bulbs.
Ring stand, rings, and clamps.
Spatula, semimicro style, nickel or stainless steel.
Sponge.
Stirring rods, $5 \times \frac{1}{8}$ in.
Test tubes, $3 \times \frac{3}{8}$ in. and $6 \times \frac{5}{8}$ in.
Test-tube brush, semimicro.
Test-tube holder, wire.
Test-tube rack, wood or metal, for $\frac{3}{8}$-in. tubes.
Towels.
Thermometer, 110°C.
Watch glass, 2 in.
Wing top for burner.
Wire gauze, 4 in. square.

INDEX